1968

This b   may be kept

ELEMENTARY CONTEMPORARY ALGEBRA

A Blaisdell Book in the Pure and Applied Sciences

Consulting Editor
JOHN KEMENY, *Dartmouth College*

Elementary
Contemporary Algebra

MERLIN M. OHMER
The University of Southwestern Louisiana

CLAYTON V. AUCOIN
Clemson University, South Carolina

MARION J. CORTEZ
Northside School

Blaisdell Publishing Company
A Division of Ginn and Company
NEW YORK · TORONTO · LONDON

TO

our wives and children

PREFACE

The Committee on the Undergraduate Program in Mathematics (CUPM) has recommended two semesters of the structure of the number system, one semester of algebra, and one semester of informal geometry for all prospective elementary school teachers (Level I). We have written this text, *Elementary Contemporary Algebra,* for the semester's course in algebra. Study of *Elementary Contemporary Algebra* should ideally follow study of the two semester sequence on the number system. However, in Chapter 1 we have included a review of the real number system and the field properties for the benefit of those students who have not studied the two semester course which should precede the algebra course. In the appendix we have included some basic definitions, theorems, and notations which would appear in the two semester course on the number system and which are used in this text.

Our companion text, *Elementary Contemporary Mathematics,* which is a complete treatment of the two semester course on the number system, as recommended by CUPM, may be used as a reference for this course by the student who has not had the benefit of such a course.

The text, which includes the topics recommended by the CUPM, is suitable either for training of prospective elementary teachers or for in-service or summer institute training of experienced teachers. We have used it successfully in both pre-service and institute courses at the University of Southwestern Louisiana.

At the University of Southwestern Louisiana we have taught the entire text in the third semester course as follows:

Chapter	Number of Lessons	
1. The Field of Real Numbers (A Review)	3	
2. Linear Equations and Linear Inequalities in One Variable	5	
3. Functions and Graphs	7	
4. Systems of Linear Equations and Inequalities	5	(45 lessons)
5. Quadratic Equations and Factoring	6	
6. The Complex Number System	5	
7. Finite Number Systems	6	
8. Algebraic Structures	3	
TESTING	5	

Although we have included many theorems and proofs in the text, we did so with the hope that the students would at least read and understand the statements of the theorems and understand those proofs presented in class by the teacher. At the University of Southwestern Louisiana we have proved approximately one-third of the theorems each semester, each teacher choosing those theorems he prefers to prove. Over a period of several semesters, each theorem has been proved at least once. Each teacher has found it beneficial to inform the students of the particular theorems which he was going to prove in a given semester. This procedure has enabled the students to read ahead with more proficiency. The end of each proof is indicated by $//$.

Some problems call for proofs of theorems. The teacher may wish to omit these problems. We hope, however, that the student will at least read and understand these theorems as well as those included in the body of the text.

The text is written so that it flows well without the proofs of the theorems. Each theorem is sufficiently motivated and explained by examples—some preceding the theorem and some following the theorem. Moreover, each definition which may be difficult is well motivated by examples.

We are indebted to many persons, especially to the many students and elementary school teachers who studied from this text in mimeographed form and to the teachers who have taught from it. In particular, we would like to express our gratitude to Dr. John G. Kemeny, Chairman of the Mathematics Department of Dartmouth College and former Chairman of the CUPM panel on Teacher Training, for his valuable suggestions, comments, and criticisms. He followed and read the entire manuscript as it was developed and re-read it after it was completed. His comments on Chapter 3 were especially valuable. We are grateful also to Dr. Z. L. Loflin, Chairman of the Mathematics Department at the University of Southwestern Louisiana; to Miss Jessie May Hoag, of the University of Southwestern Louisiana, for her valuable comments and criticisms during the development of the manuscript; to Dr. Seymour Schuster, of the University of Minnesota, for his detailed comments and suggestions; and to Dr. John Wagner of Michigan State University for his encouragement and general suggestions.

Finally, we are grateful to our wives and children for their patience, understanding, and encouragement during the preparation of the manuscript.

MERLIN M. OHMER
CLAYTON V. AUCOIN
MARION J. CORTEZ

Lafayette, Louisiana
February 1, 1965

CONTENTS

xi

ELEMENTARY CONTEMPORARY ALGEBRA

CHAPTER 1

THE FIELD OF REAL NUMBERS (A REVIEW)

1.1 The Real Number System

You are already familiar with the real numbers and most of their properties. The study of *algebra* entails the real number system; i.e., in order to study algebra one must be familiar with the real numbers and their properties. In this chapter we shall review those properties of the real numbers which are essential to a systematic study of algebra.

You will recall that the sum of any two real numbers a and b is the unique real number $a + b$; that is, the sum of any two real numbers is well-defined. Similarly, you know that the sum of three real numbers a, b, and c does not depend on the grouping. That is, if a, b, and c are any real numbers, then $(a + b) + c = a + (b + c)$. The real number 0 (called the *additive identity*) is the only real number such that $a + 0 = a$ for *every* real number a. If a is any real number, then there exists a unique real number ^-a (called the *additive inverse* of a) such that $a + {}^-a = 0$. For example, $7 + {}^-7 = 0$, $^-5 + {}^-(^-5) = 0$, and $\sqrt{2} + {}^-\sqrt{2} = 0$. Moreover, if a and b are any real numbers, then $a + b = b + a$.

These properties have familiar names.

CLOSURE PROPERTY FOR ADDITION
If a and b are any real numbers, then $a + b$ is a unique real number.

ASSOCIATIVE PROPERTY FOR ADDITION
If a, b, and c are any real numbers, then $(a + b) + c = a + (b + c)$.

IDENTITY PROPERTY FOR ADDITION

There exists a unique real number 0 (called the *additive identity*) such that $a + 0 = a$ for every real number a.

INVERSE PROPERTY FOR ADDITION

If a is any real number, then there exists a unique real number ^-a (called the *additive inverse* of a) such that $a + {}^-a = 0$.

COMMUTATIVE PROPERTY FOR ADDITION

If a and b are any real numbers, then $a + b = b + a$.

In a similar manner we can state analogous properties for multiplication.

CLOSURE PROPERTY FOR MULTIPLICATION

If a and b are any real numbers, then $a \times b$ is a unique real number.

ASSOCIATIVE PROPERTY FOR MULTIPLICATION

If a, b, and c are any real numbers, then $(a \times b) \times c = a \times (b \times c)$.

IDENTITY PROPERTY FOR MULTIPLICATION

There exists a unique real number 1 (called the *multiplicative identity*) such that $a \times 1 = a$ for every real number a.

INVERSE PROPERTY FOR MULTIPLICATION

If a is any nonzero real number, then there exists a unique real number $1/a$ (called the *multiplicative inverse* of a) such that $a \times 1/a = 1$.

COMMUTATIVE PROPERTY FOR MULTIPLICATION

If a and b are any real numbers, then $a \times b = b \times a$.

To illustrate the inverse property for multiplication we note that $5 \times 1/5 = 1$, $\sqrt{2} \times 1/\sqrt{2} = 1$, $2/7 \times \frac{1}{2/7} = 1$, and $\frac{\pi}{\sqrt{2}} \times \frac{1}{\frac{\pi}{\sqrt{2}}} = 1$. However, as there is no real number r such that $0 \times r = 1$, we see that 0 has no multiplicative inverse. Hence it is necessary to include the word *nonzero* in the inverse property for multiplication. Observe that the identity property for addition does not have this restriction. We have employed the customary notations for rational numbers. Thus a/b and $\frac{a}{b}$ both represent the same rational number.

The following property, called the *distributive property*, is another important property of the real numbers.

DISTRIBUTIVE PROPERTY

If a, b, and c are any real numbers, then $a \times (b + c) = a \times b + a \times c$.

Recall that, by convention, multiplication takes precedence over addition, unless punctuation indicates otherwise. Thus in $a \times (b + c)$, the punctuation indicates that the *sum* $b + c$ is to be computed before the *product* $a \times (b + c)$. However, in $a \times b + a \times c$, convention indicates that the two products $a \times b$ and $a \times c$ are *first* computed and *then* the sum of these is computed. As examples of the distributive property, we observe that $2 \times (3 + 7) = 2 \times 3 + 2 \times 7$, $\sqrt{2} \times (a + 8) = \sqrt{2} \times a + \sqrt{2} \times 8$, and $8 \times (10 + 5) = 8 \times 10 + 8 \times 5$. Because of the commutative property, we may write $(10 + 5) \times 8 = 8 \times (10 + 5) = 8 \times 10 + 8 \times 5 = 10 \times 8 + 5 \times 8$. In general, $(b + c) \times a = b \times a + c \times a$ for any real numbers a, b, and c. Thus the right-hand distributive property follows readily from the (left-hand) distributive property.

The real number system is an example of an abstract system known as a *field*. As you will recall from your previous study, a *system* consists of a nonempty set of elements and one or more binary operators between elements of the set. In the following definition, precise meaning is given to the term *field*.

DEFINITION 1. A mathematical system $(F, +, \times)$ consisting of a non-null set F and two binary operators $+$ and $\times$ is said to be a *field* if and only if the system possesses the properties $F1$ through $F11$.

F1. If a and b are any elements of F, then $a + b$ is a unique element of F (*closure property for addition*).

F2. If a, b, and c are any elements of F, then $(a + b) + c = a + (b + c)$ (*associative property for addition*).

F3. There exists a unique element 0 of F such that $a + 0 = a$ for any element of F (*identity property for addition*).

F4. If a is any element of F, then there exists a unique element ^{-}a of F such that $a + {}^{-}a = 0$ (*inverse property for addition*).

F5.   If a and b are any elements of F, then $a + b = b + a$ (*commutative property for addition*).

F6.   If a and b are any elements of F, then $a \times b$ is a unique element of F (*closure property for multiplication*).

F7.   If a, b, and c are any elements of F, then $(a \times b) \times c = a \times (b \times c)$ (*associative property for multiplication*).

F8.   There exists a unique element 1 of F such that $a \times 1 = a$ for any element of F (*identity property for multiplication*).

F9.   If a is any nonzero element of F, then there exists a unique element $1/a$ of F such that $a \times 1/a = 1$ (*inverse property for multiplication*).

F10. If a and b are any elements of F, then $a \times b = b \times a$ (*commutative property for multiplication*).

F11. If a, b, and c are any elements of F, then $a \times (b + c) = a \times b + a \times c$ (*distributive property*).

Throughout this text we shall employ the notation R to symbolize the *set* of real numbers. Thus the *real number system* $(R, +, \times)$ is a field. Frequently we indicate the product of a and b by $a \cdot b$, or ab, or $(a)(b)$, or $a(b)$. Thus $a \cdot b = ab = (a)(b) = a(b) = a \times b$.

Two important aspects of mathematics (*generalization* and *abstraction*) will become more evident as we study the field properties and other properties.

Let I denote the set of *integers*; that is, $I = \{\dots, {}^-3, {}^-2, {}^-1, 0, 1, 2, 3, \dots\}$. Then $I \subset R$. Is $(I, +, \times)$ a field? It is easy to prove that $(I, +, \times)$ possesses all of the field properties except the inverse property for multiplication. The only elements of I which have multiplicative inverses in I are ${}^-1$ and 1. Hence $(I, +, \times)$ is not a field. Although I is a *subset* of R, $(I, +, \times)$ is not a *subfield* of $(R, +, \times)$.

Recall that the set of *rational numbers* is a proper subset of the set of real numbers. Denoting the set of rational numbers by R_a, we may write $R_a \subset R$. It is interesting to study the rational number system $(R_a, +, \times)$ and, in particular, to determine whether $(R_a, +, \times)$ is a field. Since the sum of two rational numbers a/b and c/d is the unique rational number $(ad + bc)/bd$, we see that $(R_a, +, \times)$ has the closure property for addition; that is, if a/b and c/d are any rational numbers, then $a/b + c/d = (ad + bc)/bd$, and the sum is well-defined. It is easy to prove that $(a/b + c/d) + e/f = a/b + (c/d + e/f)$ for any rational numbers a/b, c/d, and e/f. The unique additive identity is the rational number 0, which can be expressed as $0/1, 0/2, 0/3, \ldots$. Thus $a/b + 0 = a/b$ and $0 + a/b = a/b$. The unique additive inverse of the rational number a/b is the rational number $^-a/b$; that is, if a/b is any rational number, then there exists a rational number $^-a/b$ such that $a/b + {}^-a/b = 0$ and $^-a/b + a/b = 0$. Hence $^-(\frac{a}{b}) = \frac{^-a}{b}$. The commutative property for addition follows readily from the definition of $a/b + c/d$. Thus if a/b and c/d are any rational numbers, then $a/b + c/d = c/d + a/b$.

Since the product $a/b \times c/d$ (that is, $\frac{a}{b} \times \frac{c}{d}$) of the rational numbers a/b and c/d is the unique rational number $(a \times c)/(b \times d)$, we see that $(R_a, +, \times)$ possesses the closure property for multiplication. The associative property follows readily from the definition of $a/b \times c/d$. The unique multiplicative identity is the rational number $1/1$ or simply 1. Thus, if a/b is any rational number, then $a/b \times 1 = a/b$ and $1 \times a/b = a/b$ and, moreover, 1 is the only rational number with this property. If $a/b \neq 0$ (i.e., if $a \neq 0$), then the unique rational number b/a exists such that $a/b \times b/a = 1$ and $b/a \times a/b = 1$. Thus b/a is the unique multiplicative inverse of the nonzero rational number a/b; that is, $\frac{1}{a/b} = b/a$. If a/b and c/d are any rational numbers, then $a/b \times c/d = c/d \times a/b$; that is, $(R_a, +, \times)$ possesses the commutative property for multiplication. The distributive property is readily proved. Hence if a/b, c/d, and e/f are any rational numbers, then $a/b \times (c/d + e/f) = a/b \times c/d + a/b \times e/f$.

Although the integer system $(I, +, \times)$ is *not* a field, we see that the rational number system $(R_a, +, \times)$ is a field.

Observe that the set $\{0, 1, 2, 3, \ldots \}$ of *counting numbers* is a subset of $\{ \ldots , ^-3, ^-2, ^-1, 0, 1, 2, 3, \ldots \}$. Letting $C_0 = \{0, 1, 2, 3, \ldots \}$, we see that $C_0 \subset I$. Recall that $(I, +, \times)$ is not a field. Is $(C_0, +, \times)$ a field? That is, does $(C_0, +, \times)$ possess all field properties? Since 0 is the only element of C_0 which has an additive inverse and 1 is the only element of C_0 which has a multiplicative inverse, we see that $(C_0, +, \times)$ does not possess either inverse property. Thus although $(R, +, \times)$ and $(R_a, +, \times)$ are fields, we see that $(I, +, \times)$ and $(C_0, +, \times)$ are *not* fields.

Exercise 1.1

I. (1) Prove that $(C_0, +, \times)$ possesses all field properties except F4 and F9.

(2) Prove that $(I, +, \times)$ possesses all field properties except F9.

(3) Prove that $(R_a, +, \times)$ possesses all field properties. [You may assume the properties in (1) and (2).]

(4) Let $I^+ = \{1, 2, 3, \ldots\}$ (the set of positive integers). Which field properties does $(I^+, +, \times)$ possess?

(5) Let $I^- = \{^-1, ^-2, ^-3, \ldots\}$ (the set of negative integers). Which field properties does $(I^-, +, \times)$ possess?

(6) Let $A = \{0, 1, 2\}$. Which field properties does $(A, +, \times)$ possess?

(7) Let $B = \{1\}$. Which field properties does $(B, +, \times)$ possess?

(8) Let $C = \{0\}$. Which field properties does $(C, +, \times)$ possess?

II. Let $S = \{a + b\sqrt{2} : a \in R_a \text{ and } b \in R_a\}$. Which field properties does $(S, +, \times)$ possess?

1.2   Consequences of the Field Properties

In the previous section we saw that the real number system $(R, +, \times)$ is a field and that the rational number system $(R_a, +, \times)$ is a field also. However, neither $(C_0, +, \times)$ nor $(I, +, \times)$ is a field. In this section we shall consider some properties of $(R, +, \times)$ which are consequences of the field properties. These properties, which are of frequent use in algebra, are, therefore, properties of *every* field—not merely of the real number field. Hence any deductions made from the field properties are valid in *any* field.

One important property is the *cancellation property for addition*.

CANCELLATION PROPERTY FOR ADDITION
If a, b, and c are any elements of a field such that $a + c = b + c$, then $a = b$.

To prove the cancellation property for addition, we employ the closure, associative, inverse, and identity properties for addition as follows:

$$a + c = b + c$$
$$(a + c) + {}^-c = (b + c) + {}^-c$$
$$a + (c + {}^-c) = b + (c + {}^-c)$$
$$a + 0 = b + 0$$
$$a = b.\mathbin{/\!/}$$

In a similar manner we state and prove the *cancellation property for multiplication*.

CANCELLATION PROPERTY FOR MULTIPLICATION
If a, b, and c are any elements of a field such that $ac = bc$ and $c \neq 0$, then $a = b$.

The proof depends on the closure, associative, inverse, and identity properties for multiplication as follows:

$$ac = bc \qquad (c \neq 0)$$
$$(ac) \times (1/c) = (bc) \times (1/c)$$
$$a \times (c \times 1/c) = b \times (c \times 1/c)$$
$$a \times 1 = b \times 1$$
$$a = b.\mathbin{/\!/}$$

A useful alternative statement of the cancellation property for multiplication is the *multiplication property of zero*. In a field, these two apparently different properties are equivalent. The multiplication property of zero is used extensively in algebra, particularly in the solution of quadratic equations.

MULTIPLICATION PROPERTY OF ZERO
If a and b are any elements of a field, then $ab = 0$ if and only if $a = 0$ or $b = 0$.

The multiplication property of zero is really a statement of *two* facts: (1) if $a = 0$ or $b = 0$, then $ab = 0$; (2) if $ab = 0$, then $a = 0$ or $b = 0$. The proof of the multiplication property of zero depends on the identity property for addition, the distributive property, the cancellation property for addition, and the cancellation property for multiplication as follows:

Now $a + 0 = a$
$a(a + 0) = a \cdot a$
$a \cdot a + a \cdot 0 = a \cdot a$
But $a \cdot a + 0 = a \cdot a$
Hence $a \cdot a + a \cdot 0 = a \cdot a + 0$
Thus, $a \cdot 0 = 0$ (by the cancellation property for addition).
Hence, if $b = 0$, then $ab = 0$.
Conversely, let $ab = 0$ and $a \neq 0$.
Now $a \cdot 0 = 0$.
Hence $ab = a \cdot 0$ and $a \neq 0$.
Thus $b = 0$ (by the cancellation property for multiplication)
Hence if $ab = 0$, then $a = 0$ or $b = 0.\mathbin{/\!/}$

The *double negative* property is a useful rule of algebra. According to this property, the additive inverse of the additive inverse of the real number a is a itself. For example, $^-(^-7) = 7$ and $^-(^-\sqrt{2}) = \sqrt{2}$.

DOUBLE NEGATIVE PROPERTY
If a is any real number, then $^-(^-a) = a$.

The *sign property for addition* is a useful property in algebra. In particular, it enables us to write the additive inverse (or negative) of a sum of two real numbers as the sum of the additive inverses of the two real numbers.

SIGN PROPERTY FOR ADDITION

If a and b are any elements of a field, then $^-(a + b) = {^-a} + {^-b}$.

The proof of the sign property for addition depends on the inverse, commutative, associative, identity, and cancellation properties for addition as follows:

Now $^-(a + b) + (a + b) = 0$.

Moreover, $(^-a + {^-b}) + (a + b) = (^-a + a) + (^-b + b)$
$$= 0 + 0$$
$$= 0.$$

Thus $^-(a + b) + (a + b) = (^-a + {^-b}) + (a + b)$

Hence $^-(a + b) = {^-a} + {^-b}. /\!/$

A useful rule of algebra is that the product of a positive number and a negative number is a negative number. Another useful rule is that the product of two negative numbers is a positive number. Both of these rules are special cases of the *sign property for multiplication*.

SIGN PROPERTY FOR MULTIPLICATION

If a and b are any elements of a field, then

(a) $^-a \times b = {^-(a \times b)}$;
(b) $a \times {^-b} = {^-(a \times b)}$;
(c) $^-a \times b = a \times {^-b}$;
(d) $^-a \times {^-b} = a \times b$.

The proof of the sign property for multiplication depends on the distributive property, the additive inverse property, the multiplication property of zero, and the cancellation property as follows:

(a)   Now $^-a(b) + a(b) = (^-a + a)b$
$$= (0)b$$
$$= 0.$$

Moreover, $^-(ab) + ab = 0$.

Hence $^-a(b) + a(b) = {^-(ab)} + ab$.

Thus $^-a(b) = {^-(ab)}. /\!/$

(b)   Now $a(^-b) + a(b) = a(^-b + b)$
$$= a(0)$$
$$= 0.$$

Moreover, $-(ab) + ab = 0$.

Hence $a(-b) + ab = -(ab) + ab$.

Thus $a(-b) = -(ab).//$

(c) Since $-a(b) = -(ab)$ and $a(-b) = -(ab)$, it follows that $-a(b) = a(-b).//$

(d) Now $(-a)(-b) + (-a)(b) = -a(-b + b)$
$$= -a(0)$$
$$= 0.$$

Moreover, $ab + (-a)(b) = ab + -(ab)$
$$= 0.$$

Hence $(-a)(-b) + (-a)(b) = ab + (-a)(b)$.

Thus $(-a)(-b) = ab.//$

By property F3, the real number 0 has the property that $a + 0 = a$ for every real number a. Is 0 the only real number with this property? In other words, is there another real number z such that $a + z = a$ for some real number a? To prove that there is no real number z (other than 0) such that $a + z = a$, we assume that there is and prove that $z = 0$, as follows:

Assume $a + z = a$.

But $a + 0 = a$.

Hence $a + z = a + 0$.

Thus $z = 0$.

Hence, for every real number a, $a + z = a$ if and only if $z = 0$.

Thus the additive identity is unique.$//$

In a similar manner, we prove that the multiplicative identity 1 is unique, as follows:

Assume that there exists a real number u such that $a \times u = a$
  for some real number $a \neq 0$.

But $a \times 1 = a$ for every real number $a \neq 0$.

Hence $a \times u = a \times 1$.

But $a \neq 0$.

Hence $u = 1$.

That is, the multiplicative identity is unique.$//$

The two proofs above make it unnecessary for us to use the word *unique* in F3 and F8. Even if we omitted the word, the uniqueness would follow.

Exercise 1.2

I. Use the cancellation property for addition and the cancellation property for multiplication to compute that real number a which obeys each of the following conditions.

(1) $2a + 5 = 6 + 5$
(2) $3a + 2 = 6 + 2$
(3) $2a + 7 = 3 + 7$
(4) $2a + 3 = 5 + 3$
(5) $2a = 7$

(6) $2a = 5$
(7) $6a - 3 = 4$
(8) $6a - 4 = 3$
(9) $\sqrt{2}\,a = 5\sqrt{2}$
(10) $\pi a = 6\pi$

II. Apply the sign property for addition to each of the following.

(1) $^-(6 + \pi)$
(2) $^-(\sqrt{2} + 7)$
(3) $^-(^-3 + \sqrt{2})$

(4) $^-(\pi + {}^-2)$
(5) $^-(2 + {}^-\pi + \sqrt{2})$
(6) $^-(3 + {}^-\sqrt{2} + {}^-\pi)$

III. Employ the sign property for multiplication to compute each of the following.

(1) $^-2 \times 5$
(2) $3 \times {}^-4$
(3) $^-(3 \times 2)$
(4) $^-(5 \times 7)$
(5) $^-(2 \times {}^-4)$

(6) $^-({}^-5 \times 3)$
(7) $^-(8 \times {}^-4 \times 5)$
(8) $^-(8 \times 4 \times {}^-5)$
(9) $^-({}^-2 \times {}^-3 \times {}^-4)$
(10) $^-({}^-3 \times {}^-5 \times {}^-2)$

IV. Employ the distributive property and the multiplication property of zero to prove that each of the following is 0.

(1) $6(5) + {}^-6(5)$
(2) $5(6) + 5({}^-6)$
(3) $\sqrt{2}({}^-3) + \sqrt{2}(3)$
(4) $\sqrt{3}({}^-2) + \sqrt{3}(2)$

(5) $3\pi(4) + 3\pi({}^-4)$
(6) $2\pi({}^-5) + 2\pi(5)$
(7) $\pi({}^-4) + {}^-\pi({}^-4)$
(8) $\sqrt{2}({}^-3) + {}^-\sqrt{2}({}^-3)$

V. (1) Prove that the multiplication property of zero follows from the cancellation property for multiplication.

(2) Prove that the cancellation property for multiplication follows from the multiplication property of zero.

(3) Prove that $\frac{1}{1/a} = a$ for any nonzero real number a.

1.3   Order Relation in $(R, +, \times)$

Now we recall that the real number a is less than the real number b if and only if there exists a positive real number k such that $a + k = b$. Symbolically, $a < b$ if and only if $a + k = b$ for some positive real number k. For example, $3 < 7$ because $3 + 4 = 7$, and $4 < 7$ because $4 + 3 = 7$. However, $4 \not< 4$ because $4 + 0 = 4$, and $4 \not< 3$ because $4 + {}^-1 = 3$; the real numbers 0 and $^-1$ are *not* positive. The relation $<$ between real numbers is called an *order relation*. Recall that the real number system possesses the following *order* properties.

1. If a and b are any real numbers, then $a < b$, or $a = b$, or $b < a$ (but only one).

   (The real number a is said to be *positive* if and only if $0 < a$, and is said to be *negative* if and only if $a < 0$.)

2. If a, b, and c are any real numbers and $a < b$, then $a + c < b + c$.
3. If a and b are any real numbers, and c is any positive real number, and if $a < b$, then $ac < bc$.
4. If a and b are any real numbers, and c is any negative real number, and if $a < b$, then $bc < ac$.
5. If a, b, and c are any real numbers such that $a < b$ and $b < c$, then $a < c$.

Property 4 actually follows from property 3 and such properties as the sign property. However, it is included for emphasis.

Properties 1 through 5 could have been phrased in terms of the order relation $>$. Since $a < b$ if and only if $b > a$, it is merely a matter of replacing "$<$" by "$>$." For this reason, we shall restrict our attention to the relation $<$. Whenever we study the real number system as an ordered system, we usually indicate the order relation $<$ by speaking of the *ordered real number system* $(R, +, ×, <)$. The real number system $(R, +, ×, <)$ is an example of an abstract system known as an *ordered field*. In the following definition, precise meaning is given to the term *ordered field*.

DEFINITION 2. A mathematical system $(F, +, ×, <)$ is said to be an *ordered field* if and only if the system possesses the properties $F1$ through $F11$ and $O1$ through $O5$.

$F1$.   If a and b are any elements of F, then $a + b$ is a unique element of F (closure property for addition).

$F2$.   If a, b, and c are any elements of F, then $(a + b) + c = a + (b + c)$ (associative property for addition).

$F3$.   There exists a unique element 0 of F such that $a + 0 = a$ for any element of F (identity property for addition).

$F4$.   If a is any element of F, then there exists a unique element ^-a of F such that $a + {}^-a = 0$ (inverse property for addition).

$F5$.   If a and b are any elements of F, then $a + b = b + a$ (commutative property for addition).

$F6$.   If a and b are any elements of F, then $a × b$ is a unique element of F (closure property for multiplication).

$F7$.   If a, b, and c are any elements of F, then $(a × b) × c = a × (b × c)$ (associative property for multiplication).

F8.   There exists a unique element 1 of F such that $a \times 1 = a$ for any element a of F (identity property for multiplication).

F9.   If a is any nonzero element of F, then there exists a unique element $1/a$ of F such that $a \times 1/a = 1$ (inverse property for multiplication).

F10. If a and b are any elements of F, then $a \times b = b \times a$ (commutative property for multiplication).

F11. If a, b, and c are any elements of F, then $a(b + c) = ab + ac$ (distributive property).

O1.   If a and b are any elements of F, then $a < b$, or $a = b$, or $b < a$ (but only one).

O2.   If a, b, and c are any elements of F such that $a < b$, then $a + c < b + c$.

O3.   If a, b, and c are any elements of F such that $0 < c$ and $a < b$, then $ac < bc$.

O4.   If a, b, and c are any elements of F such that $c < 0$ and $a < b$, then $bc < ac$.

O5.   If a, b, and c are any elements of F such that $a < b$ and $b < c$, then $a < c$.

Recall that every rational number can be expressed in the form a/b, in which a is an integer, b is a *positive* integer, and a and b are relatively prime. For example, the rational number 0.23 can be written $23/100$, and the rational number $0.1\overline{23}$ (in which the bar indicates that the digits 23 repeat indefinitely) can be written $61/495$. If the denominator of a rational number a/b is a negative integer, we can rewrite it with a positive denominator by multiplying numerator and denominator by $^-1$. For example, we can rewrite $5/^-8$ as $^-5/8$. If a and b are not relatively prime, we can divide numerator and denominator by the greatest common divisor of a and b, thus reducing a/b to *lowest terms*. For example, to reduce $30/75$ to lowest terms, we factor 30 and 75 and divide both by the greatest common divisor of a and b. Thus $30/75 = (2 \times 3 \times 5)/(3 \times 5 \times 5) = 2/5$. Since 2 and 5 are relatively prime, we are certain that $2/5$ is in lowest terms.

If two rational numbers a/b and c/d are expressed as above, we can prove from the definition and properties of order between real numbers that $a/b < c/d$ if and only if $ad < bc$. For example, $3/5 < 5/7$ because $3 \times 7 < 5 \times 5$.

It is easy to prove that $(R_a, +, \times, <)$ is an ordered field. However, since $(I, +, \times)$ is not a field, we see that $(I, +, \times, <)$ is not an ordered field. It is a simple exercise to prove that $(I, +, \times, <)$ possesses properties $O1$ through $O5$. In the exercises you are asked to prove that $F9$ is the only ordered field property which $(I, +, \times, <)$ does not possess.

Letting $E = \{\dots, {}^-6, {}^-4, {}^-2, 0, 2, 4, 6, \dots\}$ (the set of even integers), we may prove that $(E, +, \times, <)$ possesses properties $F1$ through $F7$, $F10$, $F11$, and $O1$ through $O5$. Thus $(E, +, \times, <)$ possesses the order properties $O1$ through $O5$ but is *not* an ordered field.

By the sign property for multiplication we know that ${}^-a \cdot {}^-b = ab$ for any real numbers a and b. In particular, the product of two negative real numbers is a positive real number. That is, if $r < 0$ and $s < 0$, then $0 < rs$ (rs is positive). Also, if $r < 0$ and $0 < s$, then $rs < 0$ (rs is negative). Moreover, if $0 < r$ and $0 < s$, then $0 < rs$ (rs is positive). In other words, *the product of two negative real numbers is a positive real number; the product of a negative real number and a positive real number is a negative real number; and the product of two positive real numbers is a positive real number.*

Actually, these properties are consequences of the order properties $O1$ through $O5$. For example, to prove that $[(r < 0) \land (s < 0)] \rightarrow [0 < rs]$, we employ property $O4$ with $r = a$, $0 = b$, and $s = c$, as follows:

$r < 0$ and $s < 0$
$0 \times s < r \times s$ (by $O4$)
$0 < rs$.

Similarly, to prove that $[(0 < r) \land (s < 0)] \rightarrow [rs < 0]$ we employ property $O4$ with $0 = a$, $r = b$, and $s = c$, as follows:

$0 < r$ and $s < 0$
$r \times s < 0 \times s$ (by $O4$)
$rs < 0$.

The proof that $[(0 < r) \land (0 < s)] \rightarrow [0 < rs]$ is similar and follows from $O3$.

These three consequences of the order properties may be restated, in condensed form, as follows:

For all real numbers a, b, and c,
   $0 < ab$ if and only if $0 < a$ and $0 < b$ or $a < 0$ and $b < 0$;
   $ab < 0$ if and only if $0 < a$ and $b < 0$ or $a < 0$ and $0 < b$.

The fact that the system of integers possesses all of the order properties but not all of the field properties leads us to suspect that the order properties are *not* consequences of the field properties. The student who is familiar with *modular number systems* already knows that there are fields which are not ordered fields. In Chapter 7 we shall actually study those modular number systems which are fields but which do not possess the order properties. In Chapter 6 we shall see another example of a field which is not ordered; namely, the *complex number system*. These examples (called *counterexamples*) will constitute *proof* that the order properties are not consequences of the field properties.

Exercise 1.3

I. (1) Prove that $(R, +, \times, <)$ is an ordered field.

   (2) Prove that $(R_a, +, \times, <)$ is an ordered field.

II. (1) Prove that $(I, +, \times, <)$ possesses all properties of an ordered field except F9.

   (2) Prove that $(E, +, \times, <)$ possesses all properties of an ordered field except F8 and F9.

   (3) Let O = the set of odd integers. Which ordered field properties does $(O, +, \times, <)$ possess?

   (4) Let I^+ = the set of positive integers = $\{1, 2, 3, \ldots\}$. Which ordered field properties does $(I^+, +, \times, <)$ possess?

   (5) Let I^- = the set of negative integers = $\{^-1, ^-2, ^-3, \ldots\}$. Which ordered field properties does $(I^-, +, \times, <)$ possess?

III. (1) Give an example in which $a/b < c/d$ but $ad \not< bc$ if b and d are not restricted to be positive integers.

   (2) Prove that the product of two positive real numbers is a positive real number. (*Hint.* Use Property O3.)

IV. (1) Prove: If the symbol "$<$" is replaced by the symbol "$>$" in the statement of Properties O1 through O5, the resulting properties are valid in an ordered field.

   (2) Prove that $a < b$ if and only if $^-b < ^-a$ for all real numbers a and b.

   (3) Prove that every negative real number is less than every positive real number.

1.4 Density of Real Numbers

Recall that the set C_0 possesses the *well-ordering property*. That is, if A is any nonempty subset of C_0, then there is one and only one element a_0 which is the smallest (or least) element of A. For example, if $A = \{5, 3, 7\}$, then $a_0 = 3$. However, if $A = C_0$, then $a_0 = 0$. The sets I, R_a, and R do not possess the well-ordering property. To prove this fact for I, for example, we note merely that $I^- \subset I$ and that I^- does not contain a least element; that is, the set $\{-1, -2, -3, \ldots\}$ does not contain a least element. To prove that R_a does not possess the well-ordering property, we observe that $B = \{r: 0 < r \land r \in R_a\}$ is a nonempty subset of R_a which does not have a least element. No matter what element r_0 we may *assume* to be the least element of B, we can compute a smaller one. For example, if we assume 0.001 to be the least element of B, we see that 0.0005 is even smaller. In general, if r_0 is assumed to be the least element of B, we see that the average (arithmetic mean) of 0 and r_0 is even less than r_0; that is, $0 < r_0/2$ and $r_0/2 < r_0$. This contradiction proves that B does not contain a least element. Hence R_a does not possess the well-ordering property. The proof that R does not possess the well-ordering property is similar.

We may employ the above technique to prove that between every pair of points on the number line (corresponding to two different real numbers) there is another point. For example, between the points corresponding to the real numbers $\sqrt{2}$ and π is the point corresponding to the real number $(\sqrt{2} + \pi)/2$. Similarly, between 6.8 and 6.9 is 6.85. These are illustrated in Figures 1.1 and 1.2, respectively.

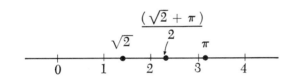

FIGURE 1.1

FIGURE 1.2

It follows readily that there are *infinitely many* points between any two different points on the number line (and hence that there are infinitely many real numbers between any two different real numbers). Thus it appears that the real numbers "fill up" the number line. The proof of this fact actually depends on an important property known as the *Dedekind property*, which is independent of the preceding properties.

DEDEKIND PROPERTY

If $A \cap B = \phi$, $A \cup B = R$, $A \neq \phi$, $B \neq \phi$, and each element of A is less than every element of B, then A contains a largest element, or B contains a least element, but not both.

If we assume that there is a one-to-one correspondence between the set of points on the number line and the set of real numbers, then the Dedekind property assures us that the real numbers "fill up" the number line. That is, there are no "holes" or "gaps" in the number line.

Another property of real numbers, closely related to the Dedekind property, is the *Archimedean property.* The Archimedean property is especially useful in geometric constructions. In the language of real numbers it may be stated as follows.

ARCHIMEDEAN PROPERTY

If a and b are any positive real numbers such that $a < b$, then there exists a positive integer k such that $b < ak$.

For example, if $a = 0.17$ and $b = 169$, then k may be chosen as 1000. Obviously, any number larger than 1000 may be used for k. Is there a positive integer smaller than 1000 which will satisfy the Archimedean property?

Recall that *the absolute value of the real number a*, denoted by $|a|$, is equal to

(a) ^-a if a is negative,

(b) 0 if $a = 0$,

(c) a if a is positive.

For example, $|^-3| = {}^-(^-3) = 3$, $|0| = 0$, $|\sqrt{2}| = \sqrt{2}$, $|\frac{-2}{3}| = \frac{2}{3}$, and $|5 + {}^-7| = 2$. The absolute value of a is the distance, on the number line, between the point a and the point 0. Thus $|^-\sqrt{2}| =$ distance between $^-\sqrt{2}$ and 0; i.e., $|^-\sqrt{2}| = \sqrt{2}$. Similarly, $|\sqrt{2}| =$ distance between $\sqrt{2}$ and 0; i.e., $|\sqrt{2}| = \sqrt{2}$.

Since the real numbers completely "fill up" the number line, the reader may be tempted to conclude that there is no further need for extension of the number system. However, in Chapter 5 we shall see the need for a more inclusive number system. In Chapter 6 we shall actually develop that larger number system, called the *complex number system.* In the meantime, we shall continue the study of the real number system with particular applications to problems of algebra.

Exercise 1.4

I. Compute the least element of each of the following subsets of C_0.

(1) $A = \{0, 1, 2, 3\}$ (4) $D = \{5, 10, 15, \ldots\}$

(2) $B = \{0, 2, 4, \ldots\}$ (5) $E = \{2, 4, 6, \ldots\}$

(3) $C = \{17\}$ (6) $F = \{10, 3, 9, 5\}$

II. Illustrate the Archimedean property in each of the following. Compute the *smallest* integer k such that $b < ak$.

(1) $a = 3.1, b = 97$ (4) $a = 0.1, b = 27$

(2) $a = 1/7, b = 22/7$ (5) $a = 0.05, b = 50,000$

(3) $a = 1/7, b = 22$ (6) $a = 0.003, b = 30,000$

III. (1) Let $A = \{r: r < 7\}$ and $B = \{s: 7 \leq s\}$.
Prove that A and B satisfy the statement of the Dedekind property. Compute the largest element of A *or* the smallest element of B.

(2) Let $A = \{r: r \leq 7\}$ and $B = \{s: 7 < s\}$.
Prove that A and B satisfy the statement of the Dedekind property. Compute the largest element of A *or* the smallest element of B.

(3) Let $A = \{r: r \leq {}^{-}5\}$ and $B = \{s: {}^{-}5 < s\}$.
Prove that A and B satisfy the statement of the Dedekind property. Compute the largest element of A *or* the smallest element of B.

(4) Let $A = \{r: r < {}^{-}5\}$ and $B = \{s: {}^{-}5 \leq s\}$.
Prove that A and B satisfy the statement of the Dedekind property. Compute the largest element of A *or* the smallest element of B.

(5) Let $A = \{r: r < 2/5\}$ and $B = \{s: 2/5 < s\}$. Does the Dedekind property apply? Why?

(6) Let $A = \{r: r \leq 6.7\}$ and $B = \{s: 6.7 \leq s\}$. Does the Dedekind property apply? Why?

IV. Compute each of the following.

(1) $|{}^{-}5|$ (2) $|2 + {}^{-}5|$ (3) $|{}^{-}3(7 + {}^{-}7)|$ (4) $|2 + \sqrt{3}|$

CHAPTER 2

LINEAR EQUATIONS
AND LINEAR INEQUALITIES
IN ONE VARIABLE

2.1 Classical Terminology

In your previous studies you have converted open sentences to true sentences by replacement of the variables by elements of the set under consideration; i.e., by elements of the universal set. For example, you have converted the open sentence $2v - 3 = 7$ to the true sentence $2(5) - 3 = 7$ by replacement of the *variable* v by the positive integer 5. You have undoubtedly referred to open sentences of the type $2x - 3 = 7$ as *equations*. Other words with which you are probably familiar are *expression, term,* and *coefficient*. In this section we shall formally define all of these words and several others.

DEFINITION 1. A symbol is said to be a *variable* if and only if it represents any member of the universal set.

For example, if the universal set is the set of all real numbers, the symbol x in the open sentence $3x + 2 = 14$ is a variable. In particular, since x represents a real number, it is frequently called a *real variable*. Henceforth, in this text, unless otherwise specified, all variables are real variables.

If x is a variable, then $x + 3$ is also a variable. Similarly $3x + 4 - 2/3x + {}^-7/5$ is also a variable. It is convenient to refer to such variables as *expressions* or *phrases*.

DEFINITION 2. An *expression* (or *phrase*) is a numeral, variable, or combination of numerals and variables.

The following examples illustrate Definition 2.

Example 1. 0 is an expression.

Example 2. 3 is an expression.

Example 3. x is an expression.

Example 4. $2/3 + {}^-x$ is an expression.

Example 5. $1/2 + 4/5x + {}^-2x/3y$ is an expression.

Example 6. $(1/2)(5/12)({}^-3x + y - 2z)$ is an expression.

Example 7. $3x + 3y + 3z$ is an expression.

Example 8. $\dfrac{({}^-4 + 0)5 + 3x}{y - t}$ is an expression.

Example 9. ${}^-16t^2 + 25t + 100$ is an expression.

Example 10. xy/z^2 is an expression.

We say that the expression $2/3 + {}^-x$ in Example 4 contains two terms, $2/3$ and ${}^-x$. The expression of Example 5 contains the three terms $1/2$, $4/5x$, and ${}^-2x/3y$, whereas the expression of Example 6 contains the single term $(1/2)(5/12)({}^-3x + y - 2z)$. The expression of Example 7 contains three terms. Similarly, the expression of Example 9 contains three terms. However, the expression of Example 8 has only the one term, $\dfrac{({}^-4 + 0)5 + 3x}{y - t}$, and the expression of Example 10 has only one term.

DEFINITION 3. The *terms* of the expression $v_1 + v_2 + \ldots + v_k$ are v_1, v_2, $\ldots$, and v_k.

Notice that each of the terms v_1, v_2, $\ldots$, v_k may, itself, be an expression containing more than one term.

Example 11. $v_1 + v_2 + v_3$ contains 3 terms.

Example 12. $(x + y) + (2x + {}^-3y) + {}^-(2t + 3u + {}^-5y) + {}^-2$ contains 4 terms.

Example 13. $5w + 5x + 5y + 5z$ contains 4 terms.

Example 14. $5(w + x + y + z)$ contains 1 term.

Example 15. $5x + 2y + 5y + z$ contains 4 terms.

Example 16. $(5x + 2y) + (5y + z)$ contains 2 terms.

The above examples illustrate the fact that the number of terms in an expression depends on the *punctuation* in the expression.

DEFINITION 4.   The *coefficient* of the variable v in the term av of an expression is a.

In Example 4 the coefficient of the variable x is ⁻1. In Example 7, the coefficient of each variable is 3. In Example 9, the coefficient of the variable t^2 is ⁻16 and the coefficient of the variable t in the term $25t$ is 25. In Example 10, the coefficient of the variable xy/z^2 is 1, the coefficient of the variable xy is $1/z^2$, the coefficient of the variable y/z^2 is x, the coefficient of the variable x/z^2 is y, etc.

Now we shall study special types of expressions. The terminology and computational techniques employed here will be useful throughout your mathematical studies. Any expression may be classified according to the number of terms it contains.

DEFINITION 5.   A *monomial* is an expression consisting of exactly one term.

DEFINITION 6.   A *binomial* is an expression consisting of exactly two terms.

DEFINITION 7.   A *multinomial* is an expression consisting of more than one term.

Example 17. $3x^2/2t$ is a monomial.

Example 18. $5(2 + {}^-3xt)$ is a monomial.

Example 19. $10 + {}^-15xt$ is a binomial.

Example 20. $2x({}^-4 + t) + {}^-7/y$ is a binomial.

Example 21. $ax^2 + bx + c$ is a multinomial.

Example 22. $2 + {}^-x + 6y/z + 2t$ is a multinomial.

Example 23. $5 + 7x$ is a multinomial.

We see that any binomial is a multinomial. If we agree that the terms of any multinomial are numbered from left to right, we may say that the first term of the multinomial in Example 21 is ax^2, the second term is bx, and the third term is c.

Now we wish to formulate a mathematical model of the following physical problem: If the sum of three consecutive integers is 15, what is the first integer? A mathematical model of this physical problem is $\{x: x + (x + 1) + (x + 2) = 15\}$, in which the variable x represents the first integer. In the classical approach to the same physical problem, one would require the *solution* or *root* of the *equation* $x + (x + 1) + (x + 2) = 15$. We introduce the second model because of its almost universal usage.

DEFINITION 8. An *equation* is a sentence or open sentence which declares that two expressions are equal.

Example 24. $6 + 3 = 9$ is an equation.

Example 25. $1 + 2 = 7$ is an equation.

Example 26. $x^2 - 2 = 0$ is an equation.

Example 27. $2x = 2x - 3$ is an equation.

Example 28. $x + 3x = 4x$ is an equation.

Example 29. $x + (x + 1) + (x + 2) = 15$ is an equation.

Example 30. $3x + 3 = 15$ is an equation.

Whenever we say that two expressions are equal, we really mean that they both represent the *same* number.

The equation of Example 24 is a true sentence, whereas the equation of Example 25 is a false sentence. The equations of Examples 26 through 30 are open sentences which cannot be classified as true or false. However, each of these equations can be converted to a sentence by the method of quantification or by the method of replacement of the variable. To convert an open sentence to a true sentence by the replacement method, we must replace the variable by some element of the universal set. For example, the open sentence $3x + 3 = 15$ can be converted to a *true* sentence by replacement of the variable x by the real number 4. If we replace x by any *other* real number, the open sentence $3x + 3 = 15$ is converted to a *false* sentence. We say that the *solution set* of $3x + 3 = 15$ is $\{4\}$. If we replace the variable x in the equation $x + 3x = 4x$ by *any* real number, that open sentence is converted to a *true* sentence. We say that the *solution set* of the equation $x + 3x = 4x$ is the universal set R (the set of reals). If we replace the variable in the open sentence $2x = 2x - 3$ by *any* real number, that open sentence is converted to a *false* sentence. We say that the *solution set* of the equation $2x = 2x - 3$ is the null set, ϕ. In general, we define the solution set of any open sentence as follows.

DEFINITION 9. The subset S of the universal set is said to be the *solution set* of an open sentence. p_x if and only if replacement of the variable x in p_x by any element of S converts the open sentence p_x to a true sentence and replacement of the variable x in p_x by any element of S converts the open sentence p_x to a false sentence.

In the following section we shall learn to compute the solution sets of some open sentences. In your previous studies when you converted open sentences to true sentences, you were computing subsets of their solution sets. In most cases, these subsets were actually the solution sets.

The following definition relates the classical words *solution* and *root* to the *solution set* of an equation.

DEFINITION 10. Any element of the solution set of an equation is called a *solution* (or *root*) of the equation.

For example, a solution (or root) of the equation $3x + 3 = 15$ is 4. We frequently *write* "$x = 4$" and *say* "4 is a solution of $3x + 3 = 15$." The words *solve the equation* mean *compute the solution set of the equation*.

Exercise 2.1

I. Identify the coefficient of the variable in each of the following expressions.

(1) $3x$ (6) $(^-2/3)x$

(2) $(^-5/3)y$ (7) $3t$

(3) $\sqrt{2}\,t$ (8) $(2/3 + ^-5/4)s$

(4) ^-5z (9) $(^-2/3 + 4)y$

(5) $17w$ (10) $10t$

II. Identify the coefficient of the variable x in each of the following expressions.

(1) ^-3x (3) ^-3ax

(2) $(^-3 + a)x$ (4) $abcx$

(5) $(a + b + c)x$ (8) $^-(2 + a)x$

(6) $(2a/3)x$ (9) $(ab^2 + ^-c)x$

(7) $axyz$ (10) $0x$

III. Identify each of the following expressions as monomial or multinomial.

(1) $2 + ^-3x$ (6) $5 + 2x + 6y$

(2) $^-3 + 2x + 7y + z$ (7) $x^2 + ^-3x + 4$

(3) $(2/3x + 4)/(5x^2 + 5x^3)$ (8) $3 + ^-2t + t^2 + 7t^3 + ^-8t^4$

(4) $(4 + 2x + 5)/(6t + ^-2/3y)$ (9) $0 + 4y + 8z$

(5) x (10) $4y + 8z$

IV. Identify each binomial in Exercise III.

V. Tell which of the following are equations.

(1) $3y = 3$

(2) $2 = 1/3$

(3) $ab = ba$

(4) $3/4 < 7/8$

(5) $4x \div 6/3$

(6) $3x = 2x + 1$

(7) The sun is larger than the earth.

(8) $3x - 2 + 1$

(9) $2(x + 5) = 2x + 5$

(10) $2(x + 5) = 2x + 10$

(11) $2(x)(3) = 5$

(12) $2(x + 5) = 2x + 3$

(13) $z + 3 + 2/3z$

(14) $|3x + 5| = 3x$

(15) $x^2 + 2x + 1 = 0$

(16) $x^2 + 2x + 1$

(17) $x^2 - 9 = (x - 3)(x + 3)$

(18) $x^2 - 9 = 0$

(19) $\sqrt{x + 4} = 4$

(20) $\sqrt{x + 4}$

VI. Tell which of the equations in Exercise V above are open sentences.

VII. Guess the solution set of each of the following equations.

(1) $x + ^-1 = 0$ (6) $\sqrt{x} = 2$

(2) $2x = 2$ (7) $x^2 = 4$

(3) $2x = 0$ (8) $3x = 1/2$

(4) $2x + 2 = 4$ (9) $3x = 1$

(5) $4x + 1 = x + 4$ (10) $12x = 4$

2.2   Addition and Multiplication of Expressions

Before studying equations and inequalities we shall consider the techniques involved in the combinations and expansions of expressions by the operations of addition and multiplication. Skills in these techniques will be useful in the computation of the solution set of an equation or inequality. The field properties and properties derivable from them are quite useful. In every example, the variable represents any real number; i.e., the universal set is the set of reals.

The following examples illustrate addition of expressions.

Example 1. $4x + 3x = (4 + 3)x = 7x.$

Example 2. $4x + (3x + {}^-7x) = 4x + 3x + {}^-7x = (4 + 3 + {}^-7)x = 0x = 0.$

Example 3. $(7xy + 3xy + {}^-4xy) + ({}^-10xy + 20xy + xy + {}^-2xy) =$
$(7 + 3 + {}^-4)xy + ({}^-10 + 20 + 1 + {}^-2)xy = 6xy + 9xy$
$= (6 + 9)xy = 15xy.$

Example 4. $(4x + 5y) + {}^-7x = 4x + 5y + {}^-7x = 4x + {}^-7x + 5y =$
$(4 + {}^-7)x + 5y = {}^-3x + 5y.$

Example 5. $2x + 4y + \sqrt{5}\,x = 2x + \sqrt{5}\,x + 4y = (2 + \sqrt{5})x + 4y.$

Example 6. $({}^-2x + 3) + y - 2(11x - 5 + 4y) = {}^-2x + 3 + y + {}^-2(11x$
$- 5 + 4y) = {}^-2x + 3 + y + {}^-22x + 10 + {}^-8y = ({}^-2 + {}^-22)x$
$+ (1 + {}^-8)y + (3 + 10) = {}^-24x + {}^-7y + 13.$

Example 7. $({}^-1/3) + ({}^-7/3)x + (4/5)xy + 3 + (1/5)xy = ({}^-7/3)x$
$+ (4/5)xy + (1/5)xy + 3 + {}^-1/3 = ({}^-7/3)x + (4/5 +$
$1/5)xy + (9/3 + {}^-1/3) = ({}^-7/3)x + xy + 8/3.$

Example 8. $2.13x - 5.26x - 7.45y - 6.35y - 2.15 = (2.13 + {}^-5.26)x$
$+ ({}^-7.45 - 6.35)y + {}^-2.15 = {}^-3.13x + {}^-13.80y + {}^-2.15.$

Example 9. $\sqrt{3}\,x + \sqrt{2}\,y + 2.1x - 6x^2 = \sqrt{3}\,x + 2.1x + \sqrt{2}\,y - 6x^2$
$= (\sqrt{3} + 2.1)x - 6x^2 + \sqrt{2}\,y.$

Example 10. ${}^-2/3 - (4/5)x + (7/3)y + (3/10)x = {}^-2/3 + ({}^-4/5)x +$
$(3/10)x + (7/3)y = {}^-2/3 + ({}^-8/10 + 3/10)x + (7/3)y$
$= {}^-2/3 + ({}^-5/10)x + (7/3)y = {}^-2/3 + ({}^-1/2)x + (7/3)y.$

The following examples illustrate the technique of multiplication of expressions.

Example 11. $\quad x(x+1) = xx + x1 = x^2 + x.$

Example 12. $\quad x^2(x^3 + {}^-3x^4) = x^2(x^3) + x^2({}^-3x^4) = x^5 + {}^-3x^6.$

Example 13. $\quad ({}^-4x^3 + {}^-3x^2)x^4 = {}^-4x^3(x^4) + {}^-3x^2(x^4) = {}^-4x^7 + {}^-3x^6.$

Example 14. $\quad (x + {}^-1)(x + 3) = (x + {}^-1)x + (x + {}^-1)3 = x^2 + {}^-1x + 3x + {}^-3 = x^2 + 2x - 3.$

Example 15. $\quad (x + y)(x - y) = (x + y)(x + {}^-y) = (x + y)x + (x + y){}^-y = x^2 + xy + x({}^-y) + y({}^-y) = x^2 + xy + {}^-xy + {}^-y^2 = x^2 + {}^-y^2 = x^2 - y^2.$

Example 16. $\quad (2x + 7)({}^-1x^2 + 5x) = (2x + 7){}^-1x^2 + (2x + 7)5x = 2x({}^-1x^2) + 7({}^-1x^2) + 2x(5x) + 7(5x) = {}^-2x^3 + {}^-7x^2 + 10x^2 + 35x = {}^-2x^3 + 3x^2 + 35x.$

Example 17. $\quad (x + 3)(x + 2y) = (x + 3)x + (x + 3)2y = x^2 + 3x + 2xy + 6y.$

Example 18. $\quad (3x + 5)(x^3 + {}^-3x^2y + 6) = (3x + 5)(x^3) + (3x + 5)({}^-3x^2y) + (3x + 5)6 = 3x^4 + 5x^3 + {}^-9x^3y + {}^-15x^2y + 18x + 30.$

Example 19. $\quad 4 + {}^-4(x + 3)5 + {}^-5 = 4 + ({}^-4)(5)(x + 3) + {}^-5 = 4 + {}^-20(x + 3) + {}^-5 = (4 + {}^-5) + {}^-20(x + 3) = {}^-1 + {}^-20x + {}^-60 = {}^-20x + {}^-61.$

Example 20. $\quad (x + y)^2 = (x + y)(x + y) = (x + y)x + (x + y)y = x^2 + yx + xy + y^2 = x^2 + 2xy + y^2.$

Example 21. $\quad (x + y + z)^2 = (x + y + z)(x + y + z)$
$$= (x + y + z)x + (x + y + z)y + (x + y + z)z$$
$$= x^2 + xy + xz + xy + y^2 + yz + xz + yz + z^2$$
$$= x^2 + y^2 + z^2 + 2xy + 2xz + 2yz.$$

Example 22. $\quad {}^-2xy(3x + {}^-4y + 5z + {}^-7) = {}^-2xy(3x) + ({}^-2xy)({}^-4y) + ({}^-2xy)(5z) + ({}^-2xy)({}^-7) = {}^-6x^2y + 8xy^2 + {}^-10xyz + 14xy.$

Example 23. $(x-y)(x^2+xy+y^2) = (x-y)x^2 + (x-y)xy + (x-y)y^2$
$$= (x + {}^-y)x^2 + (x + {}^-y)xy + (x + {}^-y)y^2$$
$$= x^3 + {}^-x^2y + x^2y + {}^-xy^2 + xy^2 + {}^-y^3$$
$$= x^3 + {}^-y^3$$
$$= x^3 - y^3.$$

Example 24. $(x-a)^2 = (x + {}^-a)^2$
$$= (x + {}^-a)(x + {}^-a)$$
$$= (x + {}^-a)x + (x + {}^-a)^-a$$
$$= x^2 + {}^-ax + {}^-ax + ({}^-a)({}^-a)$$
$$= x^2 + {}^-2ax + a^2$$
$$= x^2 - 2ax + a^2.$$

Although the techniques in this section are probably familiar to you from high school algebra, they are included as review of high school algebraic manipulations and as applications of the important field properties. You should justify each step in each of the above examples as an application of one of the field properties, or a consequence of the field properties, or a definition. We justify Example 24 as follows:

$(x-a)^2 = (x + {}^-a)^2$ (by definition of subtraction),

$(x + {}^-a)^2 = (x + {}^-a)(x + {}^-a)$ (by definition of exponent),

$(x + {}^-a)(x + {}^-a) = (x + {}^-a)x + (x + {}^-a)^-a$ (by the distributive property),

$(x + {}^-a)x + (x + {}^-a)^-a = x^2 + {}^-ax + {}^-ax + ({}^-a)({}^-a)$ (by DP and commutative property for multiplication),

$x^2 + {}^-ax + {}^-ax + ({}^-a)({}^-a) = x^2 + {}^-2ax + a^2$ (by DP, definition of addition, and sign property for multiplication),

$x^2 + {}^-2ax + a^2 = x^2 - 2ax + a^2$ (by definition of subtraction).

Exercise 2.2

I. Justify each step in Examples 2, 3, 7, 9, 10, 12, 14, 16, 19, 21, 22, and 23.

II. Write the simplest expression equal to each of the following expressions.

(1) $23ax + 2ax + {}^-25ax$

(2) $(1/2)x + (3/4)x + (3/2)x + {}^-x$

(3) $\sqrt{2}\,x + 3y + 5\sqrt{2}\,x$

(4) $101x + {}^-3c + {}^-99x + 3c$

(5) $\sqrt{5} + \sqrt{9} + \sqrt{x} + {}^-3\sqrt{5} + 4\sqrt{9}$

(6) $2.1x + (3/\text{-}2)y + 1.1x + 2x + (\text{-}4/3)y$

(7) $27/5 + z/3 + \text{-}3/5 + \text{-}3/4 + 1/5$

(8) $2 + x + y$

(9) $2 + 7x$

(10) $2xy + \text{-}3xz + 4zy + tyz + 2xz$

III. Combine or expand each of the following expressions as indicated. The final answer should not contain any parentheses or brackets.

(1) $3 + 2x(2 + \text{-}5)5 + \text{-}3$

(2) $3x + 2x(2 + 5x)4 + \text{-}3$

(3) $5[2 + 3(\text{-}2 + x)(\text{-}4x) + 2(x + \text{-}3)]$

(4) $3 + 9x + 7 + \text{-}6x + \text{-}4(x + \text{-}3)$

(5) $\text{-}4 + (7x + 3) + \text{-}2(x + 5) + (3 + 2x)7 + (3 + 3x) + 7$

(6) $2x + 4x + (3x + 5 + x)4 + \text{-}3(x + 1) + 3$

(7) $0x + x + 2x + 3x + 4x + 5$

(8) $1(x + 2) + 2(x + 1) + 3(x + 5)$

(9) $6 + \text{-}6(x + 3 + \text{-}5x + \text{-}3)$

(10) $6 + (\text{-}6x + 3 + \text{-}5x + \text{-}3)$

(11) $(6 + \text{-}6)(x + 3 + \text{-}5x + \text{-}3)$

(12) $(6 + \text{-}6)(x) + 3(\text{-}5x + \text{-}3)$

(13) $6 + \text{-}6x[3(\text{-}5x + \text{-}3)]$

(14) $6 + (\text{-}6x + 3)(\text{-}5x) + \text{-}3$

(15) $6 + \text{-}6(x + 3) + \text{-}(\text{-}5x + \text{-}3)$

(16) $6 + \text{-}6(x + 3) + \text{-}(5x + \text{-}3)$

(17) $6 + (\text{-}6x + 3) + (\text{-}5x + \text{-}3)$

(18) $(6 + \text{-}6)(x + 3) + (\text{-}5x + \text{-}3)$

(19) $(6 + \text{-}6)(x + 3 + \text{-}5x) + \text{-}3$

(20) $(6 + \text{-}6x) + 3 + \text{-}5x + \text{-}3$

(21) $(6 + \text{-}6x + 3)(\text{-}5x + \text{-}3)$

(22) $(6 + \text{-}6x)(3 + \text{-}5x + \text{-}3)$

(23) $(6 + \text{-}6x + 3)(\text{-}5x) + \text{-}3$

(24) $6 + \text{-}6[x(3 + \text{-}5x + \text{-}3)]$

(25) $\text{-}(6 + \text{-}6x) + 3 + 5x - \text{-}3$

(26) $(x + \text{-}3)(4 + 7x)$

(27) $(x + 2y)(3 + \text{-}5y)$

(28) $(2x - 3)(x + y + 3)$

(29) $(x + y + z)[4 + 2(y + 3x)]$

(30) $[(2/3)x + 4/5](\text{-}15x + 45)$

(31) $(x + 2y + 3z)^2$

(32) $(x - 2y - 3z)^2$

(33) $(a + x)^3$

(34) $(a - 2x)^3$

(35) $(x - 2a)(x + 2a)$

(36) $(x - 2)(x^2 + 2x + 4)$
(37) $(x + 2)(x^2 - 2x + 4)$
(38) $(x + y)(x^2 - xy + y^2)$
(39) $(x + 2y)(x^2 - 2xy + y^2)$
(40) $x^2yz^3(x^2 + yz - z^2 - xz - 2xy)$

2.3   Linear Equations

In this section we shall define *linear equation* in one variable and develop a method for computing its solution set. As the linear equation serves as a mathematical model for many physical problems, its solution set serves as the model for the solutions of these physical problems. After you have learned to solve any linear equation in one variable, you will be able to solve many different physical problems, without having to learn a set of different techniques for the different problems.

The following example illustrates the method of computing the solution set of an equation in one variable.

Example 1.   Compute the solution set of the equation $5x + 12 = 0$. For all x,

$(5x + 12 = 0) \rightarrow (5x + 12 + {}^-12 = 0 + {}^-12)$,
$(5x + 12 + {}^-12 = 0 + {}^-12) \rightarrow (5x = {}^-12)$,
$(5x = {}^-12) \rightarrow ([1/5]5x = [1/5][{}^-12])$,
$([1/5]5x = [1/5][{}^-12]) \rightarrow (x = {}^-12/5)$.
Hence for all x,
$(5x + 12 = 0) \rightarrow (x = {}^-12/5)$.
Conversely for all x,
$(x = {}^-12/5) \rightarrow (5x = 5 \cdot [{}^-12/5])$,
$(5x = 5 \cdot [{}^-12/5]) \rightarrow (5x = {}^-12)$,
$(5x = {}^-12) \rightarrow (5x + 12 = {}^-12 + 12)$,
$(5x + 12 = {}^-12 + 12) \rightarrow (5x + 12 = 0)$.
Hence, for all x,
$(x = {}^-12/5) \rightarrow (5x + 12 = 0)$.
Thus for all x,
$(5x + 12 = 0) \leftrightarrows (x = {}^-12/5)$.
Thus $\{x: 5x + 12 = 0\} = \{x: x = {}^-12/5\} = \{{}^-12/5\}$.

You probably recall from your study of high school algebra that you solved the above linear equation as follows:

$$5x + 12 = 0,$$
$$5x = {}^-12,$$
$$x = {}^-12/5.$$

The method you used is a short-hand method for the solution in Example 1. In fact, the short-hand method is an abbreviation for the following sequence of steps:

$$\text{for all } x, 5x + 12 = 0$$
$$\Leftrightarrow 5x = ^-12$$
$$\Leftrightarrow x = ^-12/5.$$

The important point in the latter argument is that each step is reversible, as shown by the double arrow $\Leftrightarrow$. That is, each step in the computation is of the form $p \Leftrightarrow q$. Every replacement for x which converts the open sentence $5x + 12 = 0$ to a true sentence also converts the open sentence $x = ^-12/5$ to a true sentence. Conversely, every replacement which converts the open sentence $x = ^-12/5$ to a true sentence also converts $5x + 12 = 0$ to a true sentence. In general, the open sentence p_x *is equivalent to* the open sentence q_x if and only if they have the same solution set.

The following example illustrates that certain manipulations on an equation may reduce that equation to one which is *not* equivalent to the original equation.

Example 2. Compute the solution set of $x(x - 1) = 3(x - 1)$.

$$x(x - 1) = 3(x - 1)$$
$$\frac{1}{x - 1} \cdot x(x - 1) = \frac{1}{x - 1} \cdot 3(x - 1)$$
$$x = 3.$$

The solution set of $x = 3$ is $\{3\}$. However, the solution set of $x(x - 1) = 3(x - 1)$ is $\{3, 1\}$. Thus $x = 3$ is *not* equivalent to $x(x - 1) = 3(x - 1)$. The reason that the derived equation $x = 3$ is not equivalent to the original equation $x(x - 1) = 3(x - 1)$ is that we eliminated the possibility that x could be equal to 1 when we multiplied by $\frac{1}{x - 1}$.

As the following theorem shows, we can be certain that any step which involves only addition of any expression to both members of an equation yields an equation equivalent to the given equation. Also any step involving multiplication of both members of an equation by a nonzero real number yields an equation equivalent to the given equation.

THEOREM 1. (a) If u_1 and u_2 are any expressions and u is any expression, then the equation $u_1 = u_2$ is equivalent to the equation $u_1 + u = u_2 + u$.

(b) If u_1 and u_2 are any expressions and r is any nonzero real number, then the equation $u_1 = u_2$ is equivalent to the equation $u_1 r = u_2 r$.

Proof.   (a) For all variables in u_1, u_2, and u,
$$(u_1 = u_2) \rightarrow (u_1 + u = u_2 + u).$$
Conversely, for all variables in u_1, u_2, and u,
$$(u_1 + u = u_2 + u) \rightarrow (u_1 + u + {}^-u = u_2 + u + {}^-u)$$
$$(u_1 + u + {}^-u = u_2 + u + {}^-u) \rightarrow (u_1 = u_2).$$
Hence $u_1 = u_2$ is equivalent to $u_1 + u = u_2 + u$.

(b) Left as an exercise.//

The following examples further illustrate the method of computing the solution set of an equation by use of Theorem 1.

Example 3.   Compute the solution set of $5x + 7 = 0$.

$5x + 7 = 0$
$5x + 7 + {}^-7 = 0 + {}^-7$
$5x = {}^-7$
$(1/5)(5x) = (1/5)({}^-7)$
$x = {}^-7/5.$
Thus the solution set is $\{{}^-7/5\}$.

Example 4.   Solve the equation $3x + 2 = 6 - x$.

$3x + 2 = 6 - x$
$3x + 2 + (x + {}^-2) = 6 - x + (x + {}^-2)$
$4x = 4$
$x = 1.$

Example 5.   Compute the solution set of the equation
$2x - 5 = 3 - {}^-2x.$

$2x - 5 = 3 - {}^-2x$
$2x - 5 = 3 + 2x$
$2x - 5 + ({}^-2x + 5) = 3 + 2x + ({}^-2x + 5)$
$0 = 8.$
Thus $\{x: 2x - 5 = 3 - {}^-2x\} = \{x: 0 = 8\} = \phi$.
Hence the solution set is empty; i.e., there is no replacement which converts $2x - 5 = 3 - {}^-2x$ to a true sentence.

Example 6.   Solve the equation $(3/4)x + 2/5 = 1/2 + (7/10)x$.

To simplify the computation, we multiply both members by the least common denominator: $[4, 5, 2, 10] = 20$.
Thus $20[(3/4)x + 2/5] = 20[1/2 + (7/10)x]$
$20(3/4)x + 20(2/5) = 20(1/2) + 20(7/10)x$

$$15x + 8 = 10 + 14x$$
$$15x + 8 + (^-8 + ^-14x) = 10 + 14x + (^-8 + ^-14x)$$
$$x = 2.$$

Example 7.   Compute the solution set of $2x - 5 = ^-5 + 2x$.

$$2x - 5 = ^-5 + 2x$$
$$2x - 5 + (^-2x + 5) = ^-5 + 2x + (^-2x + 5)$$
$$0 = 0$$

Thus $\{x: 2x - 5 = ^-5 + 2x\} = \{x: 0 = 0\} = R$; i.e., every real number is a root of $2x - 5 = ^-5 + 2x$.

The equations in Examples 1, 3, 4, and 6 are called *linear equations in one variable.*

DEFINITION 11.   An equation is said to be a *linear equation* in *one variable* if and only if it can be reduced to the form $ax + b = 0$, where $a \neq 0$, by means of Theorem 1.

Although the equations in Examples 5 and 7 resemble linear equations, at first glance, they are *not* linear equations. Examples 1, 3, 4, and 6 illustrate the fact that any linear equation has exactly one root. The following theorem asserts that this is true.

THEOREM 2.   The solution set of the linear equation $ax + b = 0$ is the set $\{^-b/a\}$.

Proof.   Similar to Example 1.

Exercise 2.3

I. Compute the solution set of each of the following linear equations. Check by replacement of the variable.

(1) $3x + 18 = 0$ (6) $5x + 2 = x + ^-3$
(2) $3x + ^-18 = 0$ (7) $3 + 8x + ^-4 = ^-5$
(3) $2x + 5 = 7$ (8) $x + ^-5 + 3x = 12$
(4) $5x + 2 = 12$ (9) $(1/4)x + ^-6/5 + ^-4x = ^-8/3$
(5) $5x + ^-2 = 8 + x$ (10) $(1/3)x + ^-4/5 = (1/4)x + ^-8$

II. Solve each of the following equations.

(1) $^-3x = x + 4$
(2) $^-x = 3x + 4$
(3) $(3/2) = 4/5$
(4) $3/4 + 2x + 5/6 = 11/5$

(5) $(2/3)x + 7 + (^-3/4)x = 8$
(6) $x + 2/3 + 2x + 5 = 0$
(7) $x(3 + 4) = 3(x + 10)$
(8) $(x + 2)(3 + 7) = 3/5 + (3/5)x$
(9) $(3\,1/2)x + (7\,1/2)x = 11x$
(10) $8x + 3x = 88$
(11) $3x + \,^-4 = 5 + 3x$
(12) $2x = 1 + 2x$
(13) $2x = 1 - 2x$
(14) $(3/5)x + 2 = 5 + (3/5)x - 3$
(15) $(1/2)x + 4/3 = 1/3 + (1/2)x$
(16) $(2/3)x = 4/5 + (2x)/3$
(17) $x/5 = 2/3 + (1/5)x$
(18) $x + 7 = 2(7 + x)/2$
(19) $x + 3 = 3 + x$
(20) $x + 3 = 3 - x$

III. (1) Prove Theorem 1(b).
    (2) Prove Theorem 2.

IV. Check each of the following equations to determine whether it is linear.

(1) $x + 1 = 1$ (6) $x + 3 = 2 + x$
(2) $x - 1 = 0$ (7) $7 - 2x = \,^-2x + 3$
(3) $3x + 7 = 2$ (8) $^-2x + 3 = 3 - 2x$
(4) $x = 3$ (9) $3x - 7 = 4 + 7x$
(5) $x + 3 = 3 + x$ (10) $5 - 6x = 5 - 2x$

2.4   Applications of Linear Equations

Now that we know how to solve the linear equation in one variable, we shall study some applications of linear equations. Although the mathematical models of some physical problems are more easily formulated by arithmetic methods, the models of many physical problems are most easily formulated in terms of open sentences. The following examples illustrate the applications of linear equations in one variable.

Example 1.   Compute three consecutive integers whose sum is 15.

We formulate a mathematical model as follows:
Let x represent the first integer. Then $x + 1$ represents the second integer, and $x + 2$ represents the third integer. The universal set is the set of integers. The linear equation whose solution represents the first integer is
$x + (x + 1) + (x + 2) = 15$.
We solve as in Section 2.3.

$x + (x + 1) + (x + 2) = 15$
$3x + 3 = 15$
$x = 4$.

Since the possibility exists that the mathematical model was formulated incorrectly, we should check the solution in the *given* problem.

Thus we should check whether the sum of the integers 4, 5, and 6 is equal to 15.

We see that $4 + 5 + 6 = 15$, and hence that the solution of the *given* problem is complete and correct.

Example 2.   Compute three consecutive integers whose sum is 16.

We formulate a mathematical model as follows:

Let x represent the first integer. Then $x + 1$ represents the second integer, and $x + 2$ represents the third integer. The universal set is the set of integers. We solve as in Section 2.3.

$x + (x + 1) + (x + 2) = 16$
$3x + 3 = 16$

Since $3 \mid 13$ and $U = I$, we see that the solution set of $3x = 13$ is the empty set. Thus the sum of three consecutive integers cannot be 16.

Example 3.   Barbara has $1.44 in pennies and nickels. She has 6 more pennies than nickels. How many nickels does Barbara have? How many pennies does Barbara have?

We formulate the mathematical model as follows:

Let $U = C_0$ and let x represent the number of nickels.

Then $x + 6$ represents the number of pennies.

Hence $.05x + .01(x + 6) = 1.44$ (in dollar value).

Thus $5x + (x + 6) = 144$ (in penny value).

$5x + x = 144 - 6$.
$6x = 138$.
$x = 23$.
$x + 6 = 29$.

Hence Barbara has 23 nickels and 29 pennies.

Again, we check the answer, not in the mathematical model, but in the original physical problem.

The dollar value of 23 nickels is $1.15.

The dollar value of 29 pennies is $.29.

Consequently the dollar value of 23 nickels and 29 pennies is $1.44.

Example 4.   Mr. Morris is three times as old as his daughter. In 13 years, he will be twice as old as his daughter. What is Mr. Morris's present age?

We formulate the mathematical model as follows:
Let $U = I^+$, and let x represent the daughter's age.
Then $3x$ represents Mr. Morris's age.
In 13 years, the daughter's age will be $x + 13$, and Mr. Morris's age will be $3x + 13$.
Since Mr. Morris's age in 13 years, $(3x + 13)$, will be *twice* his daughter's age in 13 years, $(x + 13)$, we see that $3x + 13 = 2(x + 13)$.
Hence $3x + 13 = 2x + 26$.
Thus $x = 13$ and $3x = 39$.
The daughter's age is 13, and the father's age is 39. As a check we observe that the daughter's age in 13 years will be 26, and the father's age in 13 years will be 52, twice the daughter's age.

Example 5.   Anthony leaves Boston for Miami at 9:00 AM and drives at an average speed of 40 mph. Jacob leaves Boston at 10:00 AM and follows Anthony at an average speed of 50 mph. At what time will Jacob overtake Anthony?

We formulate a mathematical model as follows:
Let $U = R^+$ and let t represent the number of hours Anthony has traveled when Jacob overtakes him. Then Jacob has traveled $t - 1$ hours when he overtakes Anthony. Since distance = rate × number of time units, we see that Anthony travels $40t$ miles and Jacob travels $50(t - 1)$ miles by the time Jacob overtakes Anthony. Since they both travel the same distance, we see that
$$40t = 50(t - 1)$$
$$40t = 50t - 50$$
$$^-50t + 40t = ^-50$$
$$^-10t = ^-50$$
$$t = 5.$$
Hence Jacob overtakes Anthony in 5 hours. That is, Jacob overtakes Anthony at 2:00 PM.

You may have noticed that the problem of Example 5 can be solved by arithmetic methods. Since Anthony has a 40-mile headstart on Jacob at 10:00 AM, Jacob must travel a distance of 40 miles in *addition to* the distance Anthony travels from 10:00 AM. As Jacob's average speed is 50 mph and Anthony's average speed is 40 mph, Jacob travels an additional 10 miles each hour. Hence, *in 4 hours,* Jacob travels an *additional* 40 miles. Thus Jacob overtakes Anthony 4 hours after 10:00 AM (5 hours after 9:00 AM); i.e., at 2:00 PM. While this method may appear easier to you, you should realize that there are many problems which are not so easily solved without the use of linear equations. Furthermore, Example 5 adequately and simply illustrates the application of linear equations, and simple illustrations are no less valid than difficult ones.

Example 6.   The perimeter of a rectangular lot is 500 feet. The length of the lot exceeds the width by 50 feet. Compute the width and length of the lot.

We formulate a mathematical model as follows:
Let $U = R^+$ and let x represent the width of the lot.
Then $x + 50$ represents the length of the lot.

The perimeter is represented by $x + (x + 50) + x + (x + 50)$.
However, the perimeter is 500 feet.
Thus the width of the lot is the solution of the linear equation $x + (x + 50) + x + (x + 50) = 500$.
$4x + 100 = 500$
$4x = 400$
$x = 100$.
Hence the width is 100 feet, and the length is 150 feet. As a check, we note that $100 + 150 + 100 + 150 = 500$.

Whenever you encounter a physical problem, you should not expect to be able to read it once and immediately formulate a mathematical model for its solution. Rather, you should expect to read it once for the gist of the problem, re-read it for better understanding, and then re-read it in parts, formulate the model in parts, and finally unite all parts of the model and solve. In the following exercises you will have plenty of opportunity to test your skill in this respect. Remember that the exercises are not necessarily the most practical ones but those whose mathematical models are easily formulated. The skills you acquire in this section will help you to solve the more practical problems which will be introduced later in this text and which you may encounter in your other studies.

Exercise 2.4

I. Formulate a mathematical model for each of the following problems, and solve.

(1) Compute three consecutive integers whose sum is 105.

(2) Compute three consecutive integers whose sum is 411.

(3) Compute three consecutive odd integers whose sum is 141.

(4) Compute three consecutive odd integers whose sum is 351.

(5) Compute three consecutive odd integers whose sum is 360.

(6) Compute three consecutive even integers whose sum is 361.

(7) Tommy has $2.17 in pennies and nickels. He has 7 more pennies than nickels. How many of each coin does Tommy have?

(8) Carolyn has $1.04 in pennies and nickels. She has 3 times as many pennies as nickels. How many of each coin does Carolyn have?

(9) Joyce has $3.34 in pennies, nickels, and quarters. She has 5 more nickels than pennies, and 5 fewer quarters than pennies. How many of each coin does Joyce have?

(10) Margaret has $10.60 in nickels, dimes, and quarters. She has 7 more dimes than nickels and 3 times as many quarters as nickels. How many of each coin does Margaret have?

(11) Elaine's father is 3 times as old as Elaine is now. In 10 years from now, he will be twice as old as Elaine will be. How old is Elaine now?

(12) Henry's father is twice as old as Henry is now. In 20 years from now, he will be 1½ times as old as Henry will be. How old is Henry now?

(13) Joseph is 20 years younger than his father. In 15 years he will be 3/5 of his father's age. How old is Joseph now?

(14) Willis leaves New Orleans for Chicago at 6:00 PM and drives at an average speed of 36 mph. Duane leaves New Orleans at 8:00 PM and follows Willis at an average speed of 48 mph. At what time will Duane overtake Willis?

(15) Bobby leaves Dallas for Kansas City at 7:00 AM and drives at an average speed of 30 mph. Leo leaves Dallas at 10:00 AM and follows Bobby at an average speed of 40 mph. At what time will Leo overtake Bobby?

(16) Richard leaves New York for Boston at 12:00 noon and travels at an average speed of 40 mph. Two hours later Thomas leaves New York and travels in the opposite direction at an average speed of 50 mph. At what time are they 170 miles apart?

(17) Robert leaves Lafayette for Little Rock at 6:00 AM and travels at an average speed of 35 mph. One and a half hours later Donald leaves Lafayette and travels in the opposite direction at an average speed of 40 mph. At what time are they 165 miles apart?

(18) The perimeter of a rectangular lot is 300 feet. The length of the lot is twice the width of the lot. Compute the width and the length.

(19) The perimeter of a rectangular lot is 300 feet. The length of the lot is 1½ times the width of the lot. Compute the width and the length.

(20) A farmer has 1,000 feet of fencing and wishes to fence in a part of his land along a river to restrain his cattle. From experience he knows that his cattle will not enter the river. For this reason he will need only three sides of a rectangular fence. The length of the rectangle (which parallels the river) is to be twice the width of the plot. What are the dimensions of the fenced-in plot?

(21) Compute three consecutive integers such that the sum of the first and the third is equal to 286.

(22) Compute three consecutive integers such that twice the sum of the first and the third is equal to 4 times the second.

(23) Compute three consecutive integers such that the sum of the first and the third is equal to the second.

(24) Compute three consecutive integers such that the sum of the second and the third is equal to the first.

(25) Sylvia and Yvonne leave home on their bikes and travel in opposite directions. Sylvia travels 1½ times as fast as Yvonne. After 3 hours they are 60 miles apart. Compute their rates of speed.

II. (1) The following problem appeared on a test: Jim left Atlanta for Washington, D. C., at 8:00 AM and drove at an average speed of 40 mph. Walter left Atlanta 3 hours later and drove in the opposite direction at an average speed of 50 mph. At what time were Walter and Jim 30 miles apart?

One student wrote the following solution:

$$40t + 50(t - 3) = 30$$
$$40t + 50t - 150 = 30$$
$$90t = 180$$
$$t = 2$$

That is, Jim and Walter were 30 miles apart at 10:00 AM. However, we know that Walter did not leave until 11:00 AM and at 10:00 AM Jim was 80 miles from Atlanta. Explain the apparent paradox.

(2) Would the student's mathematical model have been correct if the distance had been 130 miles rather than 30 miles?

2.5 Linear Inequalities

In this section we shall define *linear inequality* in one variable and develop a method for computing its solution set. As the linear inequality serves as a mathematical model for many physical problems, its solution set serves as the model for the solutions of these physical problems. After you have learned to solve any linear inequality in one variable, you will be able to solve many different physical problems, without having to learn a set of different techniques for the different problems.

The following example illustrates a method of computing the solution set of an open sentence which is an inequality. Observe that the *ordered field properties* are employed.

Example 1.   Compute the solution set of the inequality $5x + 12 < 0$, and represent the solution set geometrically on the number line.

Now $5x + 12 < 0$

$\Leftrightarrow 5x + 12 + {}^-12 < 0 + {}^-12$ (by $O2$)

$\Leftrightarrow 5x < {}^-12$

$\Leftrightarrow (1/5)(5x) < (1/5)({}^-12)$ (by $O3$)

$\Leftrightarrow x < {}^-12/5.$

Hence $\{x: 5x + 12 < 0\} = \{x: x < {}^-12/5\}$.

The "hollow dot" indicates that ${}^-12/5$ is not included in the solution set. The double arrows are included for emphasis. In practice we usually omit them.

Whenever the coefficient of x is negative, you must be careful not to violate property $O4$. The following example illustrates a valid procedure.

Example 2.   Compute the solution set of the inequality ${}^-5x + 12 < 0$, and represent the solution set geometrically on the number line.

$$^-5x + 12 < 0$$
$$(^-5x + 12) + {}^-12 < 0 + {}^-12$$
$$^-5x < {}^-12$$
$$(^-1/5)(^-12) < (^-1/5)(^-5x) \qquad \text{(by } O4\text{)}$$
$$12/5 < x.$$
Hence $\{x: {}^-5x + 12 < 0\} = \{x: 12/5 < x\}$.

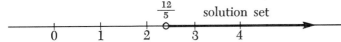

$\frac{12}{5}$ solution set

The following alternate procedure is based on property $O3$.

Example 3.   Compute the solution set of the inequality $^-5x + 12 < 0$.

$$^-5x + 12 < 0$$
$$5x + (^-5x + 12) < 5x + 0$$
$$12 < 5x$$
$$(1/5)(12) < (1/5)(5x) \qquad \text{(by } O3\text{)}$$
$$12/5 < x.$$

As in the case of an equation, certain manipulations on an inequality may reduce that inequality to an inequality which is *not* equivalent to the original inequality. The following theorem, which follows directly from the order properties, tells us which manipulations on an inequality yield an equivalent inequality.

THEOREM 3.   (a) If u_1 and u_2 are any expressions and u is any expression, then the inequality $u_1 < u_2$ is equivalent to the inequality $u_1 + u < u_2 + u$.

(b) If u_1 and u_2 are any expressions and r is any positive real number, then the inequality $u_1 < u_2$ is equivalent to the inequality $u_1 r < u_2 r$.

(c) If u_1 and u_2 are any expressions and s is any negative real number, then the inequality $u_1 < u_2$ is equivalent to the inequality $u_2 s < u_1 s$.

The following examples further illustrate the procedure for solving an inequality.

Example 4.   Compute the solution set of the inequality
$$(^-1/3)x + 1/4 < (^-1/6)x + 4.$$

To simplify the computation we multiply both members by the least common denominator: $[3, 4, 6, 1] = 12$.
Thus $12[(^-1/3)x + 1/4] < 12[(^-1/6)x + 4] \qquad \text{(by } O3\text{)}$

$$-4x + 3 < -2x + 48$$
$$-2x < 45$$
$$(-1/2)(45) < (-1/2)(-2x) \qquad \text{(by } O4\text{)}$$
$$-45/2 < x.$$

The following example illustrates that the solution set of an inequality may be empty.

Example 5.   Compute the solution set of $3x + 4 < x + 2 + 2x$.

$$3x + 4 < x + 2 + 2x$$
$$3x + 4 < 3x + 2$$
$$3x + 4 + {}^-3x + {}^-4 < 3x + 2 + {}^-3x + {}^-4$$
$$0 < {}^-2$$

Thus $\{x: 3x + 4 < x + 2 + 2x\} = \{x: 0 < {}^-2\} = \phi$.

The following example illustrates that the solution set of an inequality may be the entire set of reals.

Example 6.   Compute the solution set of $3x < 3x + 2$.

$$3x < 3x + 2$$
$$3x + {}^-3x < 3x + 2 + {}^-3x$$
$$0 < 2$$

Thus $\{x: 3x < 3x + 2\} = \{x: 0 < 2\} = R$.

The inequalities in Examples 1, 2, 3, and 4 are called *linear inequalities in one variable*.

DEFINITION 12. An inequality is said to be a *linear inequality in one variable* if and only if it can be reduced to the form $ax + b < 0$, where $a \neq 0$, by means of Theorem 3.

Although the inequalities in Example 5 and 6 resemble linear inequalities, at first glance, they are not linear inequalities.

Example 7.   Prove that $0 < 7x + 9$ is a linear inequality in one variable.

$$0 < 7x + 9$$
$$0 + ({}^-7x + {}^-9) < (7x + 9) + ({}^-7x + {}^-9)$$
$${}^-7x + {}^-9 < 0$$

It follows from Definition 12 that $0 < 7x + 9$ is a linear inequality.

Exercise 2.5

I. Determine whether each of the following is a linear inequality. In each case, justify your answer by use of Definition 12.

(1) $-3x \cdot 4 < 5$ (11) $x < 7$

(2) $4x \cdot 1 < 2x$ (12) $7 < x$

(3) $x \cdot 3/2 < 2x + 1$ (13) $3x + 2 = 5x + 2 + {}^-2x$

(4) $0 < {}^-7x + 5$ (14) $2x + 3 = x + 4 + x$

(5) $0 < 3x + 1$ (15) $x < 0$

(6) $2x + 3 < x + 3$ (16) $0 < x$

(7) $2x + 2 < x + 1 + x$ (17) $0 < 5 + 3x$

(8) $2x + 1 < 2x + 2$ (18) $-3 < {}^-1 + 4x$

(9) $2x + 3 < 3$ (19) $x < 2x$

(10) $7x + {}^-2 < {}^-2$ (20) $-5x < 2x$

II. Compute the solution set of each of the following linear inequalities, and represent the solution set geometrically on the number line.

(1) $2x + 5 < {}^-3x$ (6) $1 < (3/4)x + 1/3$

(2) $-2x + 5 < 3x$ (7) $-x < {}^-7$

(3) $0 < 2x + 7$ (8) $4x + 2 < 5x + 7 + x$

(4) $0 < {}^-2x + 7$ (9) $3x + 1/3 < 2x + 2$

(5) $(-1/3)x < 0$ (10) $-3x + 3 < 3$

2.6 Compound Inequalities

In this section we shall study *compound* inequalities in which the connective is $\vee$ (*or*) or $\wedge$ (*and*). The following examples illustrate the procedure.

Example 1.   Compute the solution set of the compound inequality $5x + 12 \leq 0$.

This inequality is really an abbrevation for $(5x + 12 < 0)$ $\vee$ $(5x + 12 = 0)$.

$(5x + 12 < 0) \vee (5x + 12 = 0)$

$5x < {}^-12 \vee 5x = {}^-12$

$x < {}^-12/5 \vee x = {}^-12/5$

$x \leq {}^-12/5$.

We see that the solution set of $5x + 12 < 0 \vee 5x + 12 = 0$ is the *union* of the solution set of $5x + 12 < 0$ and of the solution set of $5x + 12 = 0$.

In general, the solution set of $p_x \vee q_x$ is the *union* of the solution set of p_x and the solution set of q_x; i.e., $\{x: p_x \vee q_x\} = \{x: p_x\} \cup \{x: q_x\}$.

In actual practice we usually arrange the work as follows:

$$5x + 12 \leq 0$$
$$5x \leq {}^-12$$
$$x \leq {}^-12/5.$$

The only reason we included the longer method was to elaborate on the details.

Example 2. Compute the solution set of the compound inequality $^-5x + 12 \leq 0$.

$$^-5x + 12 \leq 0$$
$$^-5x \leq {}^-12$$
$$({}^-1/5)({}^-12) \leq ({}^-1/5)({}^-5x)$$
$$12/5 \leq x.$$

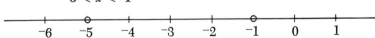

Example 3. Solve the compound inequality $^-3 < 2x + 7 < 5$.

This inequality is really an abbreviation for the compound inequality $^-3 < 2x + 7 \wedge 2x + 7 < 5$.

The solution set of $^-3 < 2x + 7 \wedge 2x + 7 < 5$ is equal to the *intersection* of the solution set of $^-3 < 2x + 7$ and $2x + 7 < 5$; i.e., $\{x: {}^-3 < 2x + 7 \wedge 2x + 7 < 5\} = \{x: {}^-3 < 2x + 7\} \cap \{x: 2x + 7 < 5\}$.

$$^-3 < 2x + 7 \qquad\qquad 2x + 7 < 5$$
$$^-3 + {}^-7 < 2x \qquad\qquad 2x < {}^-2$$
$$^-5 < x \qquad\qquad\qquad x < {}^-1$$

$\{x: {}^-5 < x\} \cap \{x: x < {}^-1\} = \{x: {}^-5 < x < {}^-1\}$.

In actual practice, we usually arrange the work as follows:

$$^-3 < 2x + 7 < 5$$
$$^-3 + {}^-7 < 2x < 5 + {}^-7$$
$$^-10 < 2x < {}^-2$$
$$^-5 < x < {}^-1$$

Example 4. Compute the solution set of the compound inequality $2 < {}^-5x + 3 \leq 15$.

$$2 < {}^-5x + 3 \le 15$$
$$2 + {}^-3 < {}^-5x \le 15 + {}^-3$$
$${}^-1 < {}^-5x < 12$$
$$({}^-1/5)(12) \le ({}^-1/5)({}^-5x) < ({}^-1/5)({}^-1) \qquad \text{(by } O4)$$
$${}^-12/5 \le x < 1/5$$

Example 5. Compute the solution set of the compound inequality $|\,2x + 3\,| < 1$.

Now $|\,2x + 3\,| < 1 \leftrightarrows {}^-1 < 2x + 3 < 1.$
$${}^-1 < 2x + 3 < 1$$
$${}^-1 + {}^-3 < 2x < 1 + {}^-3$$
$${}^-4 < 2x < {}^-2$$
$${}^-2 < x < {}^-1$$

Example 6. Compute the solution set of the compound inequality $3 \le |\,{}^-5x - 4\,|$.

Now $3 \le |\,{}^-5x - 4\,| \leftrightarrows (3 \le {}^-5x - 4) \vee ({}^-5x - 4 \le {}^-3)$
$$3 \le {}^-5x - 4 \vee {}^-5x - 4 \le {}^-3$$
$$5x \le {}^-3 - 4 \vee 3 - 4 \le 5x$$
$$5x \le {}^-7 \vee {}^-1 \le 5x$$
$$x \le {}^-7/5 \vee {}^-1/5 \le x \qquad \text{(by } O3)$$
Hence $\{x: 3 \le |\,{}^-5x - 4\,|\}$
$$= \{x: x \le {}^-7/5 \vee {}^-1/5 \le x\}$$
$$= \{x: x \le {}^-7/5\} \cup \{x: {}^-1/5 \le x\}.$$

The above examples illustrate the solution of compound inequalities. Notice that no new ideas are involved in this section. If you know how to solve a linear equation and a linear inequality, then you can solve any of the above types of compound inequalities. Of course you need to know the definition of *absolute value* and the following facts:

$$\{x: p_x \vee q_x\} = \{x: p_x\} \cup \{x: q_x\}$$
$$\{x: p_x \wedge q_x\} = \{x: p_x\} \cap \{x: q_x\}.$$

Exercise 2.6

I. Compute the solution set of each of the following inequalities and represent the solution set geometrically on the number line.

(1) $5x + 1 \leq 6$

(2) $6x + 1 \leq 5$

(3) $^-2x + 2 \leq 3$

(4) $^-6x + 5 \leq 7$

(5) $x + 1 \leq 3x + 2 + {}^-2x$

(6) $5x + 2 \leq 7x + 5 + {}^-2x$

(7) $x + 2 \leq 3x + 1 + {}^-2x$

(8) $5x + 5 \leq 7x + 2 + {}^-2x$

(9) $4 \leq {}^-5x + 9 \leq 14$

(10) $3 \leq {}^-7x + 2 \leq 5$

(11) $2x + 2 \leq 4x + 5 + {}^-2x + {}^-4$

(12) $3x + 3 \leq 6x + 7 + {}^-3x + {}^-6$

(13) $|x| \leq 5$

(14) $|2x| \leq 6$

(15) $(x \leq 5) \vee (7 \leq x)$

(16) $(x \leq 5) \vee (7 < x)$

(17) $(x \leq 5) \wedge (3 < x)$

(18) $(x \leq 5) \wedge (7 < x)$

(19) $(x \leq 5) \vee (3 < x)$

(20) $(x = 8) \wedge (x = 10)$

(21) $(x = 8) \vee (x = 10)$

(22) $(x = 8) \vee (x < 7)$

(23) $(x < 5) \wedge (2 \leq x)$

(24) $(x < 5) \wedge (15 < x)$

(25) $(x < 5) \vee (15 < x)$

(26) $3 \leq |x| + 6$

(27) $5 \leq |x| - 2$

(28) $|2x + 1| < 3$

(29) $4 \leq |5x + 1|$

(30) $|{}^-3x + 1| \leq 1$

2.7   Application of Linear Inequalities

Now that we know how to solve linear inequalities in one variable we shall study some applications of linear inequalities. The following examples illustrate the applications.

Example 1.   James is 5 years older than Betty, and the sum of their ages is less than 65. What is James's maximum possible age?

Let U be the set of positive integers.
Let the variable x represent Betty's age.
Then $x + 5$ represents James's age and $x + (x + 5)$ represents the sum of their ages.
Hence $x + (x + 5) < 65$.
Thus $2x < 60$.
Hence $x < 30$.
Betty's age is less than 30, and James's age is less than 35.
James's maximum possible age is 34.

Example 2. If there were three times as many students in a fifth grade class as there are now, there would be at least 42 more students than there are now. What is the minimum number of students in the class?

Let U be the set of positive integers.
Let x represent the number of students in the class.
Then $3x$ represents the number of students in the projected class.
$x + 42 \leq 3x$,
$42 \leq 2x$,
$21 \leq x$.
Hence there are at least 21 students in the class.

Example 3. Compute the smallest counting number such that the sum of one-third of it and 3/4 of it is larger than 39.

Let x represent the counting number.
Then $(1/3)x + (3/4)x$ is larger than 39; i.e., $39 < (1/3)x + (3/4)x$.
$39 < \frac{4 + 9}{12} x$,
$39 < (13/12)x$,
$(12/13)(39) < (12/13)(13/12)x$,
$36 < x$.
Hence the smallest counting number satisfying the given conditions is 37.

Example 4. In 6 months in one job Mr. Rayburn earned at least $7,000 and the following 6 months in another job he earned $8,000. What were his minimum average monthly earnings?

Let x represent his average monthly earnings.
Then $(7000 + 8000)/12 \leq x$.
Hence $15,000/12 \leq x$; i.e., $1250 \leq x$.
Thus Mr. Rayburn's minimum average monthly earnings were $1,250.

Example 5.   Mr. Landry has between $30,000 and $45,000 to build a house. The type of house his wife wants costs $15 per sq. ft. Compute the range of the area of his new house.

Let x represent the number of square feet in the house he will build.
Then $15x$ represents the cost of the house.
Thus $30,000 \leq 15x \leq 45,000$.
Hence $2,000 \leq x \leq 3,000$.
Thus the area of Mr. Landry's new house is from 2,000 to 3,000 sq. ft.

The simple examples above serve merely to illustrate the method employed in the formulation of a mathematical model of a physical problem. There are many more practical applications of inequalities in linear programming, probability, calculus, etc. Later we shall consider some of these applications in more detail. The skills you acquire in this section will help you to solve the more practical problems when you encounter them.

Exercise 2.7

I. Formulate a mathematical model for each of the following problems, and compute the solution set.

(1) Jim had a certain number of marbles and received twice this number more as a present. After he lost one marble he had at least 59 marbles left. What is the smallest number of marbles Jim could have had in the beginning?

(2) Joan's age is five years more than three times Mary Jane's age and Joan's age is more than 31. What is Mary Jane's minimum possible age?

(3) On a three-day hike Ann, Jessie, and Inez walked twice as far the second day as the first, and four miles the third day. If the total distance was no more than 22 miles, what is the maximum distance they could have walked the first day?

(4) Sally has more than $1.05 in pennies and nickels, and has three times as many pennies as nickels. What is the smallest number of nickels Sally could have?

(5) Mr. and Mrs. Barron want to build a house with a floor area between 1800 sq. ft. and 2400 sq. ft. The type of house they want will cost $12 per sq. ft. Compute the price range of their new house.

(6) One mathematics class contains 10 more students than a second class. If four students resign from the larger class

and 1/4 of the students resign from the smaller class, there are fewer than 76 students left in the two classes combined. What is the maximum number of students in the smaller class before resignations?

(7) A family vacation budget allowed four times as much for food as for camping expenses and five times as much for travel as for camping expenses. If the total budget is at most $450, what is the maximum amount allotted to travel?

(8) Janice sold tickets for a school play. She sold twice as many adult tickets at 50 cents each as student tickets at 25 cents each. After she lost $3, she had less than $15.75 left from the sale of tickets. What is the maximum number of tickets of each type that she sold?

(9) If the steam pressure of a boiler is increased by 50%, the greater pressure is more than 27,000 pounds per square inch. What is the minimum pressure on the boiler before the increase?

(10) Maggie's father is five times as old as Maggie. In four years the sum of their ages will be less than 56 years. What is Maggie's maximum possible present age?

CHAPTER 3

FUNCTIONS AND GRAPHS

3.1 Cartesian Product and the Coordinate Plane

In your previous study of *sets*, you have studied the binary operators $\cup$, $\cap$, and $\times$ between any two sets A and B. Recall that $A \cup B = \{x: x \in A \vee x \in B\}$, $A \cap B = \{x: x \in A \wedge y \in B\}$, and $A \times B = \{(a, b): a \in A \wedge b \in B\}$. You have learned that the ordered pair (a, b) is, in general, different from the ordered pair (b, a) and $A \times B \neq B \times A$ unless $A = \phi$, $B = \phi$, or $A = B$. The following examples will help you to review the *Cartesian product* $A \times B$ of two sets A and B and to distinguish it from union and intersection.

Example 1. $A = \{1, 3, 5\}$, $B = \{1, 2\}$.
$A \times B = \{(1, 1), (1, 2), (3, 1), (3, 2), (5, 1), (5, 2)\}$,
$A \cup B = \{1, 2, 3, 5\}$,
$A \cap B = \{1\}$.

Example 2. $A = \{2, 4\}$, $B = \{2, 4, 6, 8\}$.
$A \times B = \{(2, 2), (2, 4), (2, 6), (2, 8), (4, 2), (4, 4),$
$\qquad\qquad (4, 6), (4, 8)\}$,
$A \cup B = \{2, 4, 6, 8\}$,
$A \cap B = \{2, 4\}$.

Example 3. $A = \{1\}$, $B = \{4, 5, 6\}$.
$A \times B = \{(1, 4), (1, 5), (1, 6)\}$,
$A \cup B = \{1, 4, 5, 6\}$,
$A \cap B = \phi$.

Example 4. $A = \phi, B = \{0, 1, 4\}$.
$A \times B = \phi$,
$A \cup B = \{0, 1, 4\}$,
$A \cap B = \phi$.

Recall that R is the set of all real numbers. Then $R \times R = \{(x, y):$ $x \in R \wedge y \in R\}$; i.e., $R \times R$ is the set of all ordered pairs of real numbers. Analogous to the manner in which we established a one-to-one correspondence between the set of reals and the set of points on the number line, we establish a one-to-one correspondence between the set $R \times R$ and the set of points in a plane which we call the *coordinate plane*. First we let X and Y be two perpendicular lines and label their point of intersection *Origin*. These lines are called the *X-axis* and the *Y-axis*, respectively. According to established convention, we let the *X-axis* be horizontal and the *Y-axis* be vertical. The points on X to the *right* of Origin are labeled so that they correspond to the positive reals, and the points to the *left* of Origin are labeled so that they correspond to the negative reals. Similarly, the points on Y *above* Origin correspond to the positive reals, and the points on Y *below* Origin correspond to the negative reals. The coordinate plane is shown in Figure 3.1.

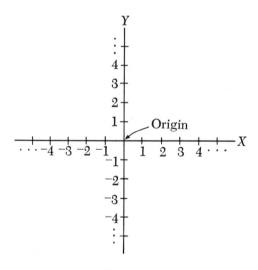

FIGURE 3.1

We establish a one-to-one correspondence between $R \times R$ and the coordinate plane as follows:

The *ordered pair* (3, 5) corresponds to the *point* in the coordinate plane 3 units to the *right* of Origin *and* 5 units above Origin. This point is labeled (3, 5) in Figure 3.2. The *ordered pair* (3, ⁻5) corresponds to the *point* 3 units to the *right* of Origin and 5 units *below* Origin. This point is labeled (3, ⁻5) in Figure 3.2. The *ordered pair* (⁻3, 5) corresponds to the *point* 3 units to the *left* of Origin and 5 units *above* Origin. This point is labeled (⁻3, 5) in Figure 3.2. The *ordered pair* (⁻3, ⁻5) corresponds to the *point* 3 units to the left of Origin and 5 units *below* Origin. This point is labeled (⁻3, ⁻5) in Figure 3.2. The *ordered pair* (0, 0) corresponds to the point 0 units to the right of Origin and 0 units above Origin. Thus this point is Origin and is labeled (0, 0) as shown in Figure 3.2.

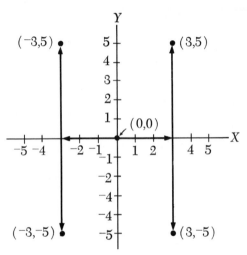

FIGURE 3.2

In general, if *a* and *b* are non-negative reals, (*a*, *b*) correspond to the unique point *a* units to the *right* of (0, 0) and *b* units *above* (0, 0). The pairs (*a*, ⁻*b*), (⁻*a*, *b*), and (⁻*a*, ⁻*b*) correspond to points located in a similar manner. Conversely, any point in the coordinate plane may be made to correspond to an ordered pair of real numbers. The point located *a* units to the *right* or *left* of (0, 0) and *b* units *above* or *below* (0, 0) corresponds to the unique ordered pair (*a*, *b*).

Thus *there is a one-to-one correspondence between the set of all ordered pairs of reals and the set of all points in the coordinate plane.* Each ordered pair corresponds to a unique point in the coordinate plane, no two ordered pairs correspond to the same point, each point in the coordinate plane correspond to a unique ordered pair, and no two points of the coordinate plane correspond to the same ordered pair. Hence we may label a point by the ordered pair to which it corresponds. For example, the point which corresponds to the ordered pair (x, y) may be labeled "(x, y)." For this reason we shall frequently refer to the point labeled "(x, y)" as *the point* (x, y). This procedure should cause no confusion or ambiguity.

DEFINITION 1. The members x and y of the ordered pair (x, y) are called the *coordinates* of the ordered pair. The first member x is called the *first coordinate,* and the second member y is called the *second coordinate.*

For example, the first coordinate of the point $(3, -5)$ is 3 and the second coordinate is -5. Whenever the universal set is $X \times Y$, the first *coordinate* is called the *x-coordinate* and the second coordinate is called the *y-coordinate.*

A physical interpretation of this one-to-one correspondence is as follows. Let $(0, 0)$ represent the main intersection of a city whose blocks are square. The ordered pair $(3, -5)$, for example, corresponds to the street corner (intersection) which one reaches by beginning at $(0, 0)$ and walking *East* 3 blocks and then *South* 5 blocks. The arrows in Figure 3.2 show the paths taken. Conversely, the corner 3 blocks East and 5 blocks South of the main intersection corresponds to the ordered pair $(3, -5)$.

The following concept is a generalization of the labeling of points on the number line.

DEFINITION 2. The *graph* of a set of ordered pairs of real numbers is the set of points in the coordinate plane which correspond to the ordered pairs.

To *sketch the graph* or to *graph* a set of ordered pairs of real numbers is to locate (approximately) the set of points corresponding to the ordered pairs and to *label* these points by means of heavy dots or coordinates (or both). The concept of the *graph* is a *mathematical* one, whereas the *sketch of a graph* is a *physical model* of a *mathematical concept.* Conversely, the *graph* is *a mathematical model* of the *physical sketch* of the graph.

In actual practice, there are many possible sketches of a graph. The particular sketch that one makes depends upon the accuracy with which he locates points corresponding to the ordered pairs. In this text we shall refer to *the sketch* even though we have not located the unique ideal graph.

Example 5.   The graph of ($^-$5, $^-$2) is the point in the coordinate plane 5 units to the left of (0, 0) and 2 units below (0, 0). The sketch of the graph is shown in the accompanying figure.

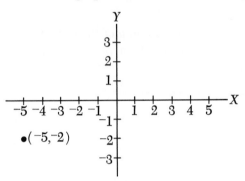

Example 6.   The graph of (0, $^-$3) is the point in the coordinate plane 0 units to the right (or left) of (0, 0) and 3 units below (0, 0). The sketch of the graph is shown in the accompanying figure.

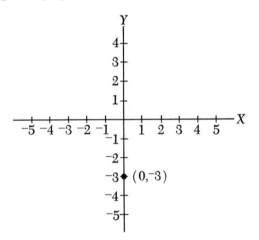

Example 7.   The graph of {($^-$5, $^-$2), (0, $^-$2), (0, 0), ($^-$5, 0)} is the union of the graphs of ($^-$5, $^-$2), (0, $^-$2), (0, 0), and ($^-$5, 0). The sketch of the graph is shown in the accompanying figure.

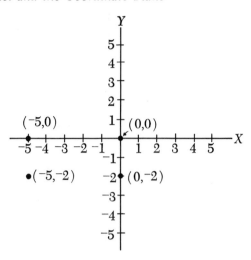

Example 8.   The graph of $\{(3,5), (3,-5), (-3,5), (-3,-5)\}$ is the union of the graphs of $(3,5)$, $(3,-5)$, $(-3,5)$, and $(-3,-5)$. The sketch of the graph is shown in the accompanying figure.

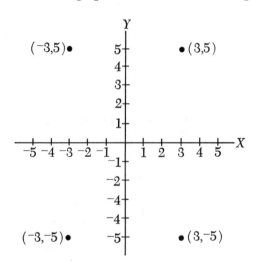

Exercise 3.1

I. Compute $A \times B$ for each of the following pairs of sets.
  (1) $A = \{2\}$, $B = \{0\}$
  (2) $A = \{2\}$, $B = \{0, 1, 2, 3\}$
  (3) $A = \{-1, 0, 1\}$, $B = \{1, 2\}$
  (4) $A = \phi$, $B = \{1, 3\}$

(5) $A = \{0, 1, 2, \ldots\}, B = \{0, 1\}$
(6) $A = \{0, 1, 2, \ldots\}, B = \{0, 1, 2, \ldots\}$
(7) $A = \{0\}, B = R$
(8) $A = \{1\}, B = R$
(9) $A = \{\text{Tom, Dick, Harry}\}, B = \{\text{Mary, Jane}\}$
(10) $A = \{\text{Bea, Gloria, Sharon}\}, B = \{110, 115, 120\}$

II. Compute $B \times A$ for each pair of sets in I above.

III. (1) Compute $A \cap B$ for each pair of sets in I above.
   (2) Compute $A \cup B$ for each pair of sets in I above.

IV. *Describe* the graph of each of the following sets of ordered pairs of reals.

(1) $\{(2, 3)\}$ (6) $\{(2, 0)\}$
(2) $\{(^-2, ^-3)\}$ (7) $\{(0, ^-3)\}$
(3) $\{(^-2, 3)\}$ (8) $\{(2, 0), (0, ^-3), (2, ^-3)\}$
(4) $\{(2, ^-3)\}$ (9) $A \times B$ where $A = R$ and $B = R$
(5) $\{(0, 3)\}$ (10) $A \times B$ where $A = R$ and $B = \{0\}$

V. Sketch the graph of each set in IV above.

VI. Compute $X \times Y \times Z$ in each of the following cases.

(1) $X = \{0, 1, 2\}, Y = \{3\}, Z = \{5, 6\}$
(2) $X = \{0\}, Y = \{1, 2\}, Z = \{3, 4, 5\}$
(3) $X = \{\}, Y = \{1, 2\}, Z = \{3, 4, 5\}$
(4) $X = C_0, Y = \{1\}, Z = \{2\}$
(5) $X = C_0, Y = C_0, Z = C_0$
(6) $X = I, Y = I, Z = I$
(7) $X = \{\text{Diane, Sally}\}, Y = \{1\}, Z = \{\text{book}\}$
(8) $X = \{^-1, ^-2\}, Y = \{0\}, Z = \{^-3\}$

3.2 Functions

One of the most useful concepts in mathematics is the concept of a *function*. The physical world abounds with examples of functions. One of the important tasks of a scientist is the formulation of a mathematical model for a given physical problem such that the relationship between two physical objects is determined by the mathematical relationship between the two corresponding mathematical entities. For example, a physicist formulates a mathematical model to express the relationship between the distance a body has moved and the time it has been in motion. Similarly, a psychologist expresses the relationship between the I.Q. of a student and the predicted performance in college. Finally, by means of a mathematical model a manufacturer expresses the relationship between his net profit and the quantity of articles he manufactures.

Observe that there are two sets involved in each of the above examples. In the first example, one set is the set of elements representing *time* (in seconds or other convenient units), and the other set is the set of elements representing *distance* (in feet or other convenient units). In the second example, one set is a set of positive numbers representing *I.Q.'s,* and the other set is a set of non-negative numbers representing *grade-point averages.* In the third example, one set is a set of positive integers representing the *number of articles manufactured,* and the other set is a set of numbers representing the *profit.* In each of these examples, the investigator is interested in a *rule of correspondence* which assigns to each element of one set some element of the second set. In the first example, to the time the rule assigns a distance; in the second example, to the I.Q., the rule assigns a grade-point average; and in the third example, to the number of articles the rule assigns a net profit.

The above examples are only three of the many examples in which each element of one set is associated with (or assigned to) some element of a second set. For this reason mathematicians study the important concept of *function.*

DEFINITION 3. A *function from a set A to a set B* is a rule of correspondence from A to B which assigns to each element of A exactly one element of B.

According to Definition 3, both a *rule* and a *set A* are necessary to define a *function from A to B.* In practice, we usually speak of a *function* (rather than a *function from A to B*) whenever the set A is understood from the context.

In each of the above examples the rule formulated by the investigator is a function. The following example further illustrates Definition 3.

Example 1.   Consider a rule which assigns to each person a weight in pounds as shown in the accompanying figure.

This rule defined on the set A (the set of all persons) is certainly a function; each person has exactly one weight (no one has two different weights). If we denote the weight of any person x by $w(x)$, we can illustrate the rule as shown

Al $\longrightarrow$ $w(\text{Al})$

Bill $\longrightarrow$ $w(\text{Bill})$

Carl $\longrightarrow$ $w(\text{Carl})$

Doris $\longrightarrow$ $w(\text{Doris})$

$\bullet\ \bullet\ \bullet\ \bullet$

a $\longrightarrow$ $w(a)$

By the rule of correspondence (the weighing machine), to the person a is assigned his weight $w(a)$.

As in Example 1, in order to indicate that element of B to which a given element of A corresponds, we introduce a special notation for *function*. For this purpose we employ the **bold-faced** letter **f**, write **f**: $A \to B$ (or simply **f** when there is no ambiguity) to mean that the function **f** from A to B assigns to each element of A a unique element of B, and write $\mathbf{f}(a)$ to represent that element of B which is assigned to the element a of A. The symbol $\mathbf{f}(a)$ is read **f** *of a*. The following examples illustrate the notation for function.

Example 2.   Consider the rule which assigns to each element of A a unique element of B as in the accompanying figure.

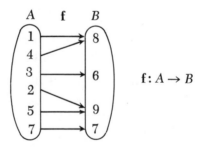

According to our notation, we write

$\mathbf{f}(1) = 8$
$\mathbf{f}(4) = 8$
$\mathbf{f}(3) = 6$

$$\mathbf{f}(2) = 9$$
$$\mathbf{f}(5) = 9$$
$$\mathbf{f}(7) = 7$$

Observe that a function may assign the same element of *B* to more than one element of *A*.

Example 3. Consider the function in the accompanying figure.

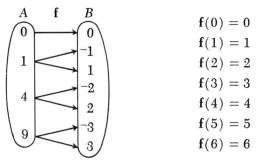

$$\mathbf{f}(0) = 0$$
$$\mathbf{f}(1) = 1$$
$$\mathbf{f}(2) = 2$$
$$\mathbf{f}(3) = 3$$
$$\mathbf{f}(4) = 4$$
$$\mathbf{f}(5) = 5$$
$$\mathbf{f}(6) = 6$$

f: *A* → *B*

Observe that *A* = *B* in this example and that $\mathbf{f}(a) = a$ for every *a* in *A*.

Example 4. Consider the function in the accompanying figure.

$$\mathbf{f}(1) = 21$$
$$\mathbf{f}(2) = 22$$
$$\mathbf{f}(3) = 22$$
$$\mathbf{f}(4) = 23$$
$$\mathbf{f}(5) = 25$$

f: *A* → *B*

Observe that some elements of *B* are not assigned to elements of *A*.

Example 5.   Consider the rule in the accompanying figure.

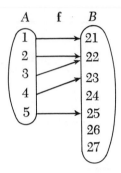

By Definition 3, this rule of correspondence is *not* a function, be-cause 4 is assigned to two different elements of *B*.

DEFINITION 4. (a) The set *A* of the function **f**: *A → B* is called the *domain of* **f**.

(b) The element **f**(*a*) which a function **f**: *A → B* assigns to the element *a* is called the *image of a under* **f** (or *the value of* **f** *at a*).

(c) The set of all images under a function **f**: *A → B* is called the *range of* **f**.

In Example 2, the domain of **f** is the set {1, 4, 3, 2, 5, 7} and the range of **f** is {8, 6, 9, 7}. In Example 3, the domain of **f** is {0, 1, 2, 3, 4, 5, 6}, and the range of **f** is also {0, 1, 2, 3, 4, 5, 6}. In Example 4, the domain of **f** is {1, 2, 3, 4, 5}, the range of **f** is {21, 22, 23, 25}, and the image of 4 under **f** is 23. Observe that the range in this case is *not* the set *B*. In fact, we are usually not interested in specifying the range but only in specifying a set which contains the range as a subset.

We frequently employ letters other than **f** to represent functions. The following example is a function with which you are already familiar.

Example 6.   Consider the function in the accompanying figure.

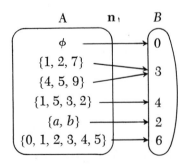

$$n(\phi) = 0$$
$$n(\{1, 2, 7\}) = 3$$
$$n(\{4, 5, 9\}) = 3$$
$$n(\{1, 5, 3, 2\}) = 4$$
$$n(\{a, b\}) = 2$$
$$n(\{0, 1, 2, 3, 4, 5\}) = 6$$

Observe that the elements of the set *A* are sets. The domain is *A* and the range is *B*. The image of ϕ is 0, the image of {1, 2, 7} is 3, the image of {4, 5, 9} is 3, the image of {1, 5, 3, 2} is 4, the image of {a, b} is 2, and the image of {0, 1, 2, 3, 4, 5} is 6.

In summary, we observe that a function is a general concept, of which there are many special examples. The domain may be a set of numbers, a set of people, a set of sets, or any set (finite or infinite). The range is completely determined by the rule of correspondence and the domain and is a subset of *B* which may be a proper subset of *B*. A function may be visualized as a machine; the elements of the range constitute the output. A simple example is the ordinary scale of Example 1. In general, the machine may appear as in Figure 3.3.

Input *a*

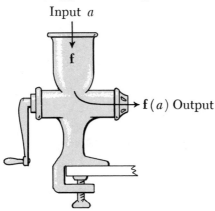

f(*a*) Output

FIGURE 3.3

Exercise 3.2

I. Determine which of the following rules of correspondence are functions.

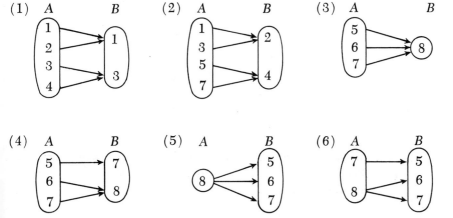

(7)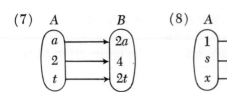

(8)

(9)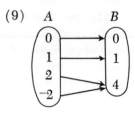

(10)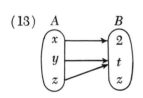

(11)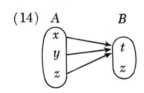

(12)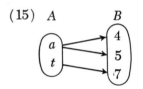

(13)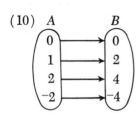

(14)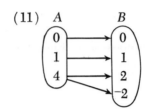

(15)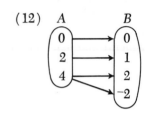

(16)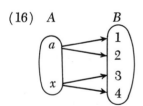

(17)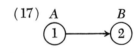

(18)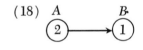

(19)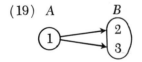

(20)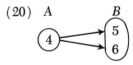

II. (1) Compute the domain and range of each *function* in Exercise I.
   (2) Compute $f(1)$ for each function in Exercise I whose domain contains 1 as an element.

III. If the domain and range of a function are interchanged, is the resulting correspondence necessarily a function?

IV. Determine which of the following are functions with the domain equal to the set of all U. S. citizens.

(1) $f(x)$ is the father of x.
(2) $m(x)$ is the mother of x.
(3) $g(x)$ is the grandfather of x.
(4) $u(x)$ is the uncle of x.
(5) $s(x)$ is the son of x.
(6) $d(x)$ is the daughter of x.
(7) $h(x)$ is the husband of x.
(8) $w(x)$ is the wife of x.
(9) $b(x)$ is the brother of x.
(10) $c(x)$ is the cousin of x.
(11) $i(x)$ is x.
(12) $p(x)$ is the paternal grandfather of x.

3.3 Function Defined by an Open Sentence and a Set of Real Numbers

In this section we shall study functions whose domains are subsets of the reals and whose ranges also are subsets of the reals. The rules of correspondence (the functions) will be given by open sentences. The following examples illustrate this type of function.

Example 1. Let $y = x + 1$ and $A = \{-3, -2, -1, 0, 1, 2, 3\}$. Then $y = x + 1$ is a function which assigns a real number to each element of A as follows:

$$-3 \rightarrow -2$$
$$-2 \rightarrow -1$$
$$-1 \rightarrow 0$$
$$0 \rightarrow 1$$
$$1 \rightarrow 2$$
$$2 \rightarrow 3$$
$$3 \rightarrow 4.$$

That is, using the standard notation for a function, we may write

$$f(-3) = -2$$
$$f(-2) = -1$$
$$f(-1) = 0$$
$$f(0) = 1$$
$$f(1) = 2$$
$$f(2) = 3$$
$$f(3) = 4.$$

Since each real number x of the domain corresponds to the real number $x + 1$ of the range, we can write the function as $f(x) = x + 1$.

Example 2. Let $y = x^2$ and $A = \{^-3, ^-2, ^-1, 0, 1, 2, 3\}$. Then $y = x^2$ is a function which assigns a real number to each element of A as follows:

$$^-3 \to 9$$
$$^-2 \to 4$$
$$^-1 \to 1$$
$$0 \to 0$$
$$1 \to 1$$
$$2 \to 4$$
$$3 \to 9.$$

Again, using the standard notation for function, we write

$$f(^-3) = 9$$
$$f(^-2) = 4$$
$$f(^-1) = 1$$
$$f(0) = 0$$
$$f(1) = 1$$
$$f(2) = 4$$
$$f(3) = 9.$$

Since each real number x of the domain corresponds to the real number x^2 of the range, we write $f(x) = x^2$.

In general, $y = $ *expression in x* is a function from A to the reals R if and only if exactly one real number y is assigned to each real number x of the domain. Observe that the domain in Examples 1 and 2 is a proper subset of the reals. Usually we do not restrict the domain in this manner. Unless we specify otherwise, it will be understood that the domain is the set of reals, or it will be clear from the problem what set the domain is. For this reason we frequently speak of the function without specifying the domain.

The following examples further illustrate the concept of function.

Example 3. $y = x^2 + 3$ is a function.

The expression in x is $x^2 + 3$.

To each real number a is assigned the real number $a^2 + 3$.

We may write $f(x) = x^2 + 3$.

The domain of $f(x) = x^2 + 3$ is the set of reals, and the range is a proper subset of the reals; namely, range $= \{y: 3 \leq y\}$.

$$f(0) = 0^2 + 3 = 3$$
$$f(1) = 1^2 + 3 = 4$$
$$f(2) = 2^2 + 3 = 7$$
$$f(^-1) = (^-1)^2 + 3 = 4$$
$$f(^-2) = (^-2)^2 + 3 = 7$$
$$f(^-3) = (^-3)^2 + 3 = 12, \text{ etc.}$$

Example 4. $y = 3$ is a function.

The expression is 3, a constant.

To each real number a is assigned the real number 3.

We may write $f(x) = 3$.

The domain of $f(x) = 3$ is the set of reals, and the range is $\{3\}$.

$$f(^-1) = 3$$
$$f(0) = 3$$
$$f(1) = 3$$
$$f(2) = 3, \text{ etc.}$$

This function is frequently called a *constant* function.

Example 5. $y = \sqrt{x}$ is a function.

The expression in x is $\sqrt{x}$.

To each non-negative real number a is assigned the non-negative real number $\sqrt{a}$.

We may write $f(x) = \sqrt{x}$.

The domain of $f(x) = \sqrt{x}$ is the set of non-negative reals, and the range is also the set of *non-negative* reals.

$$f(0) = 0$$
$$f(1) = 1$$
$$f(2) = \sqrt{2}$$
$$f(3) = \sqrt{3}$$
$$f(4) = 2, \text{ etc.}$$

Example 6. $y = 1/(x + 1)$ is a function.

The expression in x is $1/(x + 1)$.

To each real number a (except $a = ^-1$) is assigned the real number $1/(a + 1)$.

We may write $f(x) = 1/(x + 1)$.

The domain of $f(x) = 1/(x + 1)$ is the set of all real numbers except $^-1$. The reason $^-1$ is *not* included in the domain is that $f(^-1) = 1/(^-1 + 1) = 1/0$, which is not defined.

$$\mathbf{f}(0) = 1/(0+1) = 1$$
$$\mathbf{f}(1) = 1/(1+1) = 1/2$$
$$\mathbf{f}(2) = 1/(2+1) = 1/3$$
$$\mathbf{f}(^-3) = 1/(^-3+1) = 1/^-2 = ^-1/2, \text{ etc.}$$

In the study of functions the following definition is useful.

DEFINITION 5. (a) The variable x which represents any element of the domain is called the *independent variable*.

(b) The variable y which represents that element of the range corresponding to the variable x is called the *dependent variable*.

The term *independent* is used because the variable x may be *any* member of the domain. Since the variable y corresponding to x *depends* on x, y is called the *dependent* variable. You should remember that x and y are variables and that the choice of letters is arbitrary. Thus if r represents any element of the domain and s represents the corresponding element of the range, the function $y = x + 1$ of Example 1 may be written $s = r + 1$.

Exercise 3.3

I. Name the domain of each of the following functions.

(1) $\mathbf{f}(x) = x$ (6) $\mathbf{f}(v) = 2v^2 - 1$

(2) $\mathbf{f}(x) = {}^-x$ (7) $\mathbf{f}(x) = x^3 - 1$

(3) $\mathbf{f}(u) = {}^-2u + 1$ (8) $\mathbf{f}(x) = x^3 + 1$

(4) $\mathbf{f}(u) = 2u - 1$ (9) $\mathbf{f}(t) = t^2 + 1$

(5) $\mathbf{f}(v) = v^2 - 2$ (10) $\mathbf{f}(t) = t^2 - 1$

II. Name the independent variable and the dependent variable of each function in Exercise I.

III. Compute $\mathbf{f}(^-4)$ for each function in Exercise I.

IV. Compute $\mathbf{f}(4)$ for each function in Exercise I.

V. Compute $\mathbf{f}(0)$ for each function in Exercise I.

VI. The following function is defined on the set $\{1, 2, 3, 4\}$: to each element x of $\{1, 2, 3, 4\}$ the element $3x$ is assigned.

(1) Write the function as an open sentence.

(2) List the domain of the function.

(3) List the range of the function.

VII. Name the range of the function in Example 6.

3.4 Graphs of Functions

In the remainder of this chapter we shall confine our attention to the study of functions of the type discussed in Section 3.3. In Section 3.1 we defined the graph of a set of ordered pairs of real numbers. In this section we shall study the *graph of a function* $y = f(x)$. By this we mean the graph of the set of all ordered pairs of real numbers determined by the function. That is, *the graph of the function* $y = f(x)$ really means the graph of $\{(x, y): y = f(x)\}$.

In fact, some mathematicians define the function f as $\{(x, y): y = f(x)\}$. From this point of view, the function is identified with its graph.

Since it is frequently impossible to show the entire sketch of the graph of a function, we usually show a partial sketch and call it *the sketch* or *the graph*.

The following examples illustrate the method of sketching the graph of a function.

Example 1.   Sketch the graph of $y = x + 1$.

Since $y = x + 1$ is a function, we write $f(x) = x + 1$ and compute some images as follows:

$$f(-2) = -2 + 1 = -1$$
$$f(-1) = -1 + 1 = 0$$
$$f(0) = 0 + 1 = 1$$
$$f(1) = 1 + 1 = 2$$
$$f(2) = 2 + 1 = 3.$$

It is convenient to display the computation in a table which shows some of the ordered pairs.

x	$f(x)$
-2	-1
-1	0
0	1
1	2
2	3

The graph of these ordered pairs is shown in the accompanying figure.

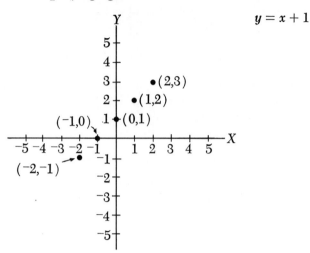

The graph of the function is shown below.

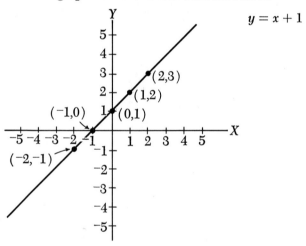

The computed points are labeled for emphasis. As we mentioned previously, we have shown only a part of the sketch. The graph actually extends indefinitely far in both directions.

Example 2.   Sketch the graph of $y = x^2$.
          A partial table and the graph are shown in the accompanying figures.

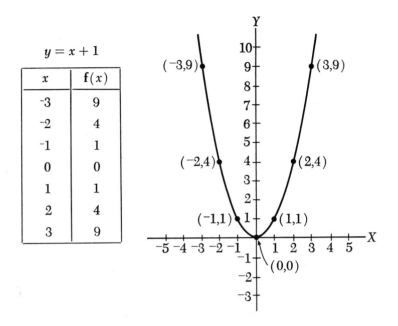

$y = x + 1$

x	f(x)
-3	9
-2	4
-1	1
0	0
1	1
2	4
3	9

Example 3. Sketch the graph of the function $f(x) = x^2 + 3$.
A partial table and the graph are shown in the accompanying figures.

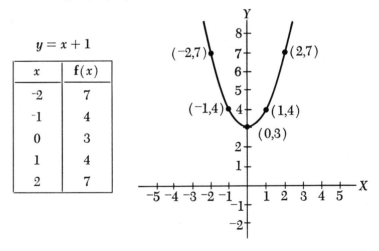

$y = x + 1$

x	f(x)
-2	7
-1	4
0	3
1	4
2	7

Example 4. Sketch the graph of the function $y = 3$.
The function $f(x) = 3$ assigns to each real number x the
real number 3.

A table and the graph are shown in the accompanying figures.

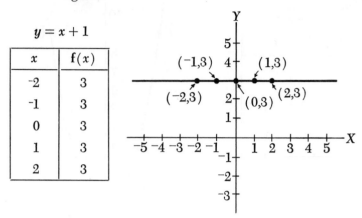

$y = x + 1$

x	$f(x)$
-2	3
-1	3
0	3
1	3
2	3

The graph is a straight line parallel to the X-axis.

Example 5.   Sketch the graph of the function $f(x) = \sqrt{x}$.
Observe that neither x nor $f(x)$ can be negative.
A table and the graph are shown in the accompanying figures.

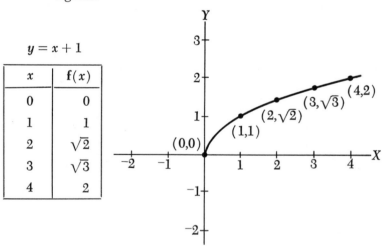

$y = x + 1$

x	$f(x)$
0	0
1	1
2	$\sqrt{2}$
3	$\sqrt{3}$
4	2

Exercise 3.4

I. Sketch the graph of each of the following functions.

(1) $f(x) = 3x$ (4) $f(x) = x^2 + 2$
(2) $f(x) = 2x$ (5) $f(x) = x^3 + 1$
(3) $f(x) = x^2 - 2$ (6) $f(x) = x^3 - 1$

(7) $f(x) = (1/2)x^2$ (9) $f(x) = 3\sqrt{x}$

(8) $f(x) = 2x^2$ (10) $f(x) = 2\sqrt{x}$

II. Sketch the graph of each of the following functions.

(1) $f(x) = 2$ (6) $f(x) = 2\,|\,x\,|$

(2) $f(x) = {}^-3$ (7) $f(x) = |\,x + 2\,|$

(3) $f(x) = 0$ (8) $f(x) = |\,x\,| + 2$

(4) $f(x) = {}^-1$ (9) $f(x) = 1/(x + 1)$

(5) $f(x) = |\,x\,|$ (10) $f(x) = 2/(x - 2)$

3.5 Linear Functions

In this section we shall study an important subset of the class of functions—the set of *linear functions*. In the preceding sections of this chapter we considered several examples of linear functions. In the exercise you will be asked to prove that $y = ax + b$ is actually a function.

DEFINITION 6. The function $y = ax + b$ is called a *linear function*.

Example 1. $y = 3x + 1$ is a linear function, in which $a = 3$ and $b = 1$. The function may be written $f(x) = 3x + 1$.
The sketch is shown in the accompanying figure.

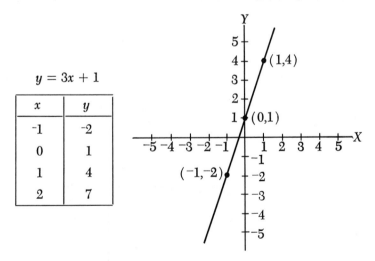

$y = 3x + 1$

x	y
-1	-2
0	1
1	4
2	7

Recall that the graph of the solution set of the function $y = 3x + 1$ is the graph of the function. That is, the graph of $y = 3x + 1$ is the graph of $\{(x, y): y = 3x + 1\}$.

Example 2. $y = 3x - 5$ is a linear function, in which $a = 3$ and $b = {}^-5$.
The function may be written $f(x) = 3x + {}^-5$.
The sketch is shown in the accompanying figure.

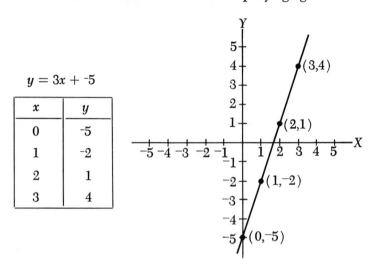

$y = 3x + {}^-5$

x	y
0	-5
1	-2
2	1
3	4

Example 3. $f(x) = 3x + 10$ is a linear function, in which $a = 3$ and $b = 10$. The sketch is shown in the accompanying figure.

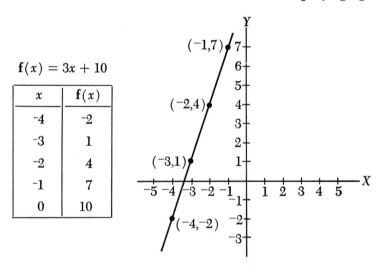

$f(x) = 3x + 10$

x	f(x)
-4	-2
-3	1
-2	4
-1	7
0	10

Example 4. $g(x) = {}^-2x$ is a linear function, in which $a = {}^-2$ and $b = 0$.

The sketch is shown in the accompanying figure.

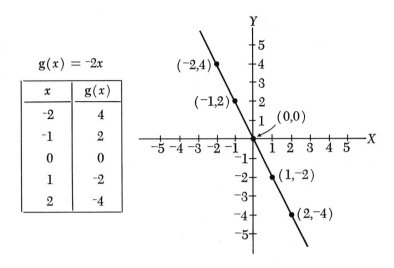

g(x) = -2x

x	g(x)
-2	4
-1	2
0	0
1	-2
2	-4

Example 5. $g(x) = -3$ is a linear function, in which $a = 0$ and $b = -3$. The sketch is shown in the accompanying figure.

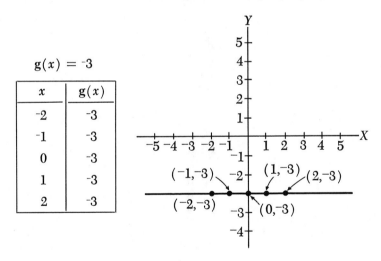

g(x) = -3

x	g(x)
-2	-3
-1	-3
0	-3
1	-3
2	-3

Observe that the graph of each of the above linear functions is a straight line. The reason for the qualifying adjective *linear* in Definition 6 is that the graph of any *linear* function is a straight *line*. The following theorem is a generalization of the observations in each of the above examples.

THEOREM 1. The solution set of the open sentence $ax + by = c$, in which $b \neq 0$, is equal to the solution set of the linear function $y = (^-a/b)x + c/b$.

Proof.
$$ax + by = c \Leftrightarrow by = {}^-ax + c$$
$$\left. \begin{array}{l} \Leftrightarrow y = (^-ax + c)/b \\ \Leftrightarrow y = (^-a/b)x + c/b \end{array} \right\} \quad b \neq 0$$

Hence $\{(x, y): ax + by = c \wedge b \neq 0\} = \{(x, y): [y = (^-a/b)x + c/b] \wedge (b \neq 0)\}.\!/\!/$

According to Theorem 1, the open sentence $ax + by = c$ generates a linear function, provided $b \neq 0$. Hence the graph of $ax + by = c$ is a straight line. The following examples illustrate Theorem 1.

Example 6. Sketch the graph of the linear function determined by the open sentence $3x + 7y = 6$.

$$3x + 7y = 6$$
$$7y = {}^-3x + 6$$
$$y = (^-3/7)x + 6/7$$

Thus the linear function is $y = (^-3/7)x + 6/7$.
The sketch of the graph is shown in the accompanying figure.

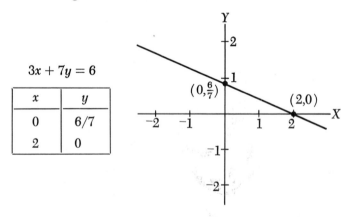

$3x + 7y = 6$

x	y
0	6/7
2	0

Example 7. Sketch the graph of the linear function determined by the open sentence $6x + 14y = {}^-7$.

$$6x + 14y = {}^-7$$
$$14y = {}^-6x + {}^-7$$

$$y = (^-6/14)x + ^-7/14$$
$$y = (^-3/7)x + ^-1/2$$

Thus the linear function is $y = (^-3/7)x + ^-1/2$.
The sketch of the graph is shown in the accompanying figure.

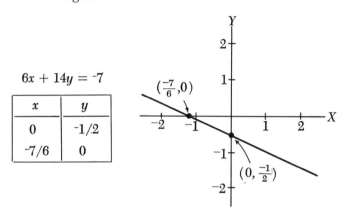

$6x + 14y = ^-7$

x	y
0	-1/2
-7/6	0

Observe that the coefficients of x in Examples 1, 2, and 3 are all equal and the lines in these examples are parallel. Because of these considerations we make the following definition.

DEFINITION 7. The *slope* of the linear function $y = ax + b$ is the real number a.

For example, the slope of each of the linear functions of Examples 1, 2, and 3 is 3, the slope of the linear function of Example 4 is $^-2$, the slope of the linear function of Example 5 is 0, and the slope of each of the linear functions of Example 6 and 7 is $^-3/7$.

The concept of slope of a linear function has a geometric interpretation. If we know that the slope of a linear function is a, we can immediately conclude that an increase of one unit in the variable x is accompanied by a change of $|a|$ units in the variable y. The following examples illustrate the geometric interpretation.

Example 8. The slope of the linear function $y = 2x - 1$ is 2. The sketch is shown in the accompanying figure.

$$y = 2x - 1$$

x	y
-2	-5
-1	-3
0	-1
1	1
2	3
3	5

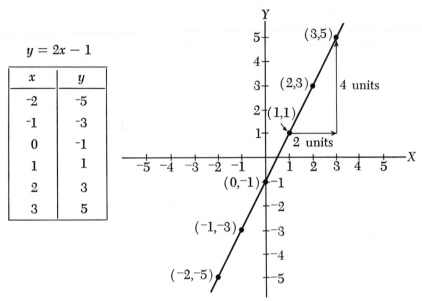

Observe that an *increase* of 1 unit in the *x*-coordinate is accompanied by an *increase* of 2 units in the *y*-coordinate. For this reason we say that the slope of the *line* is equal to 2.

Example 9.   The slope of the linear function $y = {}^-x$ is $^-1$.
The sketch is shown in the accompanying figure.

$$y = {}^-x$$

x	y
-3	3
-2	2
-1	1
0	0
1	-1
2	-2

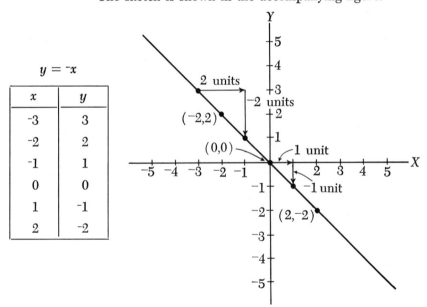

An *increase* of 1 unit in the *x*-coordinate is accompanied by a *decrease* of 1 unit in the *y*-coordinate.

Example 10. The slope of the linear function $y = (1/5)x$ is 1/5. The sketch is shown in the accompanying figure.

$$y = (1/5)x$$

x	y
-5	-1
0	0
5	1
10	2

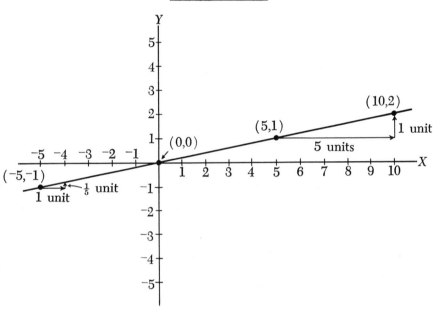

An *increase* of 1 unit in the *x*-coordinate is accompanied by an *increase* of 1/5 unit in the *y*-coordinate.

From the above examples we observe that the line is almost horizontal whenever the slope is nearly 0, and almost vertical whenever the absolute value of the slope is large. If the slope is positive, an *increase* in the *x*-coordinate is accompanied by an *increase* in the *y*-coordinate. If the slope is negative, an *increase* in the *x*-coordinate is accompanied by a *decrease* in the *y*-coordinate.

Exercise 3.5

I. (1) Decide which functions of Exercise 3.3 are linear functions.
(2) Decide which functions of Exercise 3.4 are linear functions.

II. Sketch the graph and compute the slope of each of the following linear functions.

(1) $y = x$ (6) $y = 10x - 2$
(2) $y = (1/2)x$ (7) $y = (^-1/2)x + 3$
(3) $y = ^-5x$ (8) $y = (1/4)x - 4$
(4) $y = ^-10x$ (9) $y = 6$
(5) $y = 5x - 3$ (10) $y = 0$

III. Determine the linear function $y = ax + b$ defined by each of the following open sentences, and compute its slope.

(1) $2x + 3y = 7$ (6) $x + 10y = 2$
(2) $^-2x + 3y = ^-1$ (7) $x + 5y = 0$
(3) $x - y = 3$ (8) $5x - y = 0$
(4) $x - 4y = ^-3$ (9) $^-4x + 2y = 5$
(5) $10x - y = 2$ (10) $^-3x + 2y = 5$

IV. (1) Sketch the graph of each function in Exercise III.
(2) Sketch the graph of the linear function derived in (1).

V. Sketch the graph of each of the following sets.

(1) $\{(x, y): y = x\} \cup \{(x, y): y = (1/2)x\}$
(2) $\{(x, y): y = x\} \cap \{(x, y): y = (1/2)x\}$
(3) $\{(x, y): 10x - y = 2\} \cup \{(x, y): x + 10y = 2\}$
(4) $\{(x, y): 10x - y = 2\} \cap \{(x, y): x + 10y = 2\}$
(5) $\{(x, y): [y = 3x + 1] \vee [y = (^-1/3)x]\}$
(6) $\{(x, y): [y = 3x + 1] \wedge [y = (^-1/3)x]\}$
(7) $\{(x, y): x = 0 \vee y = 0\}$
(8) $\{(x, y): x = 0 \wedge y = 0\}$
(9) $\{(x, y): 2x - 3y = 5\} \cup \{(x, y): 2x - 3y = ^-5\}$
(10) $\{(x, y): 2x - 3y = 5\} \cup \{(x, y): 6x - 9y = 15\}$

VI. Prove that $y = ax + b$ is actually a function.

(*Hint.* Prove $x_1 = x_2 \rightarrow ax_1 + b = ax_2 + b$ for *all* real numbers x_1, x_2, a, and b.)

VII. Each of the following sets has exactly one element. Compute that element.

(1) $\{(x, y): 2x + 3y = 6 \land x = 0\}$
(2) $\{(x, y): 2x - 3y = 6 \land x = 0\}$
(3) $\{(x, y): y = 3x + 5 \land x = 0\}$
(4) $\{(x, y): y = \text{-}2x - 3/4 \land x = 0\}$
(5) $\{(x, y): y = \text{-}3x \land x = 0\}$

The y-coordinate of each of the points $(0, y)$ is called the y-*intercept* of the linear function (or the y-intercept of the line).

VIII. Each of the following sets has exactly one element. Compute that element.

(1) $\{(x, y): 2x + 3y = 6 \land y = 0\}$
(2) $\{(x, y): 2x - 3y = 6 \land y = 0\}$
(3) $\{(x, y): y = 3x + 5 \land y = 0\}$
(4) $\{(x, y): y = \text{-}2x - 3/4 \land y = 0\}$
(5) $\{(x, y): y = \text{-}3x \land y = 0\}$

The x-coordinate of each of the points $(x, 0)$ is called the x-*intercept* of the linear function (or the x-intercept of the line).

3.6 Quadratic Functions

In this section we shall study another important subset of the class of functions—the set of *quadratic functions*. In Sections 3.3 and 3.4 we considered several examples of quadratic functions. In the exercises you will be asked to prove that $y = ax^2 + bx + c$ is actually a function. As the universal set is the set of reals, the coefficients a, b, and c are *real* numbers.

DEFINITION 8. The function $y = ax^2 + bx + c$, in which $a \neq 0$, is called a *quadratic function*.

Example 1. $y = x^2$ is a quadratic function, in which $a = 1$, $b = 0$, and $c = 0$.

The function may be written $\mathbf{f}(x) = x^2$.
The sketch of the graph is shown in the accompanying figure.

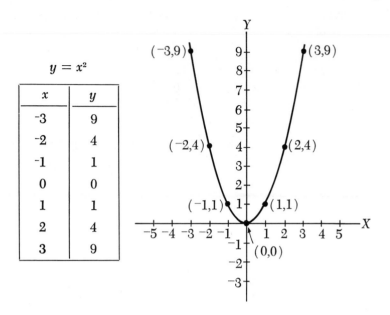

$y = x^2$

x	y
-3	9
-2	4
-1	1
0	0
1	1
2	4
3	9

Example 2. $y = {}^-x^2$ is a quadratic function, in which $a = {}^-1$, $b = 0$, and $c = 0$.

The function may be written $g(x) = {}^-x^2$.

The sketch of the graph is shown in the accompanying figure.

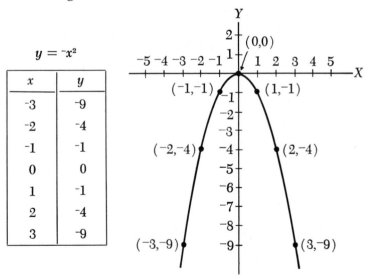

$y = {}^-x^2$

x	y
-3	-9
-2	-4
-1	-1
0	0
1	-1
2	-4
3	-9

Example 3. $y = 2x^2 - 8x$ is a quadratic function, in which $a = 2$, $b = -8$, and $c = 0$.

The sketch is shown in the accompanying figure.

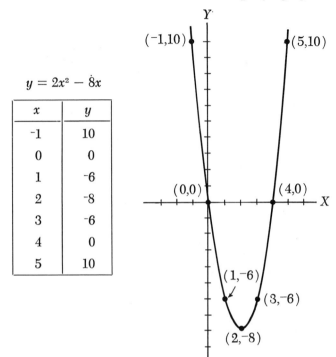

$y = 2x^2 - 8x$

x	y
-1	10
0	0
1	-6
2	-8
3	-6
4	0
5	10

Example 4. $y = -x^2 + 3x + 1$ is a quadratic function, in which $a = -1$, $b = 3$, and $c = 1$.

The sketch is shown in the accompanying figure.

$y = -x^2 + 3x + 1$

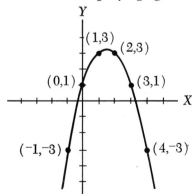

x	y
-1	-3
0	1
1	3
2	3
3	1
4	-3

Example 5. $y = x^2 + 3x + 4$ is a quadratic function, in which $a = 1$, $b = 3$, and $c = 4$.

The sketch is shown in the accompanying figure.

$y = x^2 + 3x + 4$

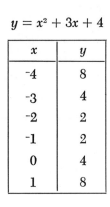

x	y
⁻4	8
⁻3	4
⁻2	2
⁻1	2
0	4
1	8

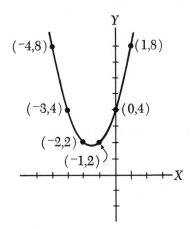

Example 6. $y = {}^-2x^2 + x + {}^-3$ is a quadratic function in which $a = {}^-2$, $b = 1$, and $c = {}^-3$.

The sketch is shown in the accompanying figure.

$y = {}^-2x^2 + x + {}^-3$

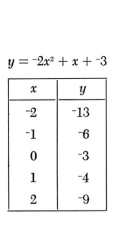

x	y
⁻2	⁻13
⁻1	⁻6
0	⁻3
1	⁻4
2	⁻9

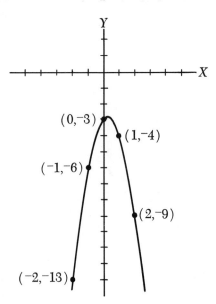

The graph of any quadratic function is called a *parabola*. The orientation of the parabola depends on the coefficients a, b, and c. If a is *negative*, the parabola opens *downward* as in Examples 2, 4, and 6. If *a* is *positive*, the parabola opens *upward* as in Examples 1, 3, and 5. If *a* is negative, there is a highest point on the parabola, and if *a* is positive, there is a lowest point on the parabola. This point is known as the *vertex* of the parabola. These ideas are very important in the applications of quadratic functions.

For example, the mathematical model of the path of a projectile is a parabola. The maximum height attained by the projectile corresponds to the *y*-coordinate of the vertex of the parabola. Moreover, the mathematical models of many problems of the physical and biological sciences, economics, psychology, social studies, etc. involve quadratic functions.

In order to determine the approximate location of the vertex of the parabola in Example 6, it is necessary to compute several points "between" the points $(0, {}^-3)$ and $(1, {}^-4)$. A more efficient method of determining the vertex *exactly* and on sketching the graph rapidly will be studied in Chapter 5.

Exercise 3.6

I. (1) Decide which functions in Exercise 3.3 are quadratic functions.
   (2) Decide which functions in Exercise 3.4 are quadratic functions.

II. Sketch the graph of each of the following quadratic functions.

  (1) $y = 2x^2 + 1$ (6) $y = {}^-5x^2 + 3x$
  (2) $y = 2x^2 - 1$ (7) $y = {}^-x^2 - x + 1$
  (3) $y = {}^-2x^2 + 1$ (8) $y = {}^-x^2 + x - 1$
  (4) $y = {}^-2x^2 - 1$ (9) $y = x^2 + 5x - 6$
  (5) $y = {}^-3x^2 + 5x$ (10) $y = x^2 - 5x + 6$

III. Estimate the vertex of each parabola in Exercise II.

IV. Sketch the graph of the quadratic function defined by each of the following open sentences.

  (1) $y = {}^-2x^2 - 5$ (6) $y = x^2 + 3x + 2$
  (2) $y = {}^-5x^2 - 2$ (7) $y - 3x^2 - 5x + 2 = 0$
  (3) $y = 4x^2 + 4x + 1$ (8) $y - 3x^2 - x + 2 = 0$
  (4) $y = 4x^2 - 4x + 1$ (9) $y - x^2 - x - 1 = 0$
  (5) $y = x^2 - 3x + 2$ (10) $y + x^2 + x + 1 = 0$

V. Estimate the vertex of each parabola in Exercise IV.

VI. Sketch the graph of each of the following sets.

  (1) $\{(x, y): y = 3x\} \cup \{(x, y): y = x^2\}$
  (2) $\{(x, y): y = 3x\} \cap \{(x, y): y = x^2\}$
  (3) $\{(x, y): y = 3x\} \cup \{(x, y): y = {}^-x^2\}$
  (4) $\{(x, y): y = 3x\} \cap \{(x, y): y = {}^-x^2\}$
  (5) $\{(x, y): y = {}^-x^2 + 1 \lor x + y = 1\}$
  (6) $\{(x, y): y = {}^-x^2 + 1 \land x + y = 1\}$

   (7) $\{(x, y): y = x^2 - 1 \lor x - y = 1\}$
   (8) $\{(x, y): y = x^2 - 1 \land x - y = 1\}$
   (9) $\{(x, y): y = x^2 + x - 6 \lor y = 0\}$
 (10) $\{(x, y): y = x^2 + x - 6 \land y = 0\}$
 (11) $\{(x, y): y = x^2 - x - 6 \land y = 0\}$
 (12) $\{(x, y): y = x^2 + 5x + 6 \land y = 0\}$
 (13) $\{(x, y): y = 6x^2 - x - 2 \land y = 0\}$
 (14) $\{(x, y): y = 6x^2 + x - 2 \land y = 0\}$
 (15) $\{(x, y): y = 6x^2 - x - 2 \land x = 0\}$
 (16) $\{(x, y): y = 6x^2 + x - 2 \land x = 0\}$
 (17) $\{(x, y): y = 6x^2 - x + 2 \land x = 0\}$
 (18) $\{(x, y): y = x^2 - x - 6 \land x = 0\}$
 (19) $\{(x, y): y = 100x^2 + 16x - 15 \land x = 0\}$
 (20) $\{(x, y): y = x^2 + 4 \land x = 0\}$

VII. Prove that $y = ax^2 + bx + c$ is actually a function.

3.7 Linear Inequalities

While linear functions have extensive applications, recent developments in mathematics and industry have caused the study of linear inequalities to gain importance. In the next chapter we shall study the applications of linear inequalities to industry. In this section we shall study the techniques of sketching the graphs of linear inequalities.

DEFINITION 9. The open sentences $ax + by < c$ and $ax + by \leq c$, in which $a \neq 0$ or $b \neq 0$, are called *linear inequalities* in two variables.

The linear inequality $ax + by \leq c$, in which $a \neq 0$ or $b \neq 0$, is sometimes called a *weak* linear inequality; similarly, $ax + by < c$ is sometimes called a *strong* linear inequality.

We shall speak of *the graph of the linear inequality* $ax + by \leq c$ to mean the *graph of its solution set*; i.e., the graph of $\{(x, y): ax + by \leq c\}$. To sketch the graph of the linear inequality $ax + by \leq c$, or of $ax + by < c$, we first sketch the graph of the linear function $ax + by = c$ and then determine whether the graph of $\{(x, y): ax + by < c\}$ lies above or below the graph of $ax + by = c$. The following examples illustrate the procedure.

Example 1.   Sketch the graph of $y < x$.

              Since $y < x \Leftrightarrow {}^-x + y < 0$ for all x and y, we see that $y < x$ is a linear inequality, in which $a = {}^-1$, $b = 1$, and $c = 0$. The sketch of the linear function $y = x$ is shown in the accompanying figure (a).

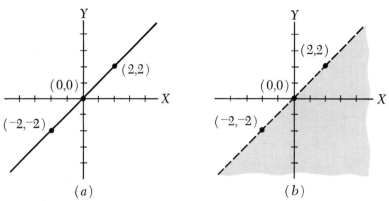

(a)   (b)

Since $y < x$ in the linear inequality and $y = x$ in the linear function, the graph of the inequality lies *below* the graph of the function. Conversely, any point of the plane below the graph of the linear function is a point of the graph of the linear inequality. Thus the graph of the linear inequality is the set of all points of the coordinate plane which lie below the graph of the linear function. The point (x, y) lies below the point (x, x) of the linear function if and only if $y < x$. The graph of the linear inequality $y < x$ is shown in the accompanying figure (b). The line is *not* part of the graph of the inequality.

Example 2.   Sketch the graph of $3x + 2 \le y$.

Since $3x + 2 \le y$ is equivalent to $3x - y \le ^-2$, the inequality is indeed a linear inequality. In this case the graph of the inequality is the set of points of the coordinate plane which lie *above* or *on* the graph of the function $y = 3x + 2$. The sketch is shown in the accompanying figure. The line is part of the graph.

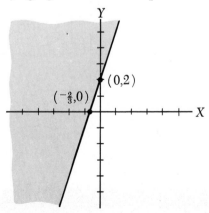

Example 3.   Sketch the graph of $y < {}^-3$.

The inequality $y < {}^-3$ is of the form $ax + by < c$, in which $a = 0$, $b = 1$, and $c = {}^-3$. The sketch of the graph is shown in the accompanying figure.

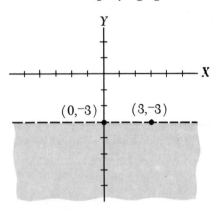

Example 4.   Sketch the graph of $5 < y$.

The inequality $5 < y$ is equivalent to the linear inequality $0x + {}^-1y < {}^-5$. The sketch of the graph is shown in the accompanying figure. The horizontal line is *not* part of the graph.

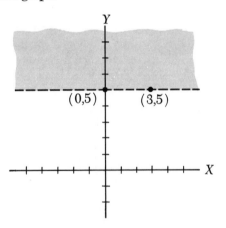

Example 5.   Sketch the graph of the inequality $x \leq 3$.

The inequality is of the form $ax + by \leq c$, in which $a = 1$, $b = 0$, and $c = 3$. The sketch is shown in the accompanying figure. The vertical line is part of the graph.

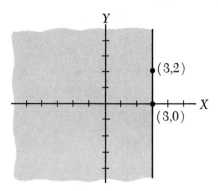

Example 6. Sketch the graph of the compound inequality
$x < 3 \;\wedge\; {}^{-}5 < x$.

The compound open sentence ${}^{-}5 < x \wedge x < 3$ is usually written as ${}^{-}5 < x < 3$. Since $\{(x, y): x < 3 \wedge {}^{-}5 < x\}$ $= \{(x, y): x < 3\} \cap \{(x, y): {}^{-}5 < x\}$, it follows that the graph of the given compound inequality is the intersection of the graph of $\{(x, y): x < 3\}$ and the graph of $\{(x, y): {}^{-}5 < x\}$. The sketch is shown in the accompanying figure. The two vertical lines are *not* part of the sketch.

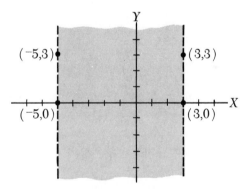

Example 7. Sketch the graph of the compound inequality
$3 \leq x \;\vee\; x \leq {}^{-}5$.

Since $\{(x, y): 3 \leq x \vee x \leq {}^{-}5\} = \{(x, y): 3 \leq x\} \cup \{(x, y): x \leq {}^{-}5\}$, it follows that the graph of the given compound inequality is the union of the graph of $\{(x, y): 3 \leq x\}$ and the graph of $\{(x, y): x \leq {}^{-}5\}$. The sketch is shown in the accompanying figure. The two vertical lines are parts of the graph.

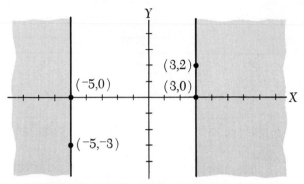

Example 8.   Sketch the graph of the compound inequality
$3 \leq y \ \wedge \ y \leq x.$

The sketch is shown in the accompanying figure. Notice that the two lines are parts of the graph.

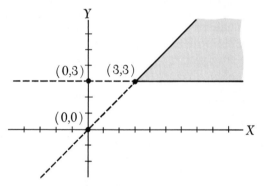

Example 9.   Sketch the graph of the compound inequality
$x < y + 1 \ \vee \ -3x + 3 < y.$

The sketch is shown in the accompanying figure. Neither dotted line is part of the graph.

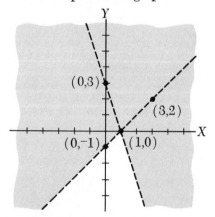

Example 10.   Sketch the graph of the compound inequality
$$0 < x \ \wedge \ 0 \leq y.$$

The sketch is shown in the accompanying figure. Notice that the X-axis is part of the graph but that the Y-axis is not.

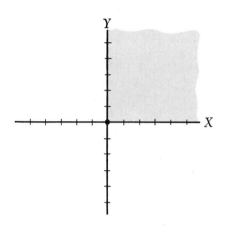

Exercise 3.7

I. Sketch the graph of each of the following inequalities. Recall that, unless otherwise restricted, the domain and the range are the reals.

(1) $x < 0$
(2) $y < {}^-x$
(3) ${}^-4x + 3 \leq y$
(4) $y < {}^-x \wedge {}^-1 < y$
(5) $y < x \wedge (1/2)x < y$
(6) ${}^-1 < x \leq 4$
(7) $1 < y \vee y < {}^-1$
(8) $1 < y \wedge y < {}^-1$
(9) $y \leq x \wedge (1/2)x < y \wedge 1 < x < 3$
(10) $y < x \wedge (1/2)x < y \wedge y < 3$
(11) $y = {}^-3x + 2 \wedge 1 < y < 2$
(12) $y \leq {}^-3x + 2 \vee 3x + 2 \leq y$
(13) $y \leq {}^-3x + 2 \wedge 3x + 2 \leq y$
(14) $(2/3)x - (4/5)y < 1/7$
(15) $(1 < y \vee y < {}^-1) \wedge (x < {}^-1 \vee 1 < x)$
(16) $(1 < y \vee y < {}^-1) \vee (x < {}^-1 \vee 1 < x)$

II. Which inequalities of Exercise I are *linear inequalities?*

3.8   Applications of Functions

Most of the functions considered in the previous sections have been purely mathematical. In this section we shall study some physical phenomena of nature and give mathematical models of these phenomena. These models will be functions. Thus, as in our previous studies, the study of functions enables us to better understand nature and the world in which we live. The following examples illustrate the application of linear and quadratic functions.

Example 1.   In physics, it is frequently necessary to convert a speed expressed in miles per hour to the corresponding speed in feet per second. The formula for the conversion is $v = (22/15)u$, in which u represents the speed in miles per hour and v represents the speed in feet per second. The sketch of the graph of the linear function $v = (22/15)u$ is shown in the accompanying figure.

$$v = (22/15)u$$

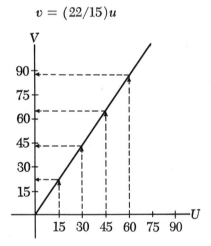

u	v
0	0
15	22
30	44
45	66
60	88
75	110
90	132

Example 2.   Phil is 3 miles west of his home. At 1:00 PM he starts a four-hour journey west on his bicycle at an average speed of 8 miles per hour. The formula which expresses the distance west of his home at any time between 1:00 PM and 5:00 PM is $s = 3 + 8t$, in which t represents the duration of his trip (in hours) and s represents the distance from home. Thus $s = 3 + 8t$ is a function with domain $= \{t: 0 \leq t \leq 4\}$. The sketch of the graph is shown in the accompanying figure. Observe from the graph that Phil is 35 miles west of home at 5:00 PM.

$$s = 3 + 8t$$

t	s
0	3
1	11
2	19
3	27
4	35

To avoid too tall a sketch, we have employed a scale on the *S-axis* different from that on the *T-axis*. Although the slope of the line appears to be affected by the different scales, it is actually not.

Example 3.   You are familiar with the fact that an increase in the volume of a gas results in a decrease in the pressure. The physical law of gases which states this phenomenon is known as *Boyle's Law*. Letting v represent the volume and p the pressure of a gas enclosed in a container (for example, a cylinder or tire), we may state Boyle's Law mathematically by the formula $p = k/v$, in which $0 < v$. Of course, the variable v may represent any positive real number, limited by the physical properties of the container, and k is a real number, known as the gas-constant, which depends on the particular gas in the container. The formula $p = k/v$ is a function whose domain is R^+. The sketch is shown in the accompanying figure for a gas-constant equal to 10.

$$p = k/v$$

v	10/v
1	10
2	5
10	1
15	2/3

$1 \to 10$
$2 \to 5$
$10 \to 1$
$15 \to 2/3$

In particular, observe that a volume of 2 units corresponds to a pressure of 5 units. In the sketch this is indicated by the vertical line segment from the point (2, 0) to the point (2, 5) and the horizontal line segment from the point (2, 5) to the point (0, 5). Thus the number 2 corresponds to the number 5.

Example 4.   The president of a canning industry wishes to produce a can which will contain a certain number of cubic inches of peas. He knows that the dimensions of the can will determine how much tin will be used in its manufacture. In the interest of economy he wishes to use the minimum amount of tin possible and still have a can of the desired volume. The amount of tin used, in square inches, is equal to the sum of the area of the top, area of the bottom, and area of the side.

If we denote the length of the radius of the base by r and the height of the can by h, we see that the area of the top is πr^2 square inches, the area of the bottom is πr^2 square inches, and the area of the side is $2\pi r h$ square inches. Thus the total amount of tin used in the can is $\pi r^2 + \pi r^2 + 2\pi r h$ square inches. Designating this area (of tin) by s, we see that the total amount of tin used is given by $s = 2\pi r^2 + 2\pi r h$. Moreover, the volume v is $\pi r^2 h$. Hence $h = v/\pi r^2$.

Thus $s = 2\pi r^2 + 2\pi r h$,

$s = 2\pi r^2 + 2\pi r \ (v/\pi r^2)$,

$s = 2\pi r^2 + 2v/r$.

If the manufacturer desires a can whose volume is 20π cubic inches, then he replaces the variable v by the real number 20π. The resulting equation is $s = 2\pi r^2 + 40\pi/r$. The sketch of the graph of $s = 2\pi r^2 + 40\pi/r$ is shown in the accompanying figure.

$$s = 2\pi r^2 + 40\pi/r$$

r	s
1	42π
2	28π
2.1	27.8π
2.2	27.8π
3	31.3π
4	42π

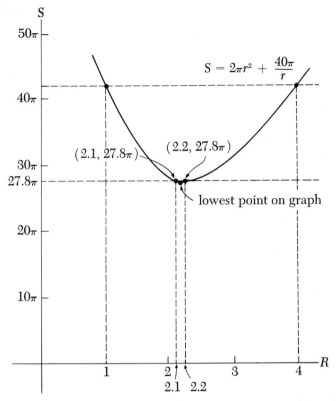

$$S = 2\pi r^2 + \frac{40\pi}{r}$$

lowest point on graph

The lowest point on the graph corresponds to the minimum value of *s*. The surface area, and hence the cost of the tin, will be minimum whenever the length of the radius is approximately equal to 2 inches. When $r = 2$ inches, $h = 20\pi/\pi(2)^2 = 20\pi/4\pi = 5$ inches.

Thus the manufacturer saves money by making a can with a radius of 2 inches and a height of 5 inches (if he wants a volume of 20π cubic inches). By the methods of a branch of mathematics known as *calculus,* one may solve the above type of problem more easily and accurately.

Much of mathematics is concerned with the study of functions. Hypotheses are stated and conclusions are derived. The resulting theorems shed much light on the nature of functions. As the theorems are stated in general terms, we may infer the conclusion of any theorem for any particular function which satisfies the hypotheses of the theorem. Thus, for example, an important theorem states certain hypotheses; the conclusion is that any function which satisfies these hypotheses has a maximum value or a minimum value. This theorem, in particular, is used in the solution of the above problem. It must be remembered, however, that not all functions have maximum and minimum values. These functions, of course, would not satisfy the hypotheses of this theorem.

Another theorem called the *fundamental theorem of algebra*, is stated as follows: $\{x: a_0 + a_1x + a_2x^2 + \ldots + a_nx^n = 0 \land n$ is a positive odd integer $\land\ a_n \neq 0\} \neq \phi$. For example, the open sentence $x^5 + 2x^4 + 3x^2 + {}^-4 = 0$ satisfies the hypotheses of the above theorem. Hence we can be certain that the solution set is not empty. That is, there is at least one real number x_0 such that the sentence $x_0^5 + 2x_0^4 + 3x_0^2 + {}^-4 = 0$ is true. In other words, the equation $x^5 + 2x^4 + 3x^2 + {}^-4 = 0$ has at least one real root. The fundamental theorem of algebra guarantees that *every* equation of the form $a_0 + a_1x + a_2x^2 + \ldots + a_nx^n = 0$, in which n is a positive odd integer and $a_n \neq 0$, has at least one real root.

Exercise 3.8

I. The formula for converting temperature in degrees centigrade to degrees Fahrenheit is $F = (9/5)C + 32$.

(1) Sketch the graph of $F = (9/5)C + 32$, $^-50 \leq C \leq 100$.
(2) Estimate the centigrade reading corresponding to a Fahrenheit reading of $86°$.
(3) Estimate the temperature at which the two readings are equal.

II. (1) Derive the formula for converting temperature in degrees Fahrenheit to temperature in degrees centigrade.
(2) Sketch the graph of the linear function derived in (1).
(3) Estimate the Fahrenheit reading corresponding to a centigrade reading of $40°$.
(4) Estimate the temperature at which the two readings are equal.

III. Ohm's Law in electricity may be written $e = ir$, in which e represents the voltage, i represents the current, and r represents the resistance. If $r = 100$ ohms, then $e = 100i$. Sketch the graph of the function $e = 100i$, $0 \leq i \leq 10$. (*Hint.* You may choose the scale on the E-axis different from the scale on the I-axis.)

IV. A boy standing on the top of a building 100 feet high throws a ball straight up with a speed of 32 feet per second. The equation describing the motion of the ball is $s = 100 + 32t + {}^-16t^2$, in which t represents the time measured in seconds and s represents the height of the ball measured in feet. Sketch the graph of $s = 100 + 32t + {}^-16t^2$.

V. In Exercise IV use the sketch to estimate (1) the time when the ball reaches its maximum height, (2) the maximum height reached by the ball, and (3) the time when the ball strikes the ground.

VI. The volume of the region enclosed by a sphere of radius r is $(4/3)\pi r^3$. Sketch the graph of $v = (4/3)\pi r^3$. Use the graph to estimate the radius when the volume is 40π units.

VII. The formula for the area of a rectangle is $k = xy$ and the perimeter is $p = 2x + 2y$. If $k = 20$ square units, determine the dimensions x and y which will yield the minimum perimeter. (*Hint.* Solve $20 = xy$ for x and replace the variable x in $p = 2x + 2y$.)

CHAPTER 4

SYSTEMS OF LINEAR EQUATIONS
AND INEQUALITIES

4.1 Systems of Linear Equations in Two Variables

In Chapter 3 we learned that the graph of a linear function in two variables is a straight line. For example, the graph of the linear function $y = x + 3$ is the straight line through the two points $(0,3)$ and $(^-3,0)$, as shown in Figure 4.1(a). Similarly, the graph of the linear function $y = ^-x$ is the straight line through the two points $(0,0)$ and $(^-3,3)$, as shown in Figure 4.1(b).

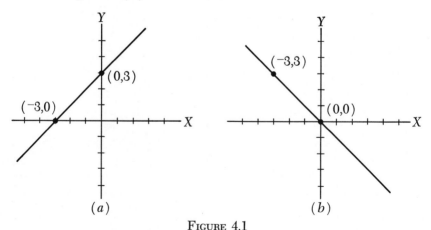

(a)   (b)

FIGURE 4.1

For convenience both graphs are sketched relative to a common set of axes, as shown in Figure 4.2.

Observe that the two straight lines of Figure 4.2 constitute the graph

94

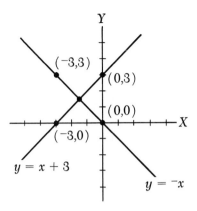

Y

$(^-3,3)$

$(0,3)$

$(0,0)$

X

$(^-3,0)$

$y = x + 3$

$y = ^-x$

FIGURE 4.2

of the set $\{(x,y): (y, = x + 3) \lor (y = {}^-x)\}$; i.e., the graph of $\{(x,y): y = x + 3\} \cup \{(x,y): y = {}^-x\}$.

Frequently we must solve a physical problem whose mathematical model consists of two linear functions $y = a_1x + b_1$ and $y = a_2x + b_2$ and whose desired solution set is the set of all ordered pairs (x,y) which satisfy both equations $y = a_1x + b_1$ and $y = a_2x + b_2$. The desired solution set is $\{(x,y): y = a_1x + b_1 \land y = a_2x + b_2\}$, which is equal to $\{(x,y): y = a_1x + b_1\} \cap \{(x,y): a_2x + b_2\}$; i.e., the intersection of the lines determined by the open sentences $y = a_1x + b_1$ and $y = a_2x + b_2$. In Section 4.3 we shall consider several physical problems which may be solved by means of linear functions. In Section 4.2 we shall discuss the various possible intersections of two linear functions. In the remainder of this section we shall discuss the commonly used procedure for computing the intersection of two linear functions. The following examples illustrate the various methods.

Example 1. Solve the *system of simultaneous linear equations*
$$\begin{bmatrix} y = 2x + 3 \\ y = x + 5 \end{bmatrix}$$; i.e., compute the set of all pairs (x,y) which satisfy both linear equations.

(1) $y = 2x + 3$
(2) $y = x + 5$
(1) $y = 2x + 3$
(2) $2x + 3 = x + 5$
$\quad\quad 2x - x = 5 - 3$
$\quad\quad\quad\quad x = 2$
$\quad\quad\quad\quad y = x + 5$
$\quad\quad\quad\quad y = 2 + 5$
$\quad\quad\quad\quad y = 7$

The solution of the system is $x = 2$, $y = 7$; i.e., the point $(2,7)$.

In effect, we *substituted* the variable $2x + 3$ of equation (1) for the variable y in equation (2). For this reason, the method of solution is usually called *solution by substitution*. The method of solution by substitution is illustrated again in Example 2.

Example 2.   Solve the system of linear equations

$$\begin{bmatrix} 2x + y = 5 \\ 3x + 2y = 9 \end{bmatrix}.$$

(1) $y = 5 - 2x$

(2) $3x + 2(5 - 2x) = 9$

   $3x + 10 - 4x = 9$

   $^-x = 9 - 10$

   $^-x = ^-1$

   $x = 1$

(1) $y = 5 - 2x$

   $y = 5 - 2(1)$

   $y = 5 - 2$

   $y = 3$

The solution of the system is $x = 1$, $y = 3$; i.e., the point $(1,3)$. The following example illustrates the method of *solution by addition*.

Example 3.   Solve the system $\begin{bmatrix} 2x + y = 5 \\ x - 2y = ^-5 \end{bmatrix}.$

(1) $2x + y = 5$

(2) $x - 2y = ^-5$

(1) $2(2x + y) = 2(5)$

(2) $x - 2y = ^-5$

(1) $4x + 2y = 10$

(2) $x - 2y = ^-5$

   $\overline{5x = 5}$

   $x = 1$

(1) $2x + y = 5$

   $2(1) + y = 5$

   $y = 3$

Thus the solution of the system is $x = 1$, $y = 3$; i.e., the point $(1,3)$. *Graphically*, the point of *intersection* of the graphs of $2x + y = 5$ and $x - 2y = ^-5$ is the point $(1,3)$, as shown in the accompanying sketch. Similar comments may be made about Examples 1 and 2. Example 4 further illustrates the method.

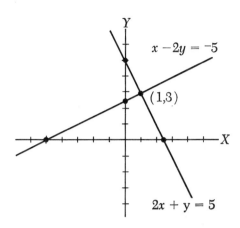

From the sketch in Example 3, we see that the point $(1,3)$ is the point which lies on both lines $x - 2y = {}^-5$ and $2x + y = 5$. That is, $(1,3)$ lies on $x - 2y = {}^-5$ *and* $2x + y = 5$. Thus $(1,3)$ is the only element in the *intersection* of the solution set of $x - 2y = {}^-5$ and the solution set of $2x + y = 5$. Symbolically, $\{(x,y): x - 2y = {}^-5 \wedge 2x + y = 5\}$ $= \{(x,y): x - 2y = {}^-5\} \cap \{(x,y): 2x + y = 5\} = \{(1,3)\}$. In other words, the intersection of the solution sets of the individual linear equations is the solution set of the *system* of linear equations.

Example 4.   Compute the point of intersection of the straight lines $3x + 2y = 4$ and $4x + 3y = 5$.

(1) $3x + 2y = 4$
(2) $4x + 3y = 5$
(1) ${}^-3(3x + 2y) = {}^-3(4)$
(2) $2(4x + 3y) = 2(5)$
(1) ${}^-9x + {}^-6y = {}^-12$
(2) $8x + 6y = 10$

$\overline{}$
${}^-x = {}^-2$
$x = 2$
(1) $3x + 2y = 4$
$3(2) + 2y = 4$
$6 + 2y = 4$
$2y = {}^-2$
$y = {}^-1$

Thus the point of intersection of $3x + 2y = 4$ and $4x + 3y = 5$ is $(2,{}^-1)$. The graph is shown in the accompanying figure.

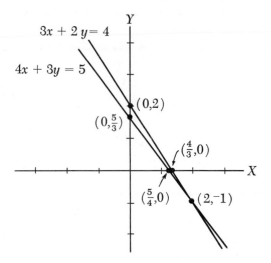

We summarize this section with the following remarks and a detailed example which shows all steps in the computation of the solution set of a system of linear equations.

To solve a system of simultaneous linear equations in two variables (i.e., to compute the intersection of the two linear functions), we employ the method of substitution or the method of addition. The method of solution guarantees that the set obtained as the solution set is the complete solution set, provided no computational error is made. In order to detect any possible computational errors, it is advisable to check the computed solution by replacing the variables x and y in the original linear equations and proving that the open sentences are converted to true sentences. The coordinates of any point in the solution set *satisfy* the two linear equations. For example, the coordinates 2 and ⁻1 satisfy the linear equations $3x + 2y = 4$ and $4x + 3y = 5$ of Example 4. We see that the solution set of a system of simultaneous linear equations in two variables is the intersection of the solution sets of the individual equations. To *solve* a system of two linear equations in two variables is *to compute the solution set of the system.*

Example 5.   Compute the intersection of

$$\{(x,y): 2x + y = 5\} \text{ and } \{(x,y): x - 2y = {}^-5\}.$$
$$\{(x,y): 2x + y = 5\} \cap \{(x,y): x - 2y = {}^-5\}$$
$$= \{(x,y): 2x + y = 5 \wedge x - 2y = {}^-5\}$$
$$= \{(x,y): y = 5 - 2x \wedge x - 2y = {}^-5\}$$
$$= \{(x,y): y = 5 - 2x \wedge x - 2(5 - 2x) = {}^-5\}$$
$$= \{(x,y): y = 5 - 2x \wedge x - 10 + 4x = {}^-5\}$$

$$= \{(x,y): y = 5 - 2x \wedge 5x = 5\}$$
$$= \{(x,y): y = 5 - 2x \wedge x = 1\}$$
$$= \{(x,y): y = 5 - 2(1) \wedge x = 1\}$$
$$= \{(x,y): y = 3 \wedge x = 1\}$$
$$= \{(x,y): x = 1 \wedge y = 3\}$$
$$= \{(1,3)\}.$$

Thus the intersection of the two solution sets is the set $\{(1,3)\}$. Hence the intersection of the lines is the point $(1,3)$.

Exercise 4.1

I. By means of the method of *substitution,* compute the intersection of each of the following pairs of linear functions. Illustrate graphically.

(1) $2x + y = 1, y = 3 - x$
(2) $x + y = 3, x = y - 2$
(3) $3x + y = 7, 2x - 3y = 1$
(4) $x - 7y = 11, x + 3y = 1$
(5) $x + 2y = 4, x + 3y = 1$
(6) $4x + y = {}^-1, 2x + y = 0$
(7) $x = 2y + 3, y = (1/2)x - 3/2$
(8) $x + y = 4, (1/6)x - (1/2)y = 2/5$
(9) $(2/5)x - (3/5)y = 4/5, 6y = 4x - 8$
(10) $(2/5)x + (3/5)y = 1/5, 4x + 3y = {}^-4$

II. By means of the method of *addition,* compute the intersection of each of the following pairs of functions. Illustrate graphically.

(1) $x + y = 0, x - y = 2$
(2) $2x - y = 0, 2x + y = {}^-4$
(3) $x + 2y = 5, 3x - y = 1$
(4) $4x + 3y = {}^-1, 2x - y = 7$
(5) $2x + 4y = 11, 4x - 3y = 0$
(6) $12x - 18y = {}^-11, 3x - 2y = 1$
(7) $3x - 5y = 15, 2x + 3y = 6$
(8) $3x - 6y = 9, 2x - 4y = 6$
(9) $3x - 9y = 6, 2x - 6y = 4$
(10) $2x - 4y = 3, 3x - 6y = 1$

III. Solve each of the following systems of linear equations. Illustrate graphically.

(1) $\begin{bmatrix} 3x + y = 5 \\ x - y = 1 \end{bmatrix}$

(2) $\begin{bmatrix} 5x = y - 5 \\ x + y = {}^-1 \end{bmatrix}$

(3) $\begin{bmatrix} 3x + 5y = 110 \\ 5y - x = 44 \end{bmatrix}$

(4) $\begin{bmatrix} 2x + 4y = 11 \\ 4x - 3y = 0 \end{bmatrix}$

(5) $\begin{bmatrix} 7x - 3y = {}^-1 \\ 3x - 2y = {}^-4 \end{bmatrix}$

(6) $\begin{bmatrix} (2/3)x + (3/4)y = 5/6 \\ 4x + 3y = 4 \end{bmatrix}$

(7) $\begin{bmatrix} 2x - 5 = 0 \\ 5x - 5y = 25 \end{bmatrix}$

(8) $\begin{bmatrix} x + 3y = {}^-1 \\ 5y = 10 \end{bmatrix}$

(9) $\begin{bmatrix} x + y/2 + y/3 = 1/6 \\ x - y = 3 \end{bmatrix}$

(10) $\begin{bmatrix} x/4 - x - y/6 = {}^-1/4 \\ x - y = 3 \end{bmatrix}$

4.2   Systems of Linear Equations in Two Variables (*continued*)

In this section we shall continue the study of systems of two linear equations in two variables. In particular, we shall discuss the various possibilities for the solution set of a system and shall learn that the intersection of the solution sets of the linear functions may be empty, infinitely many points, or a single point. Geometrically, the lines corresponding to these cases are parallel, coincident, or intersecting in a single point, respectively. The following examples illustrate the various cases.

Example 1.   Solve the system $\begin{bmatrix} x + 3y = 5 \\ 3x + 9y = 2 \end{bmatrix}$.

The solution set of the system is $\{(x,y): x + 3y = 5 \land 3x + 9y = 2\}$.

$\{(x,y): x + 3y = 5 \land 3x + 9y = 2\}$
$= \{(x,y): {}^-3x + {}^-9y = {}^-15 \land 3x + 9y = 2\}$
$= \{(x,y): [({}^-3x + {}^-9y) + (3x + 9y) = ({}^-15 + 2)]$
$\qquad\qquad\qquad\qquad\qquad\qquad \land [3x + 9y = 2]\}$
$= \{(x,y): [0 = {}^-13] \land [3x + 9y = 2]\}$
$= \{\ \}.$

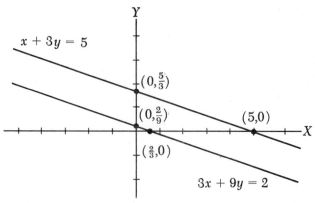

From the sketches of the graphs of the two linear functions $x + 3y = 5$ and $3x + 9y = 2$, we see that the two lines are parallel and hence do not intersect. Thus the fact that the solution set of their intersection is empty should not surprise you. Although it is really impossible to determine exactly from the *sketch* that the two lines are parallel, we can be certain that the two lines are parallel because their slopes are both equal to $^-1/3$, as the following computation shows:

$x + 3y = 5$	$3x + 9y = 2$
$3y = {}^-1x + 5$	$9y = {}^-3x + 2$
$y = ({}^-1/3)x + 5/3$	$y = ({}^-3/9)x + 2/9$
	$y = ({}^-1/3)x + 2/9$

Example 2. Solve the system $\begin{bmatrix} 3x - y = 6 \\ {}^-6x + 2y = {}^-12 \end{bmatrix}$.

The solution set of the system is $\{(x, y): 3x - y = 6 \wedge {}^-6x + 2y = {}^-12\}$.

$$\{(x, y): 3x - y = 6 \wedge {}^-6x + 2y = {}^-12\}$$
$$= \{(x, y): 3x - y = 6 \wedge ({}^-1/2)({}^-6x + 2y) = ({}^-1/2)({}^-12)\}$$
$$= \{(x, y): 3x - y = 6 \wedge 3x - y = 6\}$$
$$= \{(x, y): 3x - y = 6\}.$$

Thus the lines coincide and are really only *one* line. This is illustrated in the accompanying figure.

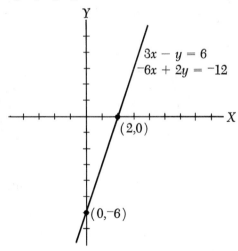

Example 3. Solve the system $\begin{bmatrix} 3x - 2y = 8 \\ x + 3y = {}^-1 \end{bmatrix}$.

The solution set of the system is $\{(x, y)\colon 3x - 2y = 8$
$\wedge\ x + 3y = {}^{-}1\}$.
(1) $3x - 2y = 8$
(2) $x + 3y = {}^{-}1$
(1) $3x - 2y = 8$
(2) $^{-}3x + {}^{-}9y = 3$

$$\overline{}$$
$^{-}11y = 11$
$y = {}^{-}1$
(2) $x + 3y = {}^{-}1$
$x + 3({}^{-}1) = {}^{-}1$
$x = 2$

Thus the two lines intersect in exactly one point, the point $(2,{}^{-}1)$. This is illustrated in the accompanying figure.

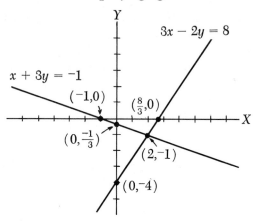

We close this section by summarizing the above results.

(1) The solution set of the system $a_1x + b_1y = c_1$, $a_2x + b_2y = c_2$ is the empty set if and only if there exists a real number k such that $a_2 = ka_1$, $b_2 = kb_1$, and $c_2 \neq kc_1$. In this case, the two lines have equal slopes and are parallel, and the system of equations is said to be *inconsistent*.

(2) The solution set of the system $a_1x + b_1y = c_1$, $a_2x + b_2y = c_2$ is the infinite set $\{(x, y)\colon a_1x + b_1y = c_1\}$ if and only if there exists a real number k such that $a_2 = ka_1$, $b_2 = kb_1$, and $c_2 = kc_1$. In this case, the two lines have equal slopes and are said to be *consistent* and *dependent*.

(3) The solution set of the system $a_1x + b_1y = c_1$, $a_2x + b_2y = c_2$ consists of exactly one point if and only if the slopes of the lines are *not* equal. In this case, the two lines intersect in exactly one point, and the system is said to be *consistent* and *independent*.

It is understood that $a_1 \neq 0$ or $b_1 \neq 0$, and $a_2 \neq 0$ or $b_2 \neq 0$ in each of the above cases. Although the above examples do not constitute proofs of these results, the method of proof is suggested by the examples. Consequently, we do not include the general proofs.

Exercise 4.2

I. Solve each of the following systems of linear equations. Illustrate graphically.

(1) $\begin{bmatrix} 3x - 5y = {}^-19 \\ 6x - y = {}^-20 \end{bmatrix}$

(2) $\begin{bmatrix} x + 3y = 5 \\ 3x - y = 5 \end{bmatrix}$

(3) $\begin{bmatrix} x + 3y = 5 \\ x + 3y = 8 \end{bmatrix}$

(4) $\begin{bmatrix} 3x + 4y = 12 \\ 6x + 8y = 10 \end{bmatrix}$

(5) $\begin{bmatrix} x + 4y = 3 \\ 2x + 8y = 6 \end{bmatrix}$

(6) $\begin{bmatrix} 3x - y = 7 \\ 6x - 2y = 14 \end{bmatrix}$

(7) $\begin{bmatrix} {}^-x = 2y - 4 \\ 2x + 4y = 1 \end{bmatrix}$

(8) $\begin{bmatrix} 2x - 3y = 4 \\ 6y + 4x = 1 \end{bmatrix}$

(9) $\begin{bmatrix} 2x - 3y = 4 \\ 6y = 4x - 8 \end{bmatrix}$

(10) $\begin{bmatrix} 2y = x - 3 \\ y = (1/2)x - 3/2 \end{bmatrix}$

(11) $\begin{bmatrix} 2y - 3x + 2 = 0 \\ 5y - 2x + 15 = 0 \end{bmatrix}$

(12) $\begin{bmatrix} y = x + 6 \\ 3x + 2y + 1 = 0 \end{bmatrix}$

(13) $\begin{bmatrix} x = y \\ x = {}^-y \end{bmatrix}$

(14) $\begin{bmatrix} 5x - 4y = 6 \\ 2y - 2.5x = {}^-3 \end{bmatrix}$

(15) $\begin{bmatrix} x - 2y = 3 \\ 4y = 2x + 7 \end{bmatrix}$

II. (1) Which systems in Exercise I are inconsistent?
   (2) Which systems in Exercise I are consistent?
   (3) Which systems in Exercise I are independent?
   (4) Which systems in Exercise I are dependent?

III. Solve each of the following systems of linear equations. Illustrate graphically.

(1) $\begin{bmatrix} x + y = 4 \\ (1/6)x = (1/2)y + 2/5 \end{bmatrix}$

(2) $\begin{bmatrix} 2x + 3y = {}^-4 \\ y - 5x = 1 \end{bmatrix}$

(3) $\begin{bmatrix} y = 2x - 4 \\ 2y - x = {}^-5 \end{bmatrix}$

(4) $\begin{bmatrix} 15x = 3y + 2 \\ 10x - 2y = 3 \end{bmatrix}$

(5) $\begin{bmatrix} 7x - 5y = 0 \\ 14x = 10y \end{bmatrix}$

(6) $\begin{bmatrix} 11x = 2y + 7 \\ 4x = 5 - 5y \end{bmatrix}$

(7) $\begin{bmatrix} 3x - 2y - 7 = 0 \\ 6x = 4y + 15 \end{bmatrix}$

(8) $\begin{bmatrix} x + y = 1 \\ 3x = y \end{bmatrix}$

(9) $\begin{bmatrix} x + 3y = 12 \\ 4x = 3y + 3 \end{bmatrix}$ (10) $\begin{bmatrix} 13x + 16y = 7 \\ 15x = 7 - 14y \end{bmatrix}$

IV. Prove each of the three summarizing statements made at the end of the section.

4.3   Applications of Systems of Linear Equations in Two Variables

Now that we know how to solve systems of linear equations in two variables, we shall study some applications to physical problems. Although the mathematical models of some physical problems can be formulated by means of linear equations in *one* variable, it is frequently easier to formulate the models by means of linear equations in *two* variables. The following examples illustrate the physical applications of systems of linear equations in two variables.

Example 1.   Lynda works for a grocer who wants her to mix some coffee which sells for 65¢ per pound with some coffee which sells for 85¢ per pound so that the mixture will weigh 80 pounds and sell for 70¢ per pound. How many pounds of each price coffee should she mix?

Let x represent the number of pounds of 65¢ coffee, and let y represent the number of pounds of 85¢ coffee.
Then $x + y = 80$ (weight),
and $.65x + .85y = .70(80)$ (dollar value).
The solution of the mathematical model is the solution of the system $\begin{bmatrix} x + y = 80 \\ 65x + 85y = 5600 \end{bmatrix}$.

(1) $x + y = 80$
(2) $65x + 85y = 5600$
(1) $y = 80 - x$
(2) $13x + 17y = 1120$
      $13x + 17(80 - x) = 1120$
      $13x + 1360 - 17x = 1120$
      $^-4x = ^-240$
      $x = 60$
(1) $y = 80 - x$
    $y = 80 - 60$
    $y = 20.$
Thus Lynda should mix 60 pounds of 65¢ coffee and 20 pounds of 85¢ coffee so that the mixture will contain 80 pounds of 70¢ coffee.

As usual, we check the solution in the *original physical problem* rather than in the *mathematical model.* Since she mixes 60 pounds of 65¢ coffee and 20 pounds of 85¢ coffee, the mixture contains 80 pounds of coffee. Since the mixture sells at 70¢ per pound, the total price of the coffee is .70(80) dollars; i.e., $56. The total price of 60 pounds of 65¢ coffee is .65(60); i.e., $39. The total price of 20 pounds of 85¢ coffee is .85(20); i.e., $17. Since $39 + $17 = $56, we conclude that the solution is correct.

Example 2.   Mary Susan has $1.44 in pennies and nickels. She has 6 more pennies than nickels. How many nickels does Mary Susan have? How many pennies does Mary Susan have? We formulate the mathematical model as follows:

Let $U = C_0$ (the set of counting numbers), let x represent the number of nickels, and let y represent the number of pennies.

Then $y = x + 6$ (because she has 6 more pennies than nickels).

Moreover, $.05x + .01y = 1.44$ (the dollar value of all coins).

Thus $5x + y = 144$ (the penny value of all coins).

The solution of the model is the solution of the system

$$\begin{bmatrix} y = x + 6 \\ 5x + y = 144 \end{bmatrix}.$$

(1) $y = x + 6$
(2) $5x + y = 144$
(2) $5x + (x + 6) = 144$
$\qquad 6x + 6 = 144$
$\qquad 6x = 138$
$\qquad x = 23$
(1) $y = x + 6$
$\qquad y = 23 + 6$
$\qquad y = 29$

Hence Mary Susan has 23 nickels and 29 pennies.

We check the solution in the original physical problem rather than in the mathematical model. Since Mary Susan has 23 nickels and 29 pennies, she has 6 more pennies than nickels. The total dollar value of Mary Susan's money is .05(23) + .01(29). Since .05(23) + .01(29) = $1.44, we conclude that the solution is correct.

Example 3.   The sum of the digits of a two-digit number is 13. If the tens digit is subtracted from the units digit, the difference is 3. What is the number?

Let u represent the units digit and t represent the tens digit.
Then $u + t = 13$,
and $u - t = 3$.
The solution of the model is the solution of the system
$$\begin{bmatrix} u + t + 13 \\ u - t = 3 \end{bmatrix}.$$

(1) $u + t = 13$
(2) $u - t = 3$
$\overline{ 2u = 16}$
$ u = 8$
(1) $t = 13 - u$
$ t = 13 - 8$
$ t = 5$

Hence the units digit is 8 and the tens digit is 5.
Thus the number is 58.

To check we note that $5 + 8 = 13$ and $8 - 5 = 3$. Thus the solution is correct.

Example 4.   Sue and Terry travel in a motorboat, at maximum speed, 30 miles upstream in 5 hours and return downstream in 3 hours. Compute the maximum speed of the boat in still water and the speed of the current.

Let x represent the speed of the boat in still water, and let y represent the speed of the current.
Then $x - y$ represents the maximum speed upstream, and $x + y$ represents the maximum speed downstream.
Since the product of time and rate is equal to distance, we obtain the system $\begin{bmatrix} 5(x - y) = 30 \\ 3(x + y) = 30 \end{bmatrix},$
which is equivalent to the system $\begin{bmatrix} x - y = 6 \\ x + y = 10 \end{bmatrix}.$
The solution is obviously $x = 8, y = 2$.
Hence the maximum speed of the boat in still water is 8 mph, and the speed of the current is 2 mph.

By actual check in the original problem, we see that the solution is correct.

Before you begin the following exercises, you should re-read the comments in the last paragraph of Section 2.3.

Exercise 4.3

I. Formulate a mathematical model for each of the following problems, and compute the solution. (Check each solution in the *original* problem).

(1) Ronny has $2.17 in pennies and nickels. He has 7 more pennies than nickels. How many of each coin does Ronny have?

(2) Norma has $1.04 in pennies and nickels. She has 3 times as many pennies as nickels. How many of each coin does Norma have?

(3) Dianne's father is 3 times as old as Dianne is now. In 6 years from now, he will be 2⅓ times as old as Dianne will be. How old is Dianne now?

(4) Brenda's father is twice as old as Brenda is now. In 13 years from now, he will be 1½ times as old as Brenda will be. How old is Brenda now?

(5) Vicky is 20 years younger than her mother. In 6 years from now, she will be half her mother's age. How old is Vicky now?

(6) Amy wants to mix enough 45¢ coffee and 60¢ coffee to form a mixture of 90 pounds of 50¢ coffee. How many pounds of each should she mix?

(7) Claudette mixed $12 per ounce perfume with $7 per ounce perfume to form a mixture of 20 ounces worth $9 per ounce. How many ounces of each type should she mix?

(8) Clifton bought 60 pounds of mixed nuts at 45¢ per pound. If the mixture consisted of peanuts and cashews worth 35¢ per pound and 50¢ per pound, respectively, how many pounds of each were in the mixture?

(9) Dudley mixes milk of 4% butterfat content with cream of 30% butterfat content to make 78 quarts of light cream of 18% butterfat content. How many quarts of milk does he use?

(10) Lurnice mixes two kinds of candy for distribution at a Christmas party. If one candy cost her 50¢ per pound, the other

cost her 75¢ per pound, and the 70 pound mixture cost her 60¢ per pound, how many pounds of each kind did she buy?

(11) The sum of the digits of Agnes's age is 12. If the tens digit is subtracted from the units digit, the difference is 6. How old is Agnes?

(12) Twice the tens digit of a two-digit number exceeds the units digit by 12. The tens digit exceeds the units digit by 3. What is the number?

(13) The units digit of a two-digit number exceeds the tens digit by 1. If the digits are interchanged, the resulting number is 6 times the sum of the digits. What is the number?

(14) The sum of the digits of a two-digit number is 15. The tens digit exceeds the units digit by 3. What is the number?

(15) A two digit number is 4 times the sum of its digits, and the units digit is twice the tens digit. What is the number?

(16) Walter and Candy are traveling in a motorboat at maximum speed. A 20 mile trip upstream takes them 5 hours and the return trip downstream takes them 2 hours. Compute the maximum speed of the boat in still water and the speed of the current.

(17) Two planes leave the same airport at 9:00 AM and travel in opposite directions (one travels North and one travels South). If one plane averages 50 mph more than the second plane and the planes are 675 miles apart at 10:30 AM, compute the average speeds of the planes.

(18) Butch and Wayne fly their two seater airplane (at full speed) a distance of 300 miles (with the wind) in 2 hours. The return trip (against the same speed wind) takes them 3 hours. Compute the air speed of the plane and the wind speed.

(19) Alexander and Jude flew (full-speed with the wind) a distance of 270 miles in 2 hours. The return trip (against the same wind at full speed) required 6 hours. Compute the air speed of the plane and the windspeed.

(20) Ursula can type 1.5 times as many words per minute as Edith can. If they begin typing at the same time and type for 20 minutes, the total number of words they type is 3000. How many words per minute does Edith type? How many words per minute does Ursula type?

II. Try to solve each of the following problems, and interpret the results.

(1) Audry has a total of 15 bills, some $5 bills and some $2 bills. Altogether she has $50. How many of each bill does Audry have?

(2) The sum of the digits of a two-digit number is 10. The sum of 3 times the tens digit and 3 times the units digit is 20. Compute the digits of the number.

(3) The sum of the digits of a two-digit number is 10. The sum of 3 times the tens digit and 3 times the units digit is 30. Compute the digits of the number.

III. Why should the solution be checked in the original problem rather than in the mathematical model?

4.4 Systems of Linear Inequalities in Two Variables

In Section 3.7 we learned to sketch the graph of any linear inequality in two variables. In addition, we learned to sketch the graph of a compound inequality composed of the conjunction or disjunction of two or more linear inequalities. For example, the graph of the compound inequality $x + y \leq 1 \wedge x - y \leq 1 \wedge y \leq 3 \wedge {}^-4 \leq x$ is the shaded region in Figure 4.3, including the line segments of the boundary.

In this section we shall review sketching the graphs of compound inequalities of the above type and shall introduce concepts which will help us to solve physical problems which involve compound inequalities. In the next section we shall solve some of these physical problems by

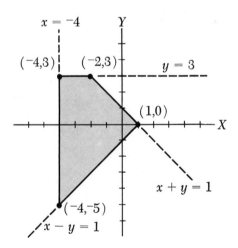

FIGURE 4.3

means of a method called *linear programming*. The following examples
will review the ideas involved in the graphing of a compound inequality
of the above type.

Example 1.   Solve the system of linear inequalities $\begin{bmatrix} 0 \leq x \\ x \leq 20 \\ 0 \leq y \\ y \leq 25 \\ x + y \leq 30 \\ 10 \leq x + y \end{bmatrix}$.

The solution set of the system is $\{(x, y): (0 \leq x \leq 20)$
$\wedge (0 \leq y \leq 25) \wedge (10 \leq x + y \leq 30)\}$, which is equal
to $\{(x, y): 0 \leq x \leq 20\} \cap \{(x, y): 0 \leq y \leq 25\} \cap$
$\{(x, y): 10 \leq x + y \leq 30\}$. To sketch the graph of the
solution set, we first sketch the graph of each of the

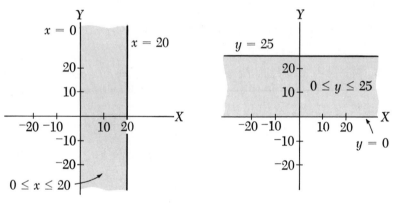

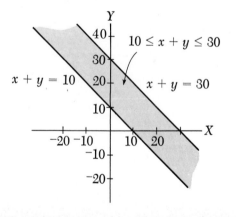

inequalities $0 \leq x \leq 20$, $0 \leq y \leq 25$, $10 \leq x + y \leq 30$, as shown in the accompanying figures.

Since the solution set of the system is the intersection of the three sets above, it follows that the graph of the system is the intersection of the three graphs above as shown in the following figure.

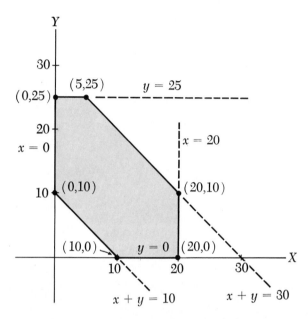

From high school geometry you will recall that the boundary of the graph of the solution set (the boundary of the shaded region) is a convex polygon. For this reason the graph is called a *convex polygonal region*.

Example 2. Solve the system of linear inequalities $\begin{bmatrix} 0 \leq x \\ x \leq 35 \\ 0 \leq y \\ x + y \leq 50 \end{bmatrix}$.

The solution set of the system is $\{(x, y): (0 \leq x \leq 35) \wedge (0 \leq y) \wedge (x + y \leq 50)\}$, which is equal to $\{(x, y): 0 \leq x \leq 35\} \cap \{(x, y): 0 \leq y\} \cap \{(x, y): x + y \leq 50\}$. The sketch of the graph of the solution set is shown in the accompanying figure.

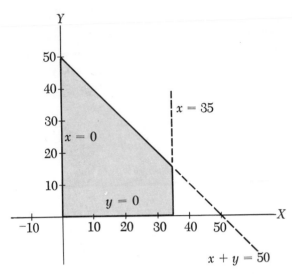

The graph is a convex polygonal region bounded by a convex polygon.

In the next section we shall need to maximize and minimize the value of an expression of the type $ax + by + c$, in which the ordered pairs (x, y) are members of a region whose boundary is a convex polygon. In more advanced mathematics a general theorem is proved which states the conditions under which the maximum value of the linear expression exists. Before we state the theorem (without proof), we shall analyze an example from an intuitive point of view.

Example 3.   Compute an ordered pair of the region of Example 1 for which the value of the expression $2x + 3y$ is maximum.

For convenience, we show the sketch of Example 1 in the accompanying figure. Since we want to maximize the value of $2x + 3y$, we let $2x + 3y = k$, in which k is a real number. For each specific k, the graph of $2x + 3y = k$ is a straight line. For example, the graph of $2x + 3y = 34$ is the straight line with slope $= -2/3$ and x-intercept $= 17$, as shown in the figure. On the other hand, the graph of $2x + 3y = 46$ is the straight line with slope $= -2/3$ and x-intercept $= 23$, as shown in the figure. In fact, for any choice of k, the graph is a straight line with slope $= -2/3$ and thus parallel to the above two lines. Observe that, as k increases, the lines move upward in the figure. Intuitively, the line with

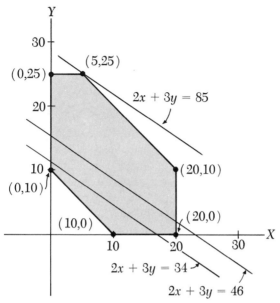

slope $= -2/3$ which passes through the point (5,25) is the line with maximum k which intersects the given region. Since $k = 85$ for this line and $k < 85$ for all other lines which intersect the region and have slope $= -2/3$, and since (5,25) lies on this line and also *in the region*, we see that, of all ordered pairs in the given region, the ordered pair (5,25) yields the maximum value of the expression $2x + 3y$. Observe that the point (5,25) is one of the vertices of the polygon.

The following theorems, which we state without proof, enable us to solve problems of the type in Example 3 without appealing to intuition.

THEOREM 1.   If the graph of the solution set of a system of *weak* linear inequalities is a region of finite area, then the boundary of the region is a convex polygon.

THEOREM 2.   (a) The maximum value of the expression $ax + by + c$ ($a \neq 0$ or $b \neq 0$) on a region of the type in Theorem 1 occurs at a vertex of the convex polygon enclosing that region.

(b) The minimum value of the expression $ax + by + c$ ($a \neq 0$ or $b \neq 0$) on a region of the type in Theorem 1 occurs at a vertex of the convex polygon enclosing that region.

In Example 3 we learned that the maximum value of $2x + 3y$ occurs at the vertex $(5,25)$. To determine the point at which the minimum value occurs, we merely compute the value at each vertex and observe that $2x + 3y$ is minimum at the vertex $(10,0)$.

Example 4.   Compute an ordered pair of the region of Example 2 for which the value of the expression $2x - y + 4$ is maximum.

By Theorem 1, the boundary of the region is a convex polygon. By Theorem 2, the maximum value of $2x - y + 4$ occurs at one of the vertices. The accompanying table exhibits the value of $2x - y + 4$ at each vertex. By inspection we see that the maximum value of $2x - y + 4$ occurs at the vertex $(35,0)$. Observe that the minimum value occurs at the vertex $(0,50)$.

Vertex	Value of $2x - y + 4$
$(0,0)$	4
$(35,0)$	74 (maximum)
$(35,15)$	59
$(0,50)$	$^-46$ (minimum)

Exercise 4.4

I. Sketch the graph of each of the following systems of linear inequalities.

(1) $\begin{bmatrix} ^-1 \le x \\ 0 \le y \\ 5x + 4y \le 20 \end{bmatrix}$

(2) $\begin{bmatrix} 0 \le x \\ ^-4 \le y \\ 5x + 4y \le 20 \end{bmatrix}$

(3) $\begin{bmatrix} x + 3y \le 12 \\ ^-6 \le 2x - 3y \\ ^-2 \le x + y \\ 2x - y \le 10 \end{bmatrix}$

(4) $\begin{bmatrix} 3x + y \le 12 \\ ^-6 \le 3x - 2y \\ 2 \le x + y \\ x - 2y \le 10 \end{bmatrix}$

(5) $\begin{bmatrix} 3x + 2y \le 6 \\ 6 \le 3x - 2y \\ 6 \le ^-3x + 2y \\ ^-3x - 2y \le 6 \end{bmatrix}$

(6) $\begin{bmatrix} 10 \le 2x - 5y \\ 10 \le ^-2x + 5y \\ 2x + 5y \le 10 \\ ^-2x - 5y \le 10 \end{bmatrix}$

(7) $\begin{bmatrix} ^-3 \le x \le 3 \\ ^-3 \le y \le 3 \end{bmatrix}$

(8) $\begin{bmatrix} 2 \le y \le 8 \\ 2 \le x \le 8 \end{bmatrix}$

II. Compute the maximum value and the minimum value of each of the following expressions on the polygonal region defined in the corresponding part of Exercise I.

(1) $2x - y$ (4) $x - 5y + 7$ (7) $x + 3$

(2) $x + 3y$ (5) $2x + 3y + 10$ (8) $y - 2$

(3) $5x + y - 6$ (6) $3x - 7y + 10$

4.5 Linear Programming

In this section we shall apply the methods of the previous sections to a class of physical problems known as *linear programming* problems, which occur in business and industry. Linear programming, as an application of mathematics, was invented so that problems concerning the allocation of resources could be solved. During World War II it gained prominence. Since the war much research has been done in linear programming and still more research is to be done in the extension of these ideas.

Linear programming is only one of the more recent applications of mathematics. The fact that mathematics now has extensive applications to economics, management, psychology, the social sciences, and the biological sciences as well as to physics, chemistry, and engineering has had an impact on the elementary school, secondary school, and college curricula. Prior to World War II, most applications of mathematics beyond arithmetic were in the physical sciences.

The following example illustrates the method of solving simple linear programming problems.

Example.   A manufacturer has two warehouses W_1 and W_2 containing 30 lathes and 35 lathes, respectively. A customer in Lafayette orders 20 lathes and a customer in Baton Rouge orders 25 lathes. The cost of shipping each lathe from each warehouse to each city is shown in the following table.

Warehouse	City	Shipping cost per lathe (dollars)
W_1	Lafayette	$28
W_1	Baton Rouge	$35
W_2	Lafayette	$32
W_2	Baton Rouge	$40

How should the manufacturer ship the lathes to insure minimum shipping charges and hence maximum profit?

Although the manufacturer has many possible ways of filling the orders, his problem is to ship the lathes so that the shipping cost will be a minimum. In order to compute the shipping cost, we let x represent the number of lathes shipped from W_1 to Lafayette and y represent the number of lathes shipped from W_1 to Baton Rouge. Then $20 - x$ represents the number of lathes shipped from W_2 to Lafayette, and $25 - y$ represents the number of lathes shipped from W_2 to Baton Rouge. Because the domains of the variables x and y are restricted by the number of lathes in W_1 and W_2, we derive the following system of linear inequalities:

$0 \leq x$ (the number of lathes shipped from W_1 to Lafayette cannot be negative),

$0 \leq y$ (the number of lathes shipped from W_1 to Baton Rouge cannot be negative),

$0 \leq 20 - x$ (the number of lathes shipped from W_2 to Lafayette cannot be negative),

$0 \leq 25 - y$ (the number of lathes shipped from W_2 to Baton Rouge cannot be negative),

$x + y \leq 30$ (the number of lathes shipped from W_1 cannot exceed 30),

$(20 - x) + (25 - y) \leq 35$ (the number of lathes shipped from W_2 cannot exceed 35).

The above system reduces to the following:

$$\begin{bmatrix} 0 \leq x \\ x \leq 20 \\ 0 \leq y \\ y \leq 25 \\ x + y \leq 30 \\ 10 \leq x + y \end{bmatrix}$$

In Example 1 of Section 4.4 we sketched the graph of this system, which, is reproduced here for convenience.

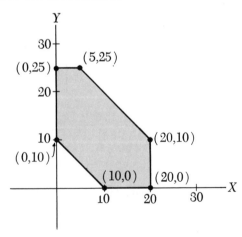

By Theorem 1, the boundary of the region is a convex polygon. The total cost of shipment is given by the expression

$$28x + 35y + 32(20 - x) + 40(25 - y),$$

which is equivalent to $^-4x - 5y + 1640$.

By Theorem 2, the minimum value of the expression $^-4x - 5y + 1640$ occurs at one of the vertices. The following table exhibits the values of $^-4x - 5y + 1640$ at each vertex of the polygon.

Vertex	Value of $^-4x - 5y + 1640$ (*Cost of shipment*)
(0,25)	1515
(0,10)	1590
(10,0)	1600
(20,0)	1560
(20,10)	1510
(5,25)	1495 (minimum)

From the above table we see that the minimum value of the expression occurs at the vertex (5,25). That is, the manufacturer minimizes the cost of shipment (and hence maximizes his profit) if he ships 5 lathes from W_1 to Lafayette and 25 lathes from W_1 to Baton Rouge. Of course, he must ship 15 lathes from W_2 to Lafayette.

The only type of linear programming problem which we can solve at this time is the type in the above example which can be formulated by means of a system of weak linear inequalities in two variables. The solution of a system of several weak linear inequalities in more than two variables is not as apparent as the solution of the above example and the solutions of the following problems. In fact, the techniques of this section are too tedious and time-consuming for use in the more complex type of linear programming. The procedures which have been developed since World War II for the solution of the more complex linear programming problems are especially adapted to high-speed electronic computers.

Exercise 4.5

I. In the above example, if the cost of shipment from W_2 to Lafayette is \$40 per lathe and the cost of shipment from W_2 to Baton Rouge is \$31 per lathe, how should the manufacturer allocate shipment of the lathes?

II. Mr. Bourgeois, who owns a 50-acre farm, wants to plant crop R and crop C. The seed for crop R costs \$25 per acre and the seed for crop C costs $40 per acre. Fertility conditions of his farm do not permit him to plant more than 35 acres in crop R but permit him to plant the entire 50 acres in crop C if he desires. Labor and machinery cost for planting, cultivating, and harvesting is $20 per acre for crop R and $15 per acre for crop C. Expected income from crop R is $200 per acre and from crop C is $175 per acre. How many acres of each crop should Mr. Bourgeois plant to insure himself maximum profit?

III. Machine M_1 produces 60 articles per hour and machine M_2 produces 45 articles per hour. The production schedule for the week specifies that a minimum of 1,800 articles be produced. The total running time available for *both* machines is no more than 40 hours, the cost of running machine M_1 is $12 per hour, and the cost of running machine M_2 is $10 per hour. How many hours should each machine operate to minimize the production cost?

IV. If the minimum number of articles in Exercise III is 2,100 and the costs of operating M_1 and M_2 are reversed, compute the number of hours each machine should operate to minimize the production cost.

V. Mr. Brown, who owns a 100-acre farm, wants to plant crop A and crop B. The seed and other costs for crop A amount to $10 per acre and for crop B amount to $40 per acre. Expected income from crop A is $40 per acre and from crop B is $120 per acre. Labor for crop A is one man-day per acre and for crop B is four man-days per acre. If Mr. Brown has a capital of $1100 and 160 man-days of labor to invest in his farm, how many acres of each crop should he plant to insure himself maximum profit?

CHAPTER 5

QUADRATIC EQUATIONS
AND FACTORING

5.1 The Quadratic Equation

The quadratic function was defined in Chapter 3 as $y = ax^2 + bx + c$, $a \neq 0$. Recall that the graph of a quadratic function is a parabola which opens upward if a is positive. The six cases which may occur are shown in Figure 5.1.

In Chapter 3, we observed that the vertex of a parabola frequently is the solution of the model of an important physical problem. The points of intersection of a parabola and the X-axis also frequently constitute the solution set of a model of an important physical problem. In this chapter we shall learn to compute the vertex and the points of intersection (whenever they exist) of any parabola and the X-axis. Since the X-axis is the graph $\{(x,y): y = 0\}$, we see that the points of intersection are given by $\{(x,y): y = ax^2 + bx + c \wedge a \neq 0\} \cap \{(x,y): y = 0\}$; i.e., the points of intersection constitute the graph of $\{(x,y): y = ax^2 + bx + c \wedge a \neq 0 \wedge y = 0\}$, which is equivalent to $\{(x,y): ax^2 + bx + c = 0 \wedge y = 0 \wedge a \neq 0\}$. Consequently, we compute the points of intersection of the parabola and the X-axis by first computing the solution set of the equation $ax^2 + bx + c = 0$ $(a \neq 0)$. Since the equation $ax^2 + bx + c = 0$ $(a \neq 0)$ is so important in mathematics, it is given a special name.

DEFINITION 1. The equation $ax^2 + bx + c = 0$, in which $a \neq 0$, is called a *quadratic equation in the variable* x (or simply a *quadratic equation*).

119

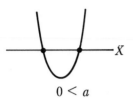

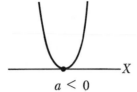

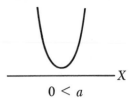

$0 < a$

Parabola intersects
X-axis in two distinct
points

$a < 0$

Parabola intersects
X-axis in a single
point

$0 < a$

Intersection of
parabola and X-
axis is the null
set

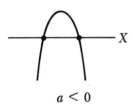

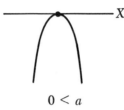

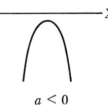

$a < 0$

Parabola intersects
X-axis in two distinct
points

$0 < a$

Parabola intersects
X-axis in a single
point

$a < 0$

Intersection of
parabola and X-
axis is the null
set

Figure 5.1

The following examples illustrate the method of computing the intersection of a parabola and the X-axis and, consequently, the method of
computing the solution set of a quadratic equation.

Example 1.   Compute the intersection of $y = x^2 + 3x + 2$ and the
X-axis; i.e., compute
$\{(x,y): y = x^2 + 3x + 2\} \cap \{(x,y): y = 0\}$.

(1) $y = x^2 + 3x + 2$
(2) $y = 0$
$\overline{}$
$0 = x^2 + 3x + 2$
$0 = (x + 1)(x + 2)$
   [since $(x + 1)(x + 2) = (x + 1)x + (x + 1)2$
                     $= x^2 + x + 2x + 2$
                     $= x^2 + 3x + 2$]
$x + 1 = 0$ or $x + 2 = 0$ (by multiplication property
$x = {}^-1$ or $x = {}^-2$ of zero)
(2) $y = 0$
Hence the intersection is the set $\{({}^-1,0), ({}^-2,0)\}$.

The accompanying sketch shows that the graph of the given quadratic function intersects the X-axis in the points $({}^-1,0)$ and $({}^-2,0)$.

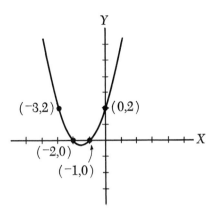

Example 2. Compute the solution set of the quadratic equation

$$x^2 - x - 6 = 0.$$

$x^2 - x - 6 = 0$
$(x - 3)(x + 2) = 0$
[since $(x - 3)(x + 2) = (x - 3)x + (x - 3)2$
$\qquad\qquad\qquad\quad = x^2 - 3x + 2x - 6$
$\qquad\qquad\qquad\quad = x^2 - x - 6]$
$x - 3 = 0$ or $x + 2 = 0$
$x = 3$ or $x = {}^-2$
Thus the solution set of $x^2 - x - 6 = 0$ is the set $\{{}^-2, 3\}$.

The sketch of the graph of the solution set is shown in the accompanying number line.

The graph of the quadratic function $y = x^2 - x - 6$ intersects the X-axis at the points $({}^-2,0)$ and $(3,0)$, as shown in the accompanying sketch.

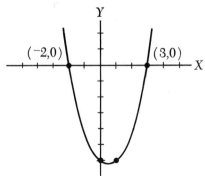

An important step in the computation of the solution set of the quadratic equation $x^2 + 3x + 2 = 0$ (or the intersection of the quadratic function $y = x^2 + 3x + 2$ and the X-axis) is the step in which $x^2 + 3x + 2$ is rewritten $(x + 1)(x + 2)$. In the following section you will have an opportunity to develop the necessary skills to *factor* such quadratic expressions. In the exercises of this section, however, you will have to guess (with the aid of the graph) the factorization of a quadratic expression $ax^2 + bx + c$, and then check the factorization by multiplication and the distributive property.

Exercise 5.1

I. Sketch the graph of each of the following quadratic functions, and label the points of intersection of the graph and the X-axis.

(1) $y = x^2 - 7x + 10$ (6) $y = x^2 - 2x + 15$
(2) $y = x^2 + 7x + 10$ (7) $y = x^2 + 8x + 12$
(3) $y = x^2 + 10x$ (8) $y = x^2 + 8x + 7$
(4) $y = x^2 - 10x$ (9) $y = x^2 - 5x$
(5) $y = x^2 + x - 12$ (10) $y = x^2 - 8x$

II. Compute the points of intersection with the X-axis of each quadratic function in Exercise I. Use the points of intersection with the X-axis to help you *guess* the necessary factorization.

5.2 Factoring

In this section we shall study some of the techniques of factoring; i.e., some methods of writing an expression as a product of two or more expressions. In the next section we shall study some of the applications of factoring. In order to write a given expression as the product of two or more expressions, we first need to consider the inverse problem of multiplying two or more expressions to form their product as a single expression. The following examples illustrate the procedure.

Example 1.   Multiply 5 by $2x + 3$.

$$5(2x + 3) = 5(2x) + 5(3) \quad \text{(by the distributive property)}$$
$$= 10x + 15.$$

Thus $5(2x + 3) = 10x + 15$.
Hence $10x + 15 = 5(2x + 3)$.

Consequently, to factor $10x + 15$, we observe that the greatest common divisor (gcd) of 10 and 15 is 5, and $5(2x + 3) = 10x + 15$.

Example 2.   Multiply $5a$ by $4x - 3y + 7$.

$$5a(4x - 3y + 7) = 5a(4x) + 5a(^-3y) + 5a(7) \quad \text{(by the}$$
$$\text{generalized distributive}$$
$$\text{property)}$$
$$= 20ax + {}^-15ay + 35a$$
$$= 20ax - 15ay + 35a.$$

Thus $5a(4x - 3y + 7) = 20ax - 15ay + 35a.$

Hence $20ax - 15ay + 35a = 5a(4x - 3y + 7).$

Consequently, to factor $20ax - 15ay + 35a$, we observe that $5 \mid a \mid$ is the gcd of $20a$, ^-15a, and $35a$, and $5a(4x - 3y + 7) = 20ax - 15ay + 35a$.

Examples 1 and 2 illustrate the simplest type of factoring—that in which all terms of the given expression have a common monomial factor. The following example further illustrates this type of factoring.

Example 3.   Factor the expression $15x^4 + 21x^3 - 9x^2 - 33x$.

We observe that $3x$ is a common factor of all the terms of the given expression.

Thus $15x^4 + 21x^3 - 9x^2 - 33x = 3x(5x^3) + 3x(7x^2) + 3x(^-3x) + 3x(^-11)$

Hence by the generalized distributive property, $15x^4 + 21x^3 - 9x^2 - 33x = 3x(5x^3 + 7x^2 - 3x - 11)$.

The following examples illustrate the method of factoring the difference of two squares.

Example 4.   Factor $x^2 - y^2$.

First consider the inverse problem of multiplying $x - y$ by $x + y$.

$$(x - y)(x + y) = (x - y)x + (x - y)y \quad \text{(by the dis-}$$
$$\text{tributive property)}$$
$$= x^2 - yx + xy - y^2$$
$$= x^2 - y^2.$$

Thus $x^2 - y^2 = (x - y)(x + y)$.

Example 5.   Factor $16a^2x^2 - 9y^2$.

$$16a^2x^2 - 9y^2 = (4ax)^2 - (3y)^2$$
$$= (4ax - 3y)(4ax + 3y).$$

The following examples illustrate the method of factoring a trinomial which is a perfect square.

Example 6.   Factor $x^2 + 6x + 9$.

First consider the inverse problem of multiplying $(x + 3)$ by $(x + 3)$.

$$(x + 3)(x + 3) = (x + 3)x + (x + 3)3$$
$$= x^2 + 3x + 3x + 3^2$$
$$= x^2 + 6x + 9.$$

Hence $x^2 + 6x + 9 = (x + 3)(x + 3) = (x + 3)^2$.

Example 7.   Factor $x^2 + 2ax + a^2$.

First consider the inverse problem of squaring $x + a$.

$$(x + a)^2 = (x + a)(x + a)$$
$$= (x + a)x + (x + a)a$$
$$= x^2 + ax + ax + a^2$$
$$= x^2 + 2ax + a^2.$$

Hence $x^2 + 2ax + a^2 = (x + a)(x + a) = (x + a)^2$.

Observe the pattern: the square of the binomial $x + a$ is

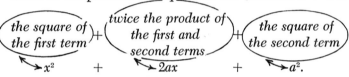

Example 8.   Factor $x^2 - 2ax + a^2$.

First consider the inverse problem of squaring $x - a$.

$$(x - a)^2 = (x - a)(x - a)$$
$$= (x - a)x + (x - a)(^-a)$$
$$= x^2 - ax - ax + a^2$$
$$= x^2 - 2ax + a^2.$$

Hence $x^2 - 2ax + a^2 = (x - a)(x - a) = (x - a)^2$.

Observe the pattern: the square of the binomial $x - a$ is

Example 9.   Factor $4t^2 - 20t + 25$.

$$4t^2 - 20t + 25 = (2t)^2 - 2(10t) + 5^2$$
$$= (2t - 5)(2t - 5)$$
$$= (2t - 5)^2.$$

The following examples illustrate a general method of factoring an expression of the form $ax^2 + bx + c$, $(a \neq 0)$.

Example 10.   Multiply $(x + d)$ by $(x + e)$.

$$(x + d)(x + e) = (x + d)x + (x + d)e$$
$$= x^2 + dx + ex + de$$
$$= x^2 + (d + e)x + de.$$

Hence $x^2 + (d + e)x + de = (x + d)(x + e)$; i.e., the factors of
$x^2 + (d + e)x + de$ are $(x + d)$ and $(x + e)$.

Example 11.   Factor $x^2 + 5x + 6$.

From Example 10, we know that $x^2 + 5x + 6 = (x + d)(x + e)$, in which $d + e = 5$ and $de = 6$.
By inspection, we see that $d = 3$ and $e = 2$.
Thus $x^2 + 5x + 6 = (x + 3)(x + 2)$.

Example 12.   Factor $x^2 - x - 6$.

$$x^2 - x - 6 = x^2 + (2 + {}^-3)(x) + 2({}^-3)$$
$$= x^2 + 2x + {}^-3x + 2({}^-3)$$
$$= (x + 2)x + (x + 2)({}^-3)$$
$$= (x + 2)[x + {}^-3]$$
$$= (x + 2)(x - 3).$$

Observe that we did not actually apply the *results* of Example 10, but, instead, *the ideas* involved in Example 10.

Example 13.   Multiply $(ax + b)$ by $(cx + d)$.

$$(ax + b)(cx + d) = (ax + b)cx + (ax + b)d$$
$$= (ax)(cx) + b(cx) + (ax)d + bd$$
$$= acx^2 + bcx + adx + bd$$
$$= acx^2 + (ad + bc)x + bd.$$

Hence $acx^2 + (ad + bc)x + bd = (ax + b)(cx + d)$.

Example 14.   Factor $6x^2 + 23x + 20$.

From Example 13 we learned that the factors $(ax + b)$ and $(cx + d)$ of $6x^2 + 23x + 20$ are such that $ac = 6$, $bd = 20$, and $(ad + bc) = 23$.

Consequently we determine factors a and c of 6, b and d of 20, and compute $ad + bc$. If $ad + bc = 23$, we have factored $6x^2 + 23x + 20$ correctly. If $ad + bc \neq 23$, we try other factors of 6 and 20.

We usually factor in this manner by first writing $6x^2 + 23x + 20$ $= (?\,x + ?)(?\,x + ?)$ and then filling in the blanks (represented by ?'s) as follows:

$$6x^2 + 23x + 20 = (3x + 5)(2x + 4).$$

Since $3(4) + 5(2) = 22$ rather than 23, we see that this factorization is *incorrect*.

Hence we try other factors of 20 and write

$$6x^2 + 23x + 20 = (3x + 4)(2x + 5).$$

Since $3(5) + 4(2) = 23$, we see that this last factorization is *correct*. Hence $6x^2 + 23x + 20 = (3x + 4)(2x + 5)$.

Example 15.   Factor $10x^2 + 3x - 18$.

$$\text{First try:}\quad 10x^2 + 3x - 18 = (10x + {}^-6)(x + 3)$$
$$= 10x^2 + (30 + {}^-6)x + {}^-18 \quad \textit{False}$$
$$\text{Second try:}\quad 10x^2 + 3x - 18 = (5x + 3)(2x + {}^-6)$$
$$= 10x^2 + ({}^-30 + 6)x + {}^-18 \quad \textit{False}$$
$$\text{Third try:}\quad 10x^2 + 3x - 18 = (5x + {}^-6)(2x + 3)$$
$$= 10x^2 + (15 + {}^-12)x + {}^-18 \quad \textit{True}$$
$$\text{Hence } 10x^2 + 3x - 18 = (5x - 6)(2x + 3).$$

We close this section with the following comments.

(1) Whenever an expression containing a variable is factored, the quantifier *all* is implied; i.e., the quantifier *all* is understood although not explicitly stated. For example, the *open sentence* "$x^2 - y^2 = (x - y)$ $(x + y)$" is written and spoken but the *sentence* "for all real numbers x and y, $x^2 - y^2 = (x - y)(x + y)$" is intended. Because a sentence, rather than an open sentence, is intended, we may write *false* or *true* as in Example 15.

(2) Although many expressions are factorable (can be factored), there are many expressions which are not factorable. For example, $x^2 + y^2$ is not factorable. (Recall that the universe is the set of *real numbers*.)

(3) Although you may employ the general procedure for factoring quadratic expressions such as $x^2 - a^2$, it is simpler to factor such expressions by use of the special techniques developed in the examples.

(4) Since the inverse of factorization of an expression is multiplication of the factors to produce the expression, proficiency in multiplying expressions yields proficiency in factoring expressions. For example, after you have learned to multiply $(x - 3)$ by $(x + 2)$ rapidly to obtain the product $x^2 - x - 6$, it will be easier for you to factor $x^2 - x - 6$ into its factors $x - 3$ and $x + 2$.

(5) Although you may not be successful in factoring a given expression, you should never guess at a factorization without checking it. After all, checking your proposed factorization is simply a matter of multiplying the proposed factors by application of the distributive property.

Exercise 5.2

I. Express each of the following indicated products as an indicated sum; i.e., multiply the first factor by the second.

(1) $3(2x^2 - 2x + 7)$
(2) $2(3x^2 - 7x + 2)$
(3) $-5x(3ax^3 + 5x^2 - 7x - 4)$
(4) $-3x(5ax^3 - 7x^2 + 4x - 6)$
(5) $-2xy(x + 3y - x^2 - 4xy + 7)$
(6) $-3xy(6 - 5x - 7y + 2x^2 + 4xy)$
(7) $(3x - 1)(3x + 1)$
(8) $(2x - 1)(2x + 1)$
(9) $(3x - 1)(3x - 1)$
(10) $(2x - 1)(2x - 1)$
(11) $(3x + 2)(3x - 2)$
(12) $(5x + 4)(5x - 4)$
(13) $(5x + 4)(5x + 4)$
(14) $(4x + 5)(4x + 5)$
(15) $(1 - 7x)(1 + 7x)$
(16) $(7 - x)(7 + x)$
(17) $(4x + 1)(4x + 1)$
(18) $(2x + 5)(2x + 5)$
(19) $(x + 1)(x + 6)$
(20) $(x + 2)(x + 3)$
(21) $(5x - 3)(x - 2)$
(22) $(3x - 5)(2x - 1)$
(23) $(2x + 7)(3x - 7)$
(24) $(4x - 3)(3x + 4)$
(25) $(8x - 5)(x + 5)$
(26) $(7x - 6)(x + 6)$
(27) $(x + 3)(3x - 4)$
(28) $(2x + 5)(x - 2)$
(29) $(9x - 6)(x + 2y)$
(30) $(2x + y)(x - 9y)$

II. Factor each of the following expressions.

(1) $7x^3 - 21x^2 + 14x + 28$
(2) $5x^3 + 20x^2 - 25x - 30$
(3) $11x^3 + 33x^2 - 55x$
(4) $13x^3 - 26x^2 - 52x$

(5) $x^2 - 25$

(6) $x^2 - 49$

(7) $9x^2 - 16y^2$

(8) $25x^2 - 9y^2$

(9) $32x^2 - 128y^2$

(10) $50x^2 - 32y^2$

(11) $x^2 + 4x + 4$

(12) $x^2 + 10x + 25$

(13) $25x^2 + 10x + 1$

(14) $4x^2 + 4x + 1$

(15) $x^2 - 12x + 36$

(16) $x^2 - 14x + 49$

(17) $x^2 + 4x + 3$

(18) $x^2 + 5x + 4$

(19) $2x^2 + 3x - 2$

(20) $2x^2 - 3x - 2$

(21) $4x^2 - 12x + 9$

(22) $9x^2 - 12x + 4$

(23) $4x^2 - 20x + 9$

(24) $9x^2 + 15x + 4$

(25) $4x^2 + 37x + 9$

(26) $9x^2 - 37x + 4$

(27) $4x^2 + 13x + 9$

(28) $9x^2 - 13x + 4$

(29) $6x^3 + 8x^2 - 8x$

(30) $10x^3 - 29x^2 - 21x$

5.3 Applications of Factoring

Now that we have studied the basic factoring techniques, we are prepared to return to the solution of the quadratic equation, which was introduced in Section 5.1. The following example will review the method.

Example 1.   Compute the solution set of the quadratic equation

$$6x^2 - 5x - 21 = 0.$$

$6x^2 - 5x - 21 = 0,$

$(3x - 7)(2x + 3) = 0,$

$3x - 7 = 0 \text{ or } 2x + 3 = 0,$

$3x = 7 \text{ or } 2x = {}^-3,$

$x = 7/3 \text{ or } x = {}^-3/2.$

Thus the solution set of $6x^2 - 5x - 21 = 0$ is the set $\{7/3, {}^-3/2\}$; i.e., replacement of the variable x in the open sentence $6x^2 - 5x - 21 = 0$ by *either* number 7/3 or ⁻3/2 converts that open sentence to a true sentence.

DEFINITION 2.   The members of the solution set of a quadratic equation are called the *roots* (or *solutions*) of the quadratic equation.

For example, the roots of $6x^2 - 5x - 21 = 0$ are 7/3 and ⁻3/2. If we let $f(x) = 6x^2 - 5x - 21$, then $f(7/3) = 0$ and $f({}^-3/2) = 0$; i.e., the graph of the quadratic function $f(x) = 6x^2 - 5x - 21$ intersects the X-axis at $(7/3,0)$ and $(^-3/2,0)$. For this reason, the *roots* of the quadratic equation $6x^2 - 5x - 21 = 0$ are also called the *zeros* of the quadratic function $f(x) = 6x^2 - 5x - 21$.

Example 2.   Solve the quadratic equation $6x^2 + 5x - 21 = 0$.

$6x^2 + 5x - 21 = 0$,
$(3x + 7)(2x - 3) = 0$,
$3x + 7 = 0$ or $2x - 3 = 0$,
$x = ^-7/3$ or $x = 3/2$.
Thus the roots are $^-7/3$ and $3/2$.

Check:
$$6(^-7/3)^2 + 5(^-7/3) - 21 = 6(49/9) + 5(^-7/3) - 21$$
$$= 98/3 - 35/3 - 63/3$$
$$= 0.$$
$$6(3/2)^2 + 5(3/2) - 21 = 6(9/4) + 15/2 - 21$$
$$= 27/2 + 15/2 - 42/2$$
$$= 0.$$

The following example illustrates that the two roots of a quadratic equation are equal when the corresponding quadratic function intersects the X-axis at one point (i.e., is *tangent* to the X-axis).

Example 3.   Compute the zeros of the quadratic function

$$f(x) = 9x^2 - 6x + 1.$$

$9x^2 - 6x + 1 = 0$
$(3x - 1)(3x - 1) = 0$
$3x - 1 = 0$ or $3x - 1 = 0$
$x = 1/3$ or $x = 1/3$
$x = 1/3$.
Both zeros are equal to $1/3$.

Check:
$$f(1/3) = 9(1/3)^2 - 6(1/3) + 1$$
$$= 1 - 2 + 1$$
$$= 0.$$

In this case, the graph of the quadratic function is tangent to the X-axis, as shown in the accompanying figure.

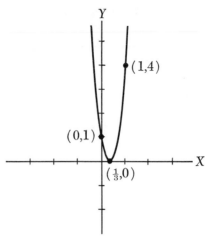

The factoring techniques studied in Section 5.2 are useful in the addition of expressions, as illustrated in the following examples. The techniques for computing the least common denominator of two or more rational numbers are applicable to the sum of two or more rational expressions. The word *compute* in each of the following examples, and in the exercises, indicates that the various rational expressions are to be combined into a single rational expression.

Example 4.   Compute the sum of $\frac{x}{x-3}$ and $\frac{2x-5}{x^2-9}$.

$$\frac{x}{x-3} + \frac{2x-5}{x^2-9} = \frac{x}{x-3} + \frac{2x-5}{(x-3)(x+3)}$$

$$= \frac{x(x+3)}{(x-3)(x+3)} + \frac{2x-5}{(x-3)(x+3)}$$

$$= \frac{x^2+3x}{(x-3)(x+3)} + \frac{2x-5}{(x-3)(x+3)}$$

$$= \frac{x^2+3x+2x-5}{(x-3)(x+3)}$$

$$= \frac{x^2+5x-5}{(x-3)(x+3)}.$$

Example 5.   Compute the sum $\frac{2x}{x+3} + \frac{5x}{x-2} + \frac{-3}{x^2+x-6}$.

$$\frac{2x}{x+3} + \frac{5x}{x-2} + \frac{-3}{x^2+x-6} = \frac{2x}{x+3} + \frac{5x}{x-2} + \frac{-3}{(x+3)(x-2)}$$

$$= \frac{2x}{x+3} \cdot \frac{x-2}{x-2} + \frac{5x}{x-2} \cdot \frac{x+3}{x+3} + \frac{-3}{(x+3)(x-2)}$$

$$= \frac{2x^2-4x}{(x+3)(x-2)} + \frac{5x^2+15x}{(x+3)(x-2)} + \frac{-3}{(x+3)(x-2)}$$

$$= \frac{2x^2-4x+5x^2+15x+-3}{(x+3)(x-2)}$$

$$= \frac{7x^2+11x-3}{(x+3)(x-2)}.$$

Example 6. Compute $\dfrac{1}{x^2 - y^2} + \dfrac{1}{x^2 + 2xy + y^2}$.

$$\frac{1}{x^2 - y^2} + \frac{1}{x^2 + 2xy + y^2} = \frac{1}{(x-y)(x+y)} + \frac{1}{(x+y)(x+y)}$$

$$= \frac{1}{(x-y)(x+y)} \cdot \frac{(x+y)}{(x+y)} +$$

$$\frac{1}{(x+y)(x+y)} \cdot \frac{(x-y)}{(x-y)}$$

$$= \frac{x+y}{(x-y)(x+y)(x+y)} +$$

$$\frac{x-y}{(x+y)(x+y)(x-y)}$$

$$= \frac{x+y+x-y}{(x-y)(x+y)(x+y)}$$

$$= \frac{2x}{(x-y)(x+y)(x+y)}$$

$$= \frac{2x}{(x-y)(x+y)^2}.$$

Example 7. Compute the difference $\dfrac{x}{2x^2 + 5x - 12} - \dfrac{2}{x^2 + 2x - 8}$.

$$\frac{x}{2x^2 + 5x - 12} - \frac{2}{x^2 + 2x - 8} = \frac{x}{(2x-3)(x+4)} - \frac{2}{(x+4)(x-2)}$$

$$= \frac{x}{(2x-3)(x+4)} \cdot \frac{(x-2)}{(x-2)} +$$

$$\frac{-2}{(x+4)(x-2)} \cdot \frac{(2x-3)}{(2x-3)}$$

$$= \frac{x^2 - 2x}{(2x-3)(x+4)(x-2)} +$$

$$\frac{-4x^2 + 6}{(x+4)(x-2)(2x-3)}$$

$$= \frac{x^2 - 2x - 4x^2 + 6}{(2x-3)(x+4)(x-2)}$$

$$= \frac{-3x^2 - 2x + 6}{(2x-3)(x+4)(x-2)}.$$

The *numerators* of the answers in Examples 4, 5, and 7 are quadratic expressions which are not factorable (with rational coefficients).† If any of these expressions were factorable (with rational coefficients), we should factor it, and if the numerator and denominator had a common factor, we should reduce the expression by diving numerator and denominator by the common factor. The following examples illustrate the technique.

Example 8. Simplify the expression $\dfrac{2x^2 + x - 6}{6x^2 - x - 12}$.

$$\frac{2x^2 + x - 6}{6x^2 - x - 12} = \frac{(2x-3)(x+2)}{(2x-3)(3x+4)}$$

$$= \frac{2x-3}{2x-3} \cdot \frac{x+2}{3x+4}$$

$$= 1 \cdot \frac{x+2}{3x+4}$$

$$= \frac{x+2}{3x+4}.$$

† Henceforth when we say that a quadratic expression with rational coefficients is not factorable, we really mean that it is not factorable with rational coefficients.

Example 9.   *Multiply* $\dfrac{2x^2 + 3x - 2}{x^2 - 6x - 7}$ by $\dfrac{x^2 + 8x + 7}{4x^2 + 12x - 7}$.

$$\frac{2x^2 + 3x - 2}{x^2 - 6x - 7} \cdot \frac{x^2 + 8x + 7}{4x^2 + 12x - 7} = \frac{(2x - 1)(x + 2)}{(x - 7)(x + 1)} \cdot \frac{(x + 1)(x + 7)}{(2x - 1)(2x + 7)}$$

$$= \frac{(2x - 1)(x + 2)(x + 1)(x + 7)}{(x - 7)(x + 1)(2x - 1)(2x + 7)}$$

$$= \frac{(2x - 1)(x + 1)}{(2x - 1)(x + 1)} \cdot \frac{(x + 2)(x + 7)}{(x - 7)(2x + 7)}$$

$$= 1 \cdot \frac{(x + 2)(x + 7)}{(x - 7)(2x + 7)}$$

$$= \frac{(x + 2)(x + 7)}{(x - 7)(2x + 7)}.$$

Example 10.   Divide $\dfrac{x^3 - xy^2}{x^2 + xy - 6y^2}$ by $\dfrac{x^2 - 2xy + y^2}{x^2 - xy - 2y^2}$.

$$\frac{x^3 - xy^2}{x^2 + xy - 6y^2} \div \frac{x^2 - 2xy + y^2}{x^2 - xy - 2y^2} = \frac{x(x - y)(x + y)}{(x - 2y)(x + 3y)} \div \frac{(x - y)(x - y)}{(x - 2y)(x + y)}$$

$$= \frac{x(x - y)(x + y)}{(x - 2y)(x + 3y)} \cdot \frac{(x - 2y)(x + y)}{(x - y)(x - y)}$$

$$= \frac{(x - y)(x - 2y)x(x + y)^2}{(x - y)(x - 2y)(x - y)(x + 3y)}$$

$$= \frac{x(x + y)^2}{(x - y)(x + 3y)}.$$

We close this section with the following comments.

(1) In Examples 4 through 10 and similar examples, the quantifier *all* is implied with the exception that all replacements of the variable which make the denominator 0 are excluded. Thus when we write $(x^2 + 2x + 1)/ (x^2 - 1) = (x + 1)(x + 1)/(x - 1)(x + 1) = (x + 1)/(x - 1)$, we mean that $(x^2 + 2x + 1)/(x^2 - 1) = (x + 1)/(x - 1)$ for *all* real numbers x *except* $x = {}^-1$ and $x = 1$. We sometimes indicate this by writing $(x^2 + 2x + 1)/(x^2 - 1) = (x + 1)/(x - 1)$, $(x \neq {}^-1, x \neq 1)$.

(2) Sometimes, factoring an expression does not simplify the computation. For example, factoring $x^2 - 9$ into its factors $x - 3$ and $x + 3$ does not simplify the computation of $1/(x + 1) + 1/(x^2 - 9)$.

Exercise 5.3

I. Compute the solution set (the set of roots) of each of the following quadratic equations.

(1) $x^2 - 25 = 0$

(2) $x^2 - 49 = 0$

(3) $9x^2 - 16 = 0$

(4) $25x^2 - 9 = 0$

(5) $32x^2 - 128 = 0$

(6) $50x^2 - 32 = 0$

(7) $x^2 + 4x + 4 = 0$

(8) $x^2 + 10x + 25 = 0$

(9) $25x^2 + 10x + 1 = 0$

(10) $4x^2 + 4x + 1 = 0$

(11) $x^2 - 12x + 36 = 0$

(12) $x^2 - 14x + 49 = 0$

(13) $x^2 + 4x + 3 = 0$

(14) $x^2 + 5x + 4 = 0$

$(15)\ 4x^2 - 12x + 9 = 0$

$(16)\ 9x^2 - 12x + 4 = 0$

$(17)\ 4x^2 - 20x + 9 = 0$

$(18)\ 9x^2 + 15x + 4 = 0$

$(19)\ 9x^2 - 13x + 4 = 0$

$(20)\ 4x^2 + 13x + 9 = 0$

II. Sketch the graph of each of the following quadratic functions.

$(1)\ f(x) = x^2 - 25$

$(2)\ f(x) = x^2 - 49$

$(3)\ f(x) = 9x^2 - 16$

$(4)\ f(x) = 25x^2 - 9$

$(5)\ f(x) = 32x^2 - 128$

$(6)\ f(x) = 50x^2 - 32$

$(7)\ f(x) = x^2 + 4x + 4$

$(8)\ f(x) = x^2 + 10x + 25$

$(9)\ f(x) = 25x^2 + 10x + 1$

$(10)\ f(x) = 4x^2 + 4x + 1$

$(11)\ f(x) = x^2 - 12x + 36$

$(12)\ f(x) = x^2 - 14x + 49$

$(13)\ f(x) = x^2 + 4x + 3$

$(14)\ f(x) = x^2 + 5x + 4$

$(15)\ f(x) = 4x^2 - 12x + 9$

$(16)\ f(x) = 9x^2 - 12x + 4$

$(17)\ f(x) = 4x^2 - 20x + 9$

$(18)\ f(x) = 9x^2 + 15x + 4$

$(19)\ f(x) = 9x^2 - 13x + 4$

$(20)\ f(x) = 4x^2 + 13x + 9$

III. Compute the zeros of each quadratic function in Exercise II.

IV. Compute each of the following sums and differences.

$(1)\ \dfrac{1}{x + 2} + \dfrac{3}{x^2 + 4x + 4}$

$(2)\ \dfrac{3}{x - 2} + \dfrac{1}{x^2 - 4x + 4}$

$(3)\ \dfrac{x}{x - 5} + \dfrac{2x}{x^2 - 25}$

$(4)\ \dfrac{2}{x + 6} + \dfrac{3x}{x^2 - 36}$

$(5)\ \dfrac{2x - 3}{2x^2 + 3x - 2} - \dfrac{3}{x^2 + x - 2}$

$(6)\ \dfrac{2x - 3}{2x^2 + 3x - 2} - \dfrac{3}{x^2 + x - 2}$

$(7)\ \dfrac{x + 1}{x^2 - 9} - \dfrac{x - 1}{x^2 - 6x + 9}$

$(8)\ \dfrac{x - 1}{x^2 - 9} - \dfrac{x + 1}{x^2 + 6x + 9}$

$(9)\ \dfrac{1}{x + 4} + \dfrac{2x}{x - 4} - \dfrac{3x^2}{x^2 - 16}$

$(10)\ \dfrac{4}{x - 5} + \dfrac{3x}{x + 5} - \dfrac{x^2}{x^2 - 25}$

V. Compute each of the following products and quotients.

$(1)\ \dfrac{3x + 2}{x^2 - 1} \cdot \dfrac{2x^2 - x - 3}{9x^2 - 4}$

$(2)\ \dfrac{2x - 3}{x^2 - 4} \cdot \dfrac{2x^2 + 7x + 6}{4x^2 - 9}$

$(3)\ \dfrac{4x^2 - y^2}{4x^2 + 4xy + y^2} \div \dfrac{4x^2 - 4xy + y^2}{2x^2 + 3xy + y^2}$

$(4)\ \dfrac{9x^2 - 16y^2}{9x^2 - 24xy + 16y^2} \div \dfrac{9x^2 + 24xy + 16y^2}{3x^2 - xy - 4y^2}$

$(5)\ \dfrac{x^2 - xy - 6y^2}{2x^2 + xy - y^2} \div \dfrac{x^2 + 3xy + 2y^2}{2x^2 - 7xy + 3y^2}$

$(6)\ \dfrac{2x^2 - 7xy + 3y^2}{x^2 + 3xy + 2y^2} \div \dfrac{2x^2 + 3xy - 2y^2}{x^2 - 2xy - 3y^2}$

$(7)\ \dfrac{x^2 - xy - 6y^2}{2x^2 + xy - y^2} \cdot \dfrac{x^2 + 3xy + 2y^2}{2x^2 - 7xy + 3y^2}$

$(8)\ \dfrac{2x^2 - 7xy + 3y^2}{x^2 + 3xy + 2y^2} \cdot \dfrac{2x^2 + 3xy - 2y^2}{x^2 - 2xy - 3y^2}$

$(9)\ \dfrac{x^2 + x - 12}{4x^2 + 4x - 15} \div \dfrac{x^2 - x - 12}{4x^2 - 4x - 15}$

$(10)\ \dfrac{x^2 - 5x - 14}{6x^2 - x - 2} \div \dfrac{x^2 + 5x + 14}{6x^2 + x - 2}$

5.4   Solution of the Quadratic Equation by Completing the Square

In this section we shall solve the quadratic equation by a technique known as *completing the square*. The procedure is to convert a quadratic expression which is not a perfect square to one which is a perfect square by adding the appropriate expression to both members of the quadratic equation. The following examples illustrate the procedure.

Example 1.   Solve the quadratic equation $x^2 - 2x - 4 = 0$.

Since all attempts to factor $x^2 - 2x - 4$ are unsuccessful, we must solve the given equation by some other method. Hence we convert the left member to a perfect square.

$$x^2 - 2x - 4 = 0$$
$$x^2 - 2x = 4$$
$$x^2 - 2x + 1 = 4 + 1$$
$$(x - 1)^2 = 5$$
$$x - 1 = -\sqrt{5} \text{ or } x - 1 = \sqrt{5}$$
$$x = 1 + {}^-\sqrt{5} \text{ or } x = 1 + \sqrt{5}$$
$$x = 1 - \sqrt{5} \text{ or } x = 1 + \sqrt{5}.$$

Hence the roots of $x^2 - 2x - 4 = 0$ are $1 - \sqrt{5}$ and $1 + \sqrt{5}$.

Let us analyze the above procedure. Since $x^2 - 2x - 4$ is not factorable, we convert it to an expression which is a perfect square, and hence factorable. Recall that $x^2 - 2x + 1 = (x - 1)^2$. If the given expression can be converted to the expression $x^2 - 2x + 1$, then factorization will be possible. To convert $x^2 - 2x - 4$ to $x^2 - 2x + 1$, we must add 5 to it. However, if we add 5 to $x^2 - 2x - 4$ we must add 5 to the right member of the equation. Hence we write

$$x^2 - 2x - 4 = 0,$$
$$x^2 - 2x - 4 + 5 = 0 + 5,$$
$$x^2 - 2x + 1 = 5$$
$$(x - 1)^2 = 5.$$

The following example suggests a more general method of completing the square.

Example 2.   Solve the quadratic equation $x^2 + 5x + 2 = 0$.

Since $x^2 + 5x + 2$ is not factorable, we complete the square. The first step is to add $^-2$ to both members of $x^2 + 5x + 2 = 0$ to obtain the equivalent equation

$x^2 + 5x = {}^-2$. Remember that we are trying to make a perfect square of the left member; i.e., we are trying to convert the left member to $(x + r)^2$. Since $(x + r)^2 = x^2 + 2rx + r^2$, we see that $2r$ must be equal to 5. Consequently $r = 5/2$ and we must add $(5/2)^2$ to both members of $x^2 + 5x = {}^-2$ if we are to complete the square.

$x^2 + 5x = {}^-2$
$x^2 + 5x + (5/2)^2 = {}^-2 + (5/2)^2$
$(x + 5/2)^2 = 17/4$
$x + 5/2 = {}^-\sqrt{17/4}$ or $x + 5/2 = \sqrt{17/4}$
$x = {}^-5/2 + {}^-\sqrt{17}/2$ or $x = {}^-5/2 + \sqrt{17}/2$
$x = {}^-5 - \sqrt{17}/2$ or $x = {}^-5 + \sqrt{17}/2$.

It is customary to indicate the two roots as follows:

$x = {}^-5 \pm \sqrt{17}/2$.

Example 3. Solve the quadratic equation $5x^2 + 20x - 8 = 0$.

We know from Example 2 that we could complete the square if the coefficient of x^2 were equal to 1 rather than 5. Consequently by multiplying both members by 1/5, we convert the given equation to an equivalent equation in which the coefficient of x^2 is 1.

$5x^2 + 20x - 8 = 0$
$5x^2 + 20x = 8$
$(1/5)(5x^2 + 20x) = (1/5)8$
$x^2 + 4x = 8/5$
$x^2 + 4x + (4/2)^2 = 8/5 + (4/2)^2$
$x^2 + 4x + (2)^2 = 8/5 + (2)^2$
$(x + 2)^2 = 28/5$
$x + 2 = {}^-\sqrt{28/5}$ or $x + 2 = \sqrt{28/5}$
$x = {}^-2 - \sqrt{28/5}$ or $x = {}^-2 + \sqrt{28/5}$
$x = {}^-2 \pm \sqrt{28/5}$.

Example 4. Solve the quadratic equation $2x^2 - 3x + 4 = 0$.

$2x^2 - 3x + 4 = 0$
$2x^2 - 3x = {}^-4$
$x^2 - (3/2)x = {}^-2$
$x^2 - (3/2)x + (1/2 \cdot 3/2)^2 = {}^-2 + (1/2 \cdot 3/2)^2$
$x^2 - (3/2)x + (3/4)^2 = {}^-2 + 9/16$
$(x - 3/4)^2 = {}^-23/16$.

The solution set is empty, since the square of every real number is non-negative and hence cannot be equal to -23/16.

Hence the open sentence $2x^2 - 3x + 4 = 0$ cannot be converted to a true sentence by replacement of the variable x by a real number.

Example 5.   Compute the intersection of the quadratic function $y = 3x^2 + 3x + 4$ and the X-axis.

Since the equation of the X-axis is $y = 0$, the intersection is the set $\{(x, y): y = 3x^2 + 3x + 4 \land y = 0\}$.

$0 = 3x^2 + 3x + 4$
$3x^2 + 3x = {}^-4$
$x^2 + x = {}^-4/3$
$x^2 + x + (1/2)^2 = {}^-4/3 + (1/2)^2$
$(x + 1/2)^2 = {}^-13/12.$

The solution set is empty, since $(x + 1/2)^2$ is non-negative for every real number x and hence cannot be equal to -13/12.

Hence the graph of the quadratic function does not intersect the X-axis. The sketch is shown in the accompanying figure.

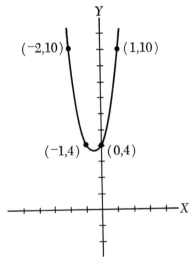

Examples 4 and 5 illustrate a serious defect of the real number system. *There exist quadratic equations which cannot be converted to*

true sentences by replacement of the variables by real numbers. We say that such a quadratic equation does not have *real roots.* Since the universe is the *real number system,* at this point in the development such an equation has no roots. If we desire that every quadratic equation shall have roots, we must extend the real number system. In the next chapter we shall extend the real number system to the *complex number system.* In the new system, every quadratic equation will have roots. In the following section we shall develop a formula for computing the real roots of a quadratic equation and in the last section we shall consider some applications of quadratic equations to physical problems.

Exercise 5.4

I. By completing the square, compute the solution set of each of the following quadratic equations.

(1) $x^2 - 5 = 0$ (6) $2x^2 - x - 2 = 0$

(2) $x^2 - 4x + 3 = 0$ (7) $2x^2 - 2x - 1 = 0$

(3) $x^2 - 4x - 2 = 0$ (8) $3x^2 + 5x - 2 = 0$

(4) $x^2 - x - 2 = 0$ (9) $x^2 + x + 1 = 0$

(5) $x^2 + 2x - 5 = 0$ (10) $2x^2 + x + 1 = 0$

II. Sketch the graph of each of the following quadratic functions, and compute the points of intersection of the graph and the X-axis.

(1) $y = x^2 - 9$ (5) $y = {}^-2x^2 + x + 1$

(2) $y = x^2 - x$ (6) $y = {}^-3x^2 + x + 2$

(3) $y = 4x^2 - 4x + 1$ (7) $y = x^2 + x + 1$

(4) $y = 4x^2 + 4x + 1$ (8) $y = x^2 - x + 1$

5.5 The Quadratic Formula

So far we have developed two methods of solving the quadratic equation—the method of factoring and the method of completing the square. As we have seen, some quadratic expressions are not factorable; hence there exist quadratic equations which cannot be solved by the factoring method. However, every quadratic equation with real roots can be solved by the method of completing the square. In this section we shall develop a formula (called the *quadratic formula*) for solving the general quadratic equation $ax^2 + bx + c = 0$, $(a \neq 0)$. We develop the formula by completing the square on $ax^2 + bx + c = 0$:

$$ax^2 + bx + c = 0 \quad (a \neq 0)$$
$$ax^2 + bx = {}^-c$$
$$(1/a)(ax^2 + bx) = {}^-c/a \quad (\text{since } a \neq 0)$$
$$x^2 + (b/a)x = {}^-c/a$$

$x^2 + (b/a)x + (1/2 \cdot b/a)^2 = {}^-c/a + (1/2 \cdot b/a)^2$

$(x + 1/2 \cdot b/a)^2 = {}^-c/a + b^2/4a^2$

$(x + b/2a)^2 = (b^2 - 4ac)/4a^2$

$x + b/2a = \sqrt{(b^2 - 4ac)/4a^2}$ or $x + b/2a = {}^-\sqrt{(b^2 - 4ac)/4a^2}$

$\qquad\qquad\qquad$ (provided $0 \le b^2 - 4ac$)

$x = {}^-b/2a + \sqrt{(b^2 - 4ac)/4a^2}$ or $x = {}^-b/2a - \sqrt{(b^2 - 4ac)/4a^2}$

$x = {}^-b/2a + \sqrt{(b^2 - 4ac)}/2a$ or $x = {}^-b/2a - \sqrt{(b^2 - 4ac)}/2a$

Hence $x = ({}^-b \pm \sqrt{b^2 - 4ac})/2a$.

Thus the roots of $ax^2 + bx + c = 0$, $(a \ne 0)$, are $({}^-b + \sqrt{b^2 - 4ac})/2a$ and $({}^-b - \sqrt{b^2 - 4ac})/2a$ (provided $b^2 - 4ac$ is *not* negative). If $b^2 - 4ac < 0$, then $(b^2 - 4ac)/4a^2 < 0$ (since $4a^2$ is positive). But $(x + b/2a)^2$ cannot be negative. Thus if $b^2 - 4ac < 0$, the open sentence $(x + b/2a)^2 = (b^2 - 4ac)/4a^2$ cannot be converted to a true sentence by replacement of the variable x by a real number. In this case, the quadratic equation $ax^2 + bx + c = 0$ has no real roots.

We summarize the above results by cases.

Case 1.　　　If $0 < b^2 - 4ac$, then the quadratic equation $ax^2 + bx + c = 0$ has the *two distinct roots* $({}^-b + \sqrt{b^2 - 4ac})/2a$ and $({}^-b - \sqrt{b^2 - 4ac})/2a$. In this case the graph of the quadratic function $y = ax^2 + bx + c$ intersects the X-axis in the distinct points $\left(\frac{{}^-b + \sqrt{b^2 - 4ac}}{2a}, 0\right)$ and $\left(\frac{{}^-b - \sqrt{b^2 - 4ac}}{2a}, 0\right)$.

Case 2.　　　If $b^2 - 4ac = 0$, then the quadratic equation $ax^2 + bx + c = 0$ has exactly one real root ${}^-b/2a$. In this case the graph of the quadratic function $y = ax^2 + bx + c$ is tangent to the X-axis at the point $({}^-b/2a, 0)$. We sometimes say that the quadratic equation has *two* real and *equal* roots.

Case 3.　　　If $b^2 - 4ac < 0$, then the quadratic equation $ax^2 + bx + c = 0$ has *no* real roots. In this case the graph of the quadratic function $y = ax^2 + bx + c$ does not intersect the X-axis.

The following examples illustrate the application of the quadratic formula to computing the roots of a quadratic equation.

Example 1.　　Solve the quadratic equation $3x^2 + 4x - 5 = 0$.

$a = 3, b = 4, c = {}^-5.$

Hence $b^2 - 4ac = 4^2 - 4(3)({}^-5) = 16 + 60 = 76$.

Since $0 < b^2 - 4ac$, this example belongs to Case 1.

$$x = (^-b \pm \sqrt{b^2 - 4ac})/2a$$
$$= (^-4 \pm \sqrt{76})/2(3)$$
$$= (^-4 \pm \sqrt{4(19)})/2(3)$$
$$= (^-4 \pm 2\sqrt{19})/2(3)$$
$$= 2(^-2 \pm \sqrt{19})/2(3)$$
$$= (^-2 \pm \sqrt{19})/3.$$

Example 2.   Solve the quadratic equation $9x^2 - 12x + 4 = 0$.

$a = 9, b = {}^-12, c = 4$.
Hence $b^2 - 4ac = (^-12)^2 - 4(9)(4) = 144 - 144 = 0$.
Since $b^2 - 4ac = 0$, this example belongs to Case 2.

$$x = (^-b \pm \sqrt{b^2 - 4ac})/2a$$
$$= [^-(^-12) \pm \sqrt{0}]/2(9)$$
$$= (12 \pm 0)/18$$
$$= 2/3.$$

Example 3.   Solve the quadratic equation $9x^2 - 11x + 4 = 0$.

$a = 9, b = {}^-11, c = 4$.
Hence $b^2 - 4ac = (^-11)^2 - 4(9)(4) = 121 - 144 = {}^-23$.
Since $b^2 - 4ac < 0$, this example belongs to Case 3.
Hence $9x^2 - 11x + 4 = 0$ has no real roots.

Example 4.   Compute the points of intersection of the X-axis and the graph of the quadratic function $\mathbf{f}(x) = {}^-x^2 + x + 2$.

The points of intersection are given by $\{(x,y): y = {}^-x^2 + x + 2 \land y = 0\}$.
Thus we solve the quadratic equation $^-x^2 + x + 2 = 0$.
$a = {}^-1, b = 1, c = 2$.
$b^2 - 4ac = (1)^2 - 4(^-1)(2) = 1 + 8 = 9$.
Since $0 < b^2 - 4ac$, this example belongs to Case 1.

$$x = (^-b \pm \sqrt{b^2 - 4ac})/2a$$
$$= (^-1 \pm \sqrt{9})/2(^-1)$$
$$= (^-1 \pm 3)/^-2$$

$x = (^-1 + 3)/^-2$ or $x = (^-1 - 3)/^-2$
$x = 2/^-2$ or $x = {}^-4/^-2$
$x = {}^-1$ or $x = 2$.
Thus $\{(x,y): y = {}^-1x^2 + x + 2 \land y = 0\} = \{(^-1,0), 2,0)\}$.
Hence the graph intersects the X-axis at $(^-1,0)$ and $(2,0)$.

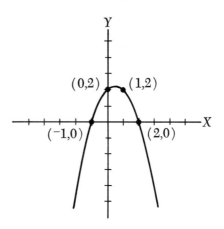

Exercise 5.5

I. Use the quadratic formula to compute the solution set of each of the following quadratic equations.

(1) $x^2 - 4x + 3 = 0$ (11) $5x^2 - 3x - 9 = 0$

(2) $x^2 + 4x + 3 = 0$ (12) $x^2 - 4x + 13 = 0$

(3) $x^2 - x - 2 = 0$ (13) $6x^2 + 5x - 6 = 0$

(4) $x^2 - 4x - 2 = 0$ (14) $7x^2 + 6x + 18 = 0$

(5) $2x^2 - x - 2 = 0$ (15) $2x^2 - 2x + 1 = 0$

(6) $x^2 + 2x - 5 = 0$ (16) $7x^2 + 8x - 4 = 0$

(7) $3x^2 + 5x - 2 = 0$ (17) $x^2 + 6x + 13 = 0$

(8) $2x^2 - 2x - 1 = 0$ (18) $x^2 + ax + 2a^2 = 0$

(9) $2x^2 + x + 1 = 0$ (19) $9x^2 - 30x + 23 = 0$

(10) $x^2 + x + 1 = 0$ (20) $x^2 + 2x + 10 = 0$

II. Sketch the graph of the quadratic function corresponding to each of the quadratic equations in Exercise I. How do the x-coordinates of the points of intersection of the graph with the X-axis compare with the roots of the corresponding quadratic equation in Exercise I?

5.6 Applications of Quadratic Equations

In this section we shall consider some of the applications of quadratic equations to certain physical problems. The mathematical model of a given problem will be formulated by means of a quadratic equation. The following examples illustrate the application.

Example 1. The area of a rectangular plot of land is 1,575 square yards. The depth of the plot exceeds the width by 10 yards. What are the dimensions of the plot?

Let x represent the width of the plot.

Then $x + 10$ represents the depth of the plot.

Thus $x(x + 10)$ represents the area of the plot.

$x(x + 10) = 1575 \qquad (x \in I^+)$

$x^2 + 10x = 1575$

$x^2 + 10x - 1575 = 0.$

$b^2 - 4ac = 10^2 - 4(1)(^-1575)$

$\qquad\qquad = 100 + 6300$

$\qquad\qquad = 6400.$

Since $b^2 - 4ac$ is positive, there are two real roots.

$x = (^-b \pm \sqrt{b^2 - 4ac})/2a$

$\quad = ^-10 \pm \sqrt{6400})/2(1)$

$\quad = (^-10 \pm 80)/2$

$\quad = (^-10 + 80)/2 \text{ or } (^-10 - 80)/2$

$\quad = 70/2 \text{ or } ^-90/2$

$\quad = 35 \text{ or } ^-45.$

Since $x \in I^+$, x cannot be equal to $^-45$. Hence $x = 35$ and $x + 10 = 45$.

Thus the width is 35 yards and the depth is 45 yards. We check the problem by computing the area of the plot from the computed width and depth. Since $35(45) = 1575$, we see that the solution is correct. Although the root $^-45$ is a valid root of the quadratic equation, it is not used in the physical problem because the width of a plot cannot be negative.

Example 2. Amy has 20 more quarters than nickels. The product of the number of quarters and the number of nickels is 800. How many of each coin does she have?

Let x represent the number of nickels.

Then $x + 20$ represents the number of quarters.

Thus $x(x + 20) = 800 \qquad (x \in I^+)$

$x^2 + 20x = 800$

$x^2 + 20x - 800 = 0 \qquad (x \in I^+)$

$(x + 40)(x - 20) = 0$

$x + 40 = 0 \text{ or } x - 20 = 0$

$x = ^-40 \text{ or } x = 20$

Since $x \in I^+$, it follows that $x = 20$.

Hence Amy has 20 nickels and 40 quarters.

As a check, we observe that $(20)(40) = 800$.

Example 3. From a motionless helicopter 150 feet high, Joel throws a ball upward with an initial speed of 20 feet/sec. The equation describing the motion of the ball is $s = -16t^2 + 20t + 150$, in which s represents the distance above ground and t represents the time in seconds. When does the ball strike the ground?

The ball strikes the ground when $s = 0$. This occurs *after* the ball has been thrown; i.e., for a positive value of t. Thus the positive root of the quadratic equation $-16t^2 + 20t + 150 = 0$ represents the time in seconds required for the ball to strike the ground.

$-16t^2 + 20t + 150 = 0 \qquad (0 < t)$

$8t^2 - 10t - 75 = 0$

$b^2 - 4ac = (-10)^2 - 4(8)(-75)$

$\qquad\qquad = 100 + 2400$

$\qquad\qquad = 2500$

$t = [-(-10) \pm \sqrt{2500}]/2(8)$

$t = (10 \pm 50)/16$

$t = 60/16$ or $t = -40/16$

$t = 15/4 = 3.75$, or $t = -5/2 = -2.5$.

But $0 < t$.

Hence the ball strikes the ground 3.75 seconds after it is thrown.

Example 4.   From experience a manufacturer knows that the unit cost is a function of the number of machines operating. The unit cost is given by the formula $y = x^2 - 20x + 105$, in which y represents the unit cost and x represents the number of machines in operation. Compute the number of machines he should operate in order to minimize the unit cost.

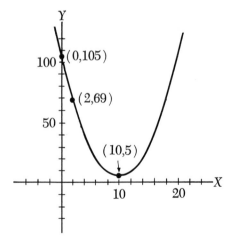

The sketch of the graph of the quadratic function for $x \in R$ is shown in the accompanying figure.

> To compute the minimum cost, we first compute the vertex of the parabola.
> In order to compute the vertex, we complete the square.
> $y = x^2 - 20x + 105$
> $y - 105 = x^2 - 20x$
> $y - 105 + 10^2 = x^2 - 20x + 10^2$
> $y - 5 = (x - 10)^2$
> $y = (x - 10)^2 + 5$
> Since $(x - 10)^2$ cannot be negative, we see that y is minimum when $(x - 10)^2 = 0$; i.e., when $x = 10$. Thus the vertex is the point $(10,5)$. Hence he should operate 10 machines to minimize the unit cost.

If the x-coordinate of the vertex had not been an integer, the manufacturer would minimize unit cost by choosing the nearest integer to the x-coordinate of the vertex.

Example 5. Paul is standing on the top of a building 100 feet high and throws a ball straight up with a speed of 32 feet per second. The equation describing the motion of the ball is $s = 100 + 32t + {}^-16t^2$, in which t represents the time measured in seconds and s represents the height of the ball measured in feet. Compute the maximum height reached by the ball.

The sketch of the graph of the quadratic function is shown in the accompanying figure.

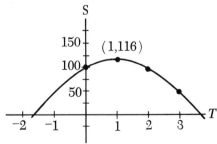

To compute the maximum height, we compute the vertex of the parabola.
In order to compute the vertex, we complete the square.
$s = {}^-16t^2 + 32t + 100$
$s - 100 = {}^-16(t^2 - 2t)$

$$s - 100 - 16 = {}^-16(t^2 - 2t + 1)$$
$$s - 116 = {}^-16(t - 1)^2$$
$$s = {}^-16(t - 1)^2 + 116.$$

Since $^-16(t - 1)^2$ cannot be positive, we see that s is maximum when $(t - 1)^2 = 0$; i.e., when $t = 1$. Thus the vertex is the point $(1, 116)$. Hence the maximum height reached by the ball is 116 feet.

Exercise 5.6

I. Formulate a mathematical model of each of the following and compute the solution set of the model. From the solution set of the model select the solution set of the given problem.

(1) The square of Theresa's age exceeds 8 times her age by 9. How old is Theresa?

(2) The square of Elizabeth's age exceeds 17 times her age by 60. How old is Elizabeth?

(3) Bud has 25 pencils more than Donald has. However, the square of the number of Donald's pencils is 5 more than the number of Bud's pencils. How many pencils does each have?

(4) Sarah can type 60 words per minute. Sixty-one times Ursula's typing speed exceeds Sarah's typing speed by the square of Ursula's typing speed. Compute Ursula's typing speed.

(5) Homer is driving 5 mph slower than William. The square of Homer's speed exceeds William's speed by 1 mph. How fast is each driving?

(6) Catherine has a rectangular field whose area is 180,000 square feet. The perimeter of the field is 1720 feet. Compute the dimensions of the field.

(7) On Tuesday Joseph worked 20 more problems than on Monday. The product of the number of problems he worked on Monday and the number he worked on Tuesday is 800. How many problems did he work on Tuesday?

(8) J.T. has 10 more nickels than pennies. The square of the number of his pennies exceeds the square of the number of his nickels by 20. How many nickels does J.T. have? How many pennies does J.T. have?

(9) On a hike Melvin traveled 23 miles more the first day than the second day. The square of the number of miles he traveled the second day exceeds by 7 the number of miles he traveled the first day. How many miles did he travel the first day? How many miles did he travel altogether?

(10) Milton observes that the tens digit of a number exceeds the

units digit by 5 and that the square of the units digit exceeds the tens digit by 7. What is the number?

(11) Velma and Laureen are working problems. Laureen notices that Velma worked 6 more problems than she did. She notices also that the square of the number of problems she worked is 6 more than the number of problems Velma worked. How many problems did Laureen work?

(12) Lester notices that the units digit of a two digit number is 3 times the tens digit. Lloyd notices that the number exceeds the square of the tens digit by 30. What is the number?

(13) Edwin asked Carol to think of a number, square it, add the number, increase the result by 10, and add twice the number. When Carol said that the result was 64, Edwin said that the number was 6. Was he correct? Is there more than one answer to the problem?

(14) Lacy notices that the square of a number is 5 times the number. Larry notices that this is true of another number. What numbers are Lacy and Larry considering?

(15) Nathan notices that the square of a number is 6 times the number. Roy notices that this is true of another number. What numbers are Nathan and Roy considering?

(16) From the top of a building 100 feet high Phil throws a baseball upward with an initial speed of 10 feet per second. The equation describing the motion of the ball is $s = {}^-16t^2 + 10t + 100$. When does the ball strike the ground? What is the significance of the negative root? (See Example 3.)

(17) From the graph of the quadratic function in (16), estimate the maximum height reached by the ball. Check your estimate by computing the vertex of the parabola. (See Example 5.)

(18) If the unit cost is given by the formula $y = x^2 + {}^-21x + 117$, compute the number of machines the manufacturer in Example 4 should operate in order to minimize the unit cost.

(19) If the unit cost is given by the formula $y = x^2 - 19x + 91$, compute the number of machines the manufacturer in Example 4 should operate in order to minimize the unit cost.

(20) If the unit cost is given by the formula $y = 4x^2 - 120x + 900$, compute the number of machines the manufacturer in Example 4 should operate in order to minimize the unit cost.

(21) Henry stapled 10 more sets of papers on Thursday than on Friday. The square of the number he stapled on Thursday exceeds 217 times the number he stapled on Friday by 700. How many sets did he staple on Thursday?

(22) James took a taxi to school. On the return trip he noticed that the driver drove 10 more blocks than on the trip to school. He observed that the square of the number of blocks on the return trip was equal to the sum of 700 and 217 times the number of blocks on the trip to school. How many blocks did James ride on the way to school? How many blocks did James ride on the return trip?

II. Compute the solution set of each of the following *quadratic inequalities*. [*Hint:* Recall that the product of two real numbers is positive if and only if they are both positive or both negative; the product of two real numbers is negative if and only if one is positive and the other is negative; the product of two real numbers is zero if and only if one of them is zero (or both are zero).]

(1) $x^2 - 2x - 3 < 0$ (6) $x^2 - x - 20 \leq 0$
(2) $x^2 - 2x < 0$ (7) $0 < x^2 - 4x - 21$
(3) $x^2 - 5x < 0$ (8) $0 < x^2 + 4x - 21$
(4) $x^2 - x - 2 < 0$ (9) $0 \leq x^2 - 3x$
(5) $x^2 + x - 20 \leq 0$ (10) $0 \leq 3x^2 - x$

CHAPTER 6

THE COMPLEX NUMBER SYSTEM

6.1   Equality, Addition, and Multiplication of Complex Numbers

Recall that not every quadratic equation has a real root; i.e., there are quadratic equations which do not have real roots. For example, the quadratic equation $x^2 + 1 = 0$ has no real root. The purpose of this chapter is to extend the real number system to a more inclusive number system so that *every* quadratic equation shall have roots. First we consider the quadratic equation $x^2 = {}^-1$. Since the square of every real number is non-negative, we must invent a new kind of number if the quadratic equation $x^2 = {}^-1$ shall have one or more roots. Consequently, we invent a new number, denote it by i, and extend the binary operator $\cdot$ so that $i \cdot i = {}^-1$; i.e., $i^2 = {}^-1$. In order to extend the real number system to include the new number i, we need to define the binary operators $+$ and $\cdot$ so that all of the field properties which are true in the real number system shall still be true in the extended system. How should we define the product of a real number b and the number i? Obviously, if we wish to retain the multiplication property of 0, we must define $\cdot$ so that $0 \cdot i = i \cdot 0 = 0$. If $b \neq 0$, we might be tempted to define $\cdot$ so that $b \cdot i = r$, a real number. However, if the field properties are retained, then the following sequence of steps must be valid.

$$bi = r$$
$$(1/b)(bi) = (1/b)(r)$$
$$i = r/b.$$

But i is *not* a real number and r/b is a real number. Consequently, if we wish to retain the field properties, we cannot define the product of i

147

and a nonzero real number b to be a real number. Obviously, if we wish to retain the identity property for multiplication, we must define • so that $1 \cdot i = i$ and $i \cdot 1 = i$; moreover, if $b \neq 1$, then we must define • so that $bi \neq i$. Since we wish to retain the closure property for multiplication, we must invent a new number for the product of b and i. It is natural to denote the new number for the product of b and i by the symbol bi and say that the product of b and i is the number bi. Now the real number system has been extended to include other numbers which are not real numbers. For example, the numbers i, ^-1i, ^-7i, $(4/3)i$, $(^-2/5)i$, $\sqrt{3}\,i$, i, and $0.4\overline{58}i$ are included in the new number system.

If we wish to retain the field properties, how should we define the binary operator $+$ between any two numbers of the new system? Obviously, if we wish to retain the identity property for addition, we must define $+$ so that $0 + bi = bi + 0 = bi$ for any real number b. If $a \neq 0$, $b \neq 0$, and we wish to retain the field properties, then we must invent a new number for the sum of a and bi. It is natural to denote the new number for the sum of a and bi by the symbol $a + bi$ and say that the sum of a and bi is the number $a + bi$. For example, the numbers $1 + i$, $^-1 + i$, $1 + 3i$, $^-1 + {}^-2i$, $3 + 2i$, $^-4/5 + (7/3)\,i$, $0 + 0i$, $4/5 + 0i$, and $0 + {}^-7i$ are included in the new number system.

Now that we have invented a new system of numbers and have defined addition and multiplication so that the sum and the product of any real number a and any number bi are in the system, we need to extend the definition of $+$ and • so that $(a + bi) + (c + di)$ and $(a + bi)(c + di)$ are also in the system (and the field properties are retained). The following examples illustrate the method by which the definitions of $+$ and • will be made.

Example 1.   How should we define $(a + bi) + (c + di)$ if we wish to retain the field properties?

If we retain the field properties, then we retain the generalized commutative and associative property for addition and the distributive property. Consequently we may write

$(a + bi) + (c + di) = (a + c) + (bi + di)$ (by GCAAPFA)

$= (a + c) + (b + d)i$ (by DP).

Thus we should define $+$ so that $(a + bi) + (c + di)$ $= (a + c) + (b + d)i$ (if the field properties are to be retained).

Example 2.   How should we define $(a + bi) \cdot (c + di)$ if we wish to retain the field properties?

If we retain the field properties, then we retain the generalized commutative and associative property for multiplication, and the distributive property. Consequently we may write

$$(a + bi)(c + di) = (a + bi)c + (a + bi)di$$
$$= ac + (bi)c + (a)(di) + (bi)(di)$$
$$= ac + bci + adi + bdi^2$$
$$= ac + bci + adi + bd(^-1)$$
$$= ac + {}^-bd + bci + adi$$
$$= (ac - bd) + (bc + ad)i.$$

Thus we should define · or × so that $(a + bi) \cdot (c + di) = (ac - bd) + (bc + ad)i$ (if the field properties are to be retained).

Because of the above considerations we make the following definition of the *complex number system.*

DEFINITION 1. The *complex number system* is the system $(C, +, \times)$, in which

(a) $C = \{a + bi: a \in R \wedge b \in R \wedge i^2 = {}^-1\}$,
(b) $a + bi = c + di$ if and only if $a = c$ and $b = d$,
(c) $0 \times i = 0$,
(d) $1 \times i = i$,
(e) $(a + bi) + (c + di) = (a + c) + (b + d)i$,
(f) $(a + bi) \times (c + di) = (ac - bd) + (bc + ad)i$.

Since $a = a + 0i$, we see that every real number is a complex number; i.e., $R \subset C$. Moreover, the definitions of addition and multiplication of any two complex numbers are consistent with the corresponding definitions for any two real numbers.

The following examples illustrate computations with complex numbers.

Example 3. If $(a + 3) + 5i = {}^-7 + 3di$, compute a and d.

By Definition 1, $(a + 3) + 5i = {}^-7 + 3di$ if and only if $a + 3 = {}^-7$ and $5 = 3d$.
Hence $a = {}^-10$ and $d = 5/3$.

Example 4. Compute the sum of $^-3 + 7i$ and $^-1 + {}^-2i$.

$$({}^-3 + 7i) + ({}^-1 + {}^-2i) = ({}^-3 + {}^-1) + (7 + {}^-2)i$$
$$= {}^-4 + 5i.$$

Example 5.   Compute the product of $(3 + ^-2i)$ and $(^-4 + 5i)$.

$$(3 + ^-2i)(^-4 + 5i) = [3(^-4) - (^-2)(5)] + [(^-2)(^-4) + (3)(5)]i$$
$$= [^-12 + 10] + [8 + 15]i$$
$$= ^-2 + 23i.$$

In the next section we shall prove that the complex number system is a field.

Exercise 6.1

I. Convert each of the following open sentences to a true sentence by replacement of each variable by a real number or prove that no replacement will convert the open sentence to a true sentence.

    (1) $a + 5i = ^-7 + di$
    (2) $3 + bi = c + ^-5i$
    (3) $6 + ^-3i = ^-c + di$
    (4) $a + ^-bi = 5 + ^-7i$
    (5) $6 + ^-7i = 7 + di$
    (6) $a + ^-3i = 6 + 5i$
    (7) $(a + ^-4) + bi = 6 + 5i$
    (8) $a + (b + ^-3)i = ^-5 + 7i$
    (9) $(2a + 5) + (^-3b + ^-7)i = ^-5/3 + (^-3/2)i$
    (10) $(^-2a + 7) + (4b + ^-3)i = 6/5 + (^-4/3)i$

II. Compute the sum of each of the following pairs of complex numbers.

    (1) $2 + ^-13i, ^-4 + 7i$ (6) $^-3 + ^-4i, ^-3 + 4i$
    (2) $^-1 + 5i, 2 + ^-3i$ (7) $1 + 3i, ^-1 + 3i$
    (3) $^-5/2 + 0i, 0 + ^-7i$ (8) $1 + ^-3i, 1 + 3i$
    (4) $0 + (^-3/4)i, 6 + 0i$ (9) $2 + ^-3i, ^-2 + 3i$
    (5) $7 + 3i, 7 + ^-3i$ (10) $^-6 + 3i, 6 + ^-3i$

III. Compute the product of each pair of complex numbers in Exercise II.

IV. Assume that the complex number system obeys the field properties. State the field properties for the system $(C, +, \times)$.

6.2   Field Properties of the Complex Number System

We have already observed that the set of real numbers is a proper subset of the set of complex numbers. In Definition 1 we set the stage so that the complex number system $(C, +, \times)$ would be a field and that

$(R, +, \times)$ would be a subfield of $(C, +, \times)$. In this section we shall prove that $(C, +, \times)$ is actually a field; i.e., $(C, +, \times)$ obeys the following properties:

F1. If $a + bi$ and $c + di$ are any elements of C, then $(a + bi) + (c + di)$ is a unique element of C (*closure property for addition*).

F2. If $a + bi$, $c + di$, and $e + fi$ are any elements of C, then $[(a + bi) + (c + di)] + (e + fi) = (a + bi) + [(c + di) + (e + fi)]$ (*associative property for addition*).

F3. There exists a unique element 0 of C such that $(a + bi) + 0 = (a + bi)$ for any element $a + bi$ of C (*identity property for addition*).

F4. If $a + bi$ is any element of C, then there exists a unique element $^{-}a + {}^{-}bi$ of C such that $(a + bi) + ({}^{-}a + {}^{-}bi) = 0$ (*inverse property for addition*).

F5. If $a + bi$ and $c + di$ are any elements of C, then $(a + bi) + (c + di) = (c + di) + (a + bi)$ (*commutative property for addition*).

F6. If $a + bi$ and $c + di$ are any elements of C, then $(a + bi)(c + di)$ is a unique element of C (*closure property for multiplication*).

F7. If $(a + bi)$, $(c + di)$, and $(e + fi)$ are any elements of C, then $[(a + bi)(c + di)](e + fi) = (a + bi)[(c + di)(e + fi)]$ (*associative property for multiplication*).

F8. There exists a unique element 1 of C such that $(a + bi) \times 1 = a + bi$ for any element $a + bi$ of C (*identity property for multiplication*).

F9. If $a + bi$ is any nonzero element of C, then there exists a unique element $\left[\left(\frac{a}{a^2 + b^2}\right) + \left(\frac{-b}{a^2 + b^2}\right)i\right]$ of C such that $(a + bi)\left[\frac{a}{a^2 + b^2} + \left(\frac{-b}{a^2 + b^2}\right)i\right] = 1$ (*inverse property for multiplication*).

F10. If $a + bi$ and $c + di$ are any elements of C, then $(a + bi)(c + di) = (c + di)(a + bi)$ (*commutative property for multiplication*).

*F*11. If $(a + bi)$, $(c + di)$, and $(e + fi)$ are any elements of C, then $(a + bi)[(c + di) + (e + fi)] = (a + bi)(c + di) + (a + bi)(e + fi)$ (*distributive property*).

To prove $F1$ we observe from Definition 1(e) that $(a + bi) + (c + di) = (a + c) + (b + d)i$. Since $a + c$ is a unique real number and $b + d$ is a unique real number, we see that $(a + c) + (b + d)i$ is a unique complex number.

We prove $F2$ as follows:

$$[(a+bi) + (c+di)] + (e+fi) = [(a+c) + (b+d)i] + (e+fi)$$
$$\text{(by Definition 1(e))}$$
$$= [(a+c) + e] + [(b+d) + f]i$$
$$\text{(by Definition 1(e))}$$
$$= [a + (c+e)] + [b + (d+f)]i$$
$$= (a+bi) + [(c+e) + (d+f)i]$$
$$\text{(by Definition 1(e))}$$
$$= (a+bi) + [(c+di) + (e+fi)]$$
$$\text{(by Definition 1(e)).}$$

We prove $F3$ as follows:

$$(a+bi) + 0 = (a+bi) + (0+0)$$
$$= (a+bi) + (0+0i) \qquad \text{(by Definition 1(c))}$$
$$= (a+0) + (b+0)i \qquad \text{(by Definition 1(e))}$$
$$= a + bi.$$

The uniqueness follows from the uniqueness of the additive identity for real numbers.

We prove $F4$ as follows:

$$(a+bi) + (^-a + {}^-bi) = (a + {}^-a) + (b + {}^-b)i$$
$$\text{(by Definition 1(e))}$$
$$= 0 + 0i$$
$$= 0 + 0 \qquad \text{(by Definition 1(c))}$$
$$= 0.$$

Since the inverse property for addition of real numbers guarantees that ^-a is the only real number such that $a + {}^-a = 0$ and ^-b is the only real number such that $b + {}^-b = 0$, we are assured that $^-a + {}^-bi$ is the only complex number such that $(a + bi) + (^-a + {}^-bi) = 0$. That is, the additive inverse of any given complex number is *unique*.

We prove *F*5 as follows:

$$(a + bi) + (c + di) = (a + c) + (b + d)i$$
$$\text{(by Definition 1(e))}$$
$$= (c + a) + (d + b)i$$
$$= (c + di) + (a + bi)$$
$$\text{(by Definition 1(e))}.$$

To prove *F*6 we observe from definition 1(f) that $(a + bi)(c + di)$ $= (ac - bd) + (bc + ad)i$. Since $(ac - bd)$ is a unique real number and $(bc + ad)$ is a unique real number, we see that $(ac - bd)$ $+ (bc + ad)i$ is a unique complex number.

We prove *F*7 as follows:

$$[(a + bi)(c + di)](e + fi) = [(ac - bd) + (bc + ad)i](e + fi)$$
$$\text{(by Definition 1(f))}$$
$$= [(ac - bd)e - (bc + ad)f] + [(bc + ad)e + (ac - bd)f]i$$
$$\text{(by Definition 1(f))}$$
$$= [ace - bde - bcf - adf] + [bce + ade + acf - bdf]i \quad \text{(by Definition 1(f))}$$
$$= [ace - adf - bde - bcf] + [bce - bdf + ade + acf]i$$
$$= [a(ce - df) - b(de + cf)] + [b(ce - df) + a(de + cf)]i$$
$$= (a + bi)[(ce - df) + (de + cf)i]$$
$$\text{(by Definition 1(f))}$$
$$= (a + bi)[(c + di)(e + fi)]$$
$$\text{(by Definition 1(f))}.$$

We prove *F*8 as follows:

$$(a + bi)1 = (a + bi)(1 + 0)$$
$$= (a + bi)(1 + 0i) \qquad \text{(by Definition 1(c))}$$
$$= (a \cdot 1 - b \cdot 0) + (b \cdot 1 + a \cdot 0)i \qquad \text{(by Definition 1(f))}$$
$$= (a - 0) + (b + 0)i \qquad \text{(by Definition 1(c))}$$
$$= a + bi.$$

The uniqueness follows from the uniqueness of the multiplicative identity for real numbers.

To prove *F*9, we consider the complex number $a + bi$, where $ab \neq 0$, and let $(a + bi)(c + di) = 1$ and prove that $c = a/(a^2 + b^2)$ and $d = \,^-b/(a^2 + b^2)$.

$(a + bi)(c + di) = 1$

$(ac - bd) + (bc + ad)i = 1 + 0i$ (by Definition 1(c) and 1(f))

$ac - bd = 1$ and $bc + ad = 0$ (by Definition 1(b))

$a(ac - bd) = a \cdot 1$ and $b(bc + ad) = b \cdot 0$

$a^2c - abd = a$ and $b^2c + abd = 0$

$(a^2c - abd) + (b^2c + abd) = a + 0$ and $b^2c + abd = 0$

$(a^2 + b^2)c = a$ and $b^2c + abd = 0$

$c = a/(a^2 + b^2)$ and $b^2 \cdot a/(a^2 + b^2) + abd = 0$ $(ab \neq 0)$

$c = a/(a^2 + b^2)$ and $abd = {}^-b^2a/(a^2 + b^2)$

$c = a/(a^2 + b^2)$ and $d = {}^-b/(a^2 + b^2)$, $(ab \neq 0)$.

Although this *proof* is valid *only if* $ab \neq 0$, the *result* is valid even if $a = 0$ or $b = 0$ (but not both).

As a check, we compute the product of $(a + bi)$ and $\left(\frac{a}{a^2 + b^2}\right) + \left(\frac{-b}{a^2 + b^2}\right)i$

$$(a + bi)\left[\left(\frac{a}{a^2 + b^2}\right) + \left(\frac{-b}{a^2 + b^2}\right)i\right] = \left[a\left(\frac{a}{a^2 + b^2}\right) - b\left(\frac{-b}{a^2 + b^2}\right)\right] +$$
$$\left[b'\frac{a}{a^2 + b^2}\right) + a\left(\frac{-b}{a^2 + b^2}\right)\right]i$$
$$\text{(by Definition 1(f))}$$

$$= \left[\frac{a^2}{a^2 + b^2} + \frac{b^2}{a^2 + b^2}\right] + \left[\frac{ab}{a^2 + b^2} + \right.$$
$$\left. \frac{-ab}{a^2 + b^2}\right]i$$

$$= \frac{a^2 + b^2}{a^2 + b^2} + 0i$$

$$= 1 + 0i$$

$$= 1.$$

We prove $F10$ as follows:

$$(a + bi)(c + di) = (ac - bd) + (bc + ad)i \quad \text{(by Definition 1(f))}$$
$$= (ca - db) + (da + cb)i$$
$$= (c + di)(a + bi) \quad \text{(by Definition 1(f))}.$$

We prove $F11$ as follows:

$$(a + bi)[(c + di) + (e + fi)] = (a + bi)[(c + e) + (d + f)i]$$
$$\text{(by Definition 1(e))}$$
$$= [a(c + e) - b(d + f)] + [b(c + e)$$
$$+ a(d + f)]i \quad \text{(by Definition 1(f))}$$
$$= [ac + ae - bd - bf] + [bc + be + ad$$
$$+ af]i$$
$$= [(ac - bd) + (ae - bf)] + [(bc +$$
$$ad) + (be + af)]i$$

$$= [(ac - bd) + (bc + ad)i] + [(ae$$
$$- bf) + (be + af)i]$$
$$= [(a + bi)(c + di)] + [(a + bi)(e$$
$$+ fi)] \qquad \text{(by Definition 1(f))}.$$

Observe that the manner in which we defined $(C, +, \times)$ in Definition 1 enabled us to prove the field properties for $(C, +, \times)$ from Definition 1 and the field properties for $(R, +, \times)$. That is, from Definition 1 and the knowledge that the real number system is a field, we have proved that the complex number system is also a field. Recalling that the real number system is an ordered field, you may wonder whether the complex number system is an ordered field also. In Section 6.5 we shall consider this question. In the next section we shall discuss subtraction and division of complex numbers.

Exercise 6.2

I. Compute the additive inverse of each of the following complex numbers.

(1) 5

(2) -8

(3) $(6/7) i$

(4) i

(5) $1 + 3i$

(6) $7 + 8i$

(7) $-5 + 3i$

(8) $3 + -5i$

(9) $-6/5 + (-2/3) i$

(10) $-7/8 + (-3/5) i$

(11) $0 + 0i$

(12) 0

II. Compute the multiplicative inverse of each of the following complex numbers.

(1) $2/3$

(2) $-3/5$

(3) $0 + 3i$

(4) $-7i$

(5) $3 + -4i$

(6) $-4 + 3i$

(7) $-7 + 24i$

(8) $24 + -7i$

III. Denote the multiplicative inverse of each of the following complex numbers by $c + di$ and compute the inverse by the *method* of proof of $F9$ in the text.

(1) $3 + -4i$

(2) $-4 + 3i$

(3) $-7 + 24i$

(4) $24 + -7i$

IV. Illustrate the commutative property for addition of each of the following pairs of complex numbers.

(1) $2 + -3i, -5 + 7i$

(2) $-6 + 7i, 4 + -3i$

(3) $0 + -6i, 3 + 0i$

(4) $-5 + 0i, 0 + 3i$

(5) $1 + i, 2 + {}^{-}1i$

(6) ${}^{-}2 + {}^{-}1i, 3 + i$

(7) ${}^{-}7 + 8i, 7 + 8i$

(8) $6 + 5i, {}^{-}6 + {}^{-}2i$

(9) ${}^{-}3 + 2i, 3 + {}^{-}2i$

(10) $7 + {}^{-}5i, {}^{-}7 + 5i$

V. Illustrate the commutative property for multiplication of each of the pairs of complex numbers in Exercise IV.

VI. Illustrate the associative property for addition for each of the following triplets of complex numbers.

(1) $1 + 0i, 2 + 5i, {}^{-}3 + i$

(2) $1 + i, 3 + {}^{-}2i, 2 + 3i$

(3) ${}^{-}4 + 3i, 4 + {}^{-}3i, 5 + 7i$

(4) $6 + 3i, {}^{-}7 + 4i, 7 + {}^{-}4i$

(5) $0 + 3i, 4 + {}^{-}1i, {}^{-}3 + 7i$

(6) $1 + {}^{-}4i, 3 + 2i, 0 + i$

VII. Illustrate the associative property for multiplication for each triplet of complex numbers in Exercise VI.

VIII. Illustrate the distributive property for each triplet of complex numbers in Exercise VI.

6.3   Subtraction and Division of Complex Numbers

We have proved that the complex number system $(C, +, \cdot)$, or $(C, +, \times)$, is a field, in which addition and multiplication are as defined in Definition 1. In this section we shall define subtraction and division. For convenience we shall denote ${}^{-}1i$ by ${}^{-}i$; i.e., ${}^{-}i = {}^{-}1i$. This is consistent with the fact that $1i = i$. The binary operator $-$, the operation *subtraction*, and the *difference* of two complex numbers is given in Definition 2.

DEFINITION 2.   The *difference* in the subtraction of the complex number $c + di$ from the complex number $a + bi$ [written $(a + bi)$ $- (c + di)$] is the complex number $e + fi$ if and only if $a + bi = (c + di) + (e + fi)$. [That is, $(a + bi) -$ $(c + di) = e + fi$ if and only if $a + bi = (c + di) +$ $(e + fi)$.]

It follows immediately from F4 that $(a + bi) - (c + di) = (a + bi)$ $+ ({}^{-}c + {}^{-}di)$. The following examples illustrate the method of subtraction.

Example 1.   Compute $(3 + {}^{-}7i) - ({}^{-}6 + 5i)$.

$$(3 + {}^{-}7i) - ({}^{-}6 + 5i) = (3 + {}^{-}7i) + (6 + {}^{-}5i)$$
$$= (3 + 6) + ({}^{-}7 + {}^{-}5)i$$
$$= 9 + {}^{-}12i$$

$$= (9 + 0i) + (0 + {}^-12i)$$
$$= (9 \div 0i) - ({}^-0 + 12i)$$
$$= 9 - 12i.$$

Example 2. Compute $({}^-4 + 3i) - (1 + {}^-2i)$

$$({}^-4 + 3i) - (1 + {}^-2i) = ({}^-4 + 3i) + ({}^-1 + 2i)$$
$$= ({}^-4 + {}^-1) + (3 + 2)i$$
$$= {}^-5 + 5i.$$

We observe from Definition 2 and the above examples that $(a + bi) - (c + di) = (a - c) + (b - d)i$. The following example illustrates this fact.

Example 3. Compute $(5 + 3i) - (2 + 7i)$.

$$(5 + 3i) - (2 + 7i) = (5 - 2) + (3 - 7)i$$
$$= 3 + {}^-4i$$

The binary operator $\div$, the operation *division*, and the *quotient* of two complex numbers is given in Definition 3.

DEFINITION 3. The *quotient* in the division of the complex number $a + bi$ by the nonzero complex number $c + di$ [written $(a + bi) \div (c + di)$ or $(a + bi)/(c + di)$] is the complex number $e + fi$ if and only if $a + bi = (c + di)(e + fi)$. [That is, $(a + bi)/(c + di) = e + fi$ if and only if $a + bi = (c + di)(e + fi)$.]

To actually compute the quotient $(a + bi)/(c + di)$, we may proceed as follows:

$$a + bi = (a + bi) \cdot 1 \qquad \text{(by F8)}$$
$$= (a + bi)[(c + di)(\tfrac{c}{c^2 + d^2} + \tfrac{-d}{c^2 + d^2}i)] \qquad \text{(by F9)}$$
$$= (c + di)[(a + bi)(\tfrac{c}{c^2 + d^2} + \tfrac{-d}{c^2 + d^2}i)] \qquad \text{(by F7 and F10)}.$$

But $\left[(a + bi)(\tfrac{c}{c^2 + d^2} + \tfrac{-d}{c^2 + d^2}i)\right]$ is a complex number $e + fi$ (by F6).

Thus $a + bi = (c + di)(e + fi)$.

Hence $(a + bi)/(c + di) = e + fi$ (by Definition 3).

Consequently $(a + bi)/(c + di) = (a + bi)(\tfrac{c}{c^2 + d^2} + \tfrac{-d}{c^2 + d^2}i)$.

In particular, $1/(c + di) = (1 + 0i)/(c + di) = (\tfrac{c}{c^2 + d^2} + \tfrac{-d}{c^2 + d^2}i)$.

The following examples illustrate the computation of the quotient of two complex numbers.

Example 4.   Compute $(^-6 + 5i)/(3 + ^-4i)$.

$$
\begin{aligned}
(^-6 + 5i)/(3 + ^-4i) &= (^-6 + 5i)\left(\tfrac{3}{3^2 + (^-4)^2} + \tfrac{^-(^-4)}{3^2 + (^-4)^2}i\right) \\
&= (^-6 + 5i)[3/25 + (4/25)i] \\
&= (1/25)[(^-6(3) - 5(4)) + (5(3) \\
&\qquad + (^-6)(4))i] \\
&= (1/25)[(^-18 - 20) + (15 - 24)i] \\
&= (1/25)[^-38 + ^-9i] \\
&= ^-38/25 + (^-9/25)i.
\end{aligned}
$$

Example 5.   Compute $2i/(1 + 3i)$.

$$
\begin{aligned}
2i/(1 + 3i) &= (2i)\left(\tfrac{1}{1^2 + 3^2} + \tfrac{^-3}{1^2 + 3^2}i\right) \\
&= 2i\,[1/10 + (^-3/10)i] \\
&= 2i\,(1/10) + 2i\,(^-3/10)i \\
&= (1/5)i + (^-3/5)i^2 \\
&= (1/5)i + (^-3/5)(^-1) \\
&= 3/5 + (1/5)i.
\end{aligned}
$$

Traditionally quotients are computed in another way, which elimi-
nates the necessity of memorizing that $\tfrac{a}{a^2 + b^2} + \tfrac{^-b}{a^2 + b^2}\,i$ is the multiplicative inverse of $a + bi$, $(a \neq 0$ or $b \neq 0)$. Before we introduce this
method, we define the *conjugate* of a complex number.

DEFINITION 4.   The *conjugate* of the complex number $a + bi$ is the complex number $a + ^-bi$.

For example, the conjugate of $2 + ^-7i$ is $2 + 7i$, and the conjugate
of $2 + 7i$ is $2 + ^-7i$. The product of the complex number $a + bi$ and its
conjugate $a + ^-bi$ is the real number $a^2 + b^2$. Thus any division problem
is reducible to a multiplication problem. The following examples illustrate the traditional method of computing a quotient by use of the
conjugate.

Example 6.   Compute $(^-4 + 3i)/(5 + 2i)$.

$$
\begin{aligned}
\frac{^-4 + 3i}{5 + 2i} &= \frac{^-4 + 3i}{5 + 2i} \times \frac{5 + ^-2i}{5 + ^-2i} \\
&= \frac{[(^-4)(5) - (3)(^-2)] + [3(5) + (^-4)(^-2)]i}{[5(5) - 2(^-2)] + [2(5) + 5(^-2)]i} \\
&= \frac{(^-20 + 6) + (15 + 8)i}{(5^2 + 2^2) + (10 - 10)i} \\
&= (^-14 + 23i)/29 \\
&= \frac{^-14}{29} + \frac{23}{29}\,i.
\end{aligned}
$$

Example 7. Compute $(1 + 3i)/(^-2 - 7i)$.

$$(1 + 3i)/(^-2 - 7i) = (1 + 3i)/(^-2 + ^-7i)$$
$$= \frac{1 + 3i}{^-2 + ^-7i} \times \frac{^-2 + 7i}{^-2 + 7i}$$
$$= \frac{[1(^-2) - (3)(7)] + [3(^-2) + 1(7)]i}{[(^-2)(^-2) - (^-7)(7)] + [(^-7)(^-2) + (^-2)(7)]i}$$
$$= (^-23 + i)/53$$
$$= ^-(23/53) + (1/53)i.$$

For each real number property which follows from the field properties $F1$ through $F11$, there is a corresponding complex number property. For example, the generalized commutative and associative property for addition and for multiplication and the generalized distributive property are true for complex numbers as well as for real numbers. We close this section by listing three of the more important of these properties.

CANCELLATION PROPERTY FOR ADDITION OF COMPLEX NUMBERS (CPFAOCN)
If $(a + bi) + (c + di) = (a + bi) + (e + fi)$, then $(c + di) = (e + fi)$.

CANCELLATION PROPERTY FOR MULTIPLICATION OF COMPLEX NUMBERS (CPFMOCN).
If $(a + bi)(c + di) = (a + bi)(e + fi)$, and $a + bi \neq 0$, then $c + di = e + fi$.

MULTIPLICATION PROPERTY OF ZERO (MPOZ)
$(a + bi)(c + di) = 0$ if and only if $a + bi = 0$ or $c + di = 0$.

Exercise 6.3

I. Compute each of the following differences.

(1) $(2 + 7i) - (3 + 2i)$
(2) $(5 + 3i) - (4 + 5i)$
(3) $(^-4 + 7i) - (2 + ^-3i)$
(4) $(4 + ^-7i) - (^-2 + 3i)$
(5) $2i - (5 + i)$
(6) $4 - (5 + i)$
(7) $i - 5i$
(8) $^-i - ^-5i$
(9) $[(k + 2) + 3i] - [(k - 1) + ^-3i]$
(10) $[(m - 3) + ^-2i] - [(m + 1) + 2.1]$

II. Compute each of the following quotients.

(1) $(2 + 7i)/(3 + 2i)$ (6) $^-2/(4 + {}^-i)$

(2) $(5 + 3i)/(4 + 5i)$ (7) $2i/(3 + 2i)$

(3) $(5 + {}^-3i)/({}^-4 + 5i)$ (8) $^-3i/(2 + {}^-3i)$

(4) $(5 + {}^-3i)/({}^-4 + {}^-5i)$ (9) $(3 + {}^-2i)/{}^-2i$

(5) $4/(5 + i)$ (10) $(1 + 5i)/5i$

III. (1) Prove that $(a + bi) - (c + di) = (a + bi) + ({}^-c + {}^-di)$.

    (2) Prove that $(a + bi) - (c + di) = (a - c) + (b - d)i$.

6.4 The Quadratic Formula

Since $i^2 = {}^-1$ and $({}^-i)^2 = ({}^-i)({}^-i) = ({}^-1i)({}^-1i) = ({}^-1)({}^-1)(i \times i)$ $= 1 \times i^2 = i^2 = {}^-1$, we see that the quadratic equation $x^2 = {}^-1$ has the *two* roots i and ${}^-i$. Before we extended the real number system to the complex number system, the quadratic equation $x^2 = {}^-1$ had *no* roots. The reason we extended the real number system to the complex number system was that we desired every quadratic equation to have at least one root. Now we shall prove (*in the field of complex numbers*) that every quadratic equation has two roots, provided that we count the real root a in the equation $(x - a)^2 = 0$ as *two real and equal* roots. In Chapter 5 we proved that the quadratic equation $ax^2 + bx + c = 0$ has two real roots if and only if $0 \le b^2 - 4ac$. Now we prove that the quadratic equation $ax^2 + bx + c = 0$ has two complex roots which are *not* real if and only if $b^2 - 4ac < 0$.

Let $ax^2 + bx + c = 0$, $a \ne 0$, and $b^2 - 4ac < 0$.

$ax^2 + bx = {}^-c$

$x^2 + (b/a)x = {}^-c/a$

$x^2 + (b/a)x + (b/2a)^2 = {}^-c/a + (b/2a)^2$

$(x + b/2a)^2 = ({}^-4ac + b^2)/4a^2$

$(x + b/2a)^2 + (4ac - b^2)/4a^2 = 0$

$[(x + b/2a) + \sqrt{4ac - b^2/4a^2}\, i]\, [(x + b/2a) - \sqrt{4ac - b^2/4a^2}\, i] = 0$
                                    (by Definition 1(f))

$x + b/2a + \sqrt{4ac - b^2/4a^2}\, i = 0$ or $x + b/2a - \sqrt{4ac - b^2/4a^2}\, i = 0$
                              (by multiplication property of 0)

$x = {}^-b/2a - (\sqrt{4ac - b^2}/2a) \times i$, or $x = {}^-b/2a + (\sqrt{4ac - b^2}/2a) \times i$.

Thus there are two complex roots of the quadratic equation $ax^2 + bx + c = 0$ if $b^2 - 4ac < 0$. Observe that the two roots ${}^-b/2a - (\sqrt{4ac - b^2}/2a)i$ and ${}^-b/2a + (\sqrt{4ac - b^2}/2a)i$ are conjugates.

In order to consolidate *all cases* ($b^2 - 4ac < 0$, $b^2 - 4ac = 0$, and $0 < b^2 - 4ac$) into *one case*, we introduce the notation $\sqrt{{}^-a}$ for $\sqrt{a} \times i$

if a is a positive real; i.e., $\sqrt{a} \times i = \sqrt{-a}$. It follows immediately that $\sqrt{1} \times i = \sqrt{-1}$; i.e., $i = \sqrt{-1}$. If $b^2 - 4ac < 0$, then $(\sqrt{4ac - b^2}/2a) \times i = \sqrt{-(4ac - b^2)}/2a = \sqrt{b^2 - 4ac}/2a$, and the quadratic equation $ax^2 + bx + c = 0$ has the complex roots $(-b \pm \sqrt{b^2 - 4ac})/2a$. Thus, *in all cases*, the roots of the quadratic equation $ax^2 + bx + c = 0$ are $(-b \pm \sqrt{b^2 - 4ac})/2a$. Consequently we have extended the quadratic formula of Section 5.5 so that the roots of *any* quadratic equation may be computed from it; i.e., $ax^2 + bx + c = 0$, $a \neq 0$, if and only if $x = (-b \pm \sqrt{b^2 - 4ac})/2a$. Henceforth, the *new* formula, $x = (-b \pm \sqrt{b^2 - 4ac})/2a$, will be called the *quadratic formula*.

The following examples illustrate the application of the quadratic formula to the solution of quadratic equations.

Example 1. Solve the quadratic equation $2x^2 + 5x - 12 = 0$

$a = 2, b = 5, c = -12$
$x = (-b \pm \sqrt{b^2 - 4ac})/2a$
$x = (-5 \pm \sqrt{5^2 - 4(2)(-12)})/2(2)$
$x = (-5 \pm \sqrt{121})/4$
$x = (-5 \pm 11)/4$
$x = (-5 + 11)/4 \text{ or } x = (-5 - 11)/4$
$x = 3/2 \text{ or } x = -4.$

The roots are *real and unequal.*

Example 2. Solve the quadratic equation $x^2 - x + 1 = 0$.

$a = 1, b = -1, c = 1$
$x = (-b \pm \sqrt{b^2 - 4ac})/2a$
$x = (1 \pm \sqrt{(-1)^2 - 4(1)(1)})/2(1)$
$x = (1 \pm \sqrt{-3})/2$
$x = (1 \pm \sqrt{3}\,i)/2$
$x = 1/2 + (\sqrt{3}/2)i \text{ or } x = 1/2 - (\sqrt{3}/2)i.$

The roots are *complex conjugates.*

Example 3. Solve the quadratic equation $9x^2 - 12x + 4 = 0$.

$a = 9, b = -12, c = 4$
$x = (-b \pm \sqrt{b^2 - 4ac})/2a$
$x = (12 \pm \sqrt{(-12)^2 - 4(9)(4)})/2(9)$
$x = (12 \pm \sqrt{144 - 144})/18$
$x = (12 \pm 0)/18$
$x = 2/3.$

The roots are *real and equal.* Observe that the given quadratic equation can be written $(3x - 2)^2 = 0$, from which it follows readily that both roots are 2/3.

Example 4.   Solve the quadratic equation $9x^2 - 11x + 4 = 0$.

$a = 9, b = -11, c = 4$

$x = (-b \pm \sqrt{b^2 - 4ac})/2a$

$x = (11 \pm \sqrt{(-11)^2 - 4(9)(4)})/2(9)$

$x = (11 \pm \sqrt{-23})/18$

$x = (11 \pm \sqrt{23}\,i)/18$

$x = 11/18 + (\sqrt{23}/18)\,i$ or $x = 11/18 - (\sqrt{23}/18)\,i$.

The roots are *complex conjugates.*

Exercise 6.4

I. Solve each of the following quadratic equations by use of the quadratic formula.

(1) $2x^2 - 3x + 2 = 0$ (11) $2x^2 + 3x + 1 = x^2$

(2) $3x^2 + x - 1 = 0$ (12) $4x^2 + 3x + 2 = 1$

(3) $x^2 - x + 6 = 0$ (13) $2x^2 = -4$

(4) $5x^2 - 11x - 12 = 0$ (14) $3x^2 = -5x$

(5) $x^2 + 7x + 9 = 0$ (15) $3x^2 = 7x$

(6) $2x^2 + 2x + 5 = 0$ (16) $5 = -3x^2$

(7) $3x^2 + 1 + 5x = 0$ (17) $x^2 + 9 = 0$

(8) $6x + 1 - 2x^2 = 0$ (18) $x^2 + 16 = 0$

(9) $x^2 - 5 + 4x = 0$ (19) $x^2 = 2 + 6x$

(10) $1 + 2x - 3x^2 = 0$ (20) $x^2 = 5 - 4x$

II. If the roots of any quadratic equation of Exercise I are rational numbers, check your results by factoring the quadratic function and solving the quadratic equation by the method of factoring.

6.5   Geometric Representation of Complex Numbers, Imaginary Numbers

You have already learned that the set of real numbers may be represented geometrically on the number line. Since $a + bi = c + di$ if and only if $a = c$ and $b = d$, we see that any complex number determines exactly one ordered pair of real numbers and, conversely, any ordered pair of real numbers determines exactly one complex number. That is, the set of complex numbers is in one-to-one correspondence with the set of ordered pairs of real numbers. The correspondence is illustrated in Figure 6.1.

$$3 + 2i \leftrightarrow (3, 2)$$
$$-3 + 2i \leftrightarrow (-3, 2)$$
$$3 + -2i \leftrightarrow (3, -2)$$
$$-3 + -2i \leftrightarrow (-3, -2)$$
$$a + bi \leftrightarrow (a, b)$$

FIGURE 6.1

Thus we see that each complex number can be represented geometrically by a point in the Cartesian plane, as illustrated in Figure 6.2. *To graph the complex number a + bi, we graph the ordered pair (a, b).* The Cartesian plane of Figure 6.2 is sometimes called the *complex plane.*

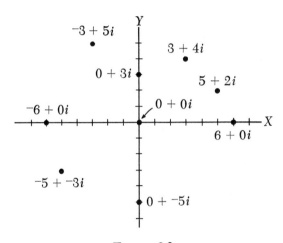

FIGURE 6.2

The length of the line segment from the origin to the point which represents a given complex number can be computed by the Pythagorean Theorem. For example, we compute the length of the line segment from $(0,0)$ to $(-3,4)$ by observing that the base of the triangle in Figure 6.3 is $|-3|$ units long and the altitude is $|4|$ units long. By the *Pythagorean Theorem*, the hypotenuse is $\sqrt{|-3|^2 + |4|^2}$ units long; i.e., the length of the hypotenuse is 5 units. In general, the length of the line segment from the origin to the point (a, b) is $\sqrt{|a|^2 + |b|^2}$ units. Since $|a|^2 = a^2$ and $|b|^2 = b^2$ for any real numbers a and b, we can write this length as $\sqrt{a^2 + b^2}$. Whenever the point which represents a complex number lies on one of the axes, there is no triangle. Nevertheless, the length of the line segment from $(0,0)$ to that point can still be computed from $\sqrt{a^2 + b^2}$. In this case, however, $a = 0$ or $b = 0$. For example, if the point representing the complex number lies on the X-axis, then

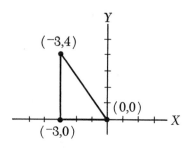

FIGURE 6.3

$b = 0$, and the length of the segment from $(0,0)$ to the point $(a, 0)$ is $\sqrt{a^2}$, which is equal to $|a|$. To illustrate, we consider the point $(-5,0)$ corresponding to the complex number $-5 + 0i$. The length of the line segment from $(0,0)$ to $(-5,0)$ is $\sqrt{(-5)^2 + 0^2} = \sqrt{25} = 5 = |-5|$.

The above discussion enables us to extend the concept of absolute value of a real number.

DEFINITION 4.   The *absolute value* of the complex number $a + bi$ (denoted by $|a + bi|$) is the real number $\sqrt{a^2 + b^2}$; i.e., $|a + bi| = \sqrt{a^2 + b^2}$.

For example, the absolute value of $-3 + 4i$ is $\sqrt{(-3)^2 + (4)^2}$, i.e., $|-3 + 4i| = \sqrt{9 + 16} = 5$. Similarly, $|0 + -5i| = 5$ and $|-7 + 0i| = 7$. We see that $|a + bi| = \sqrt{(a + bi)(a - bi)}$; i.e., the absolute value of a complex number is the square root of the product of that complex number and its conjugate.

We are now prepared to discuss the possibility of ordering the complex numbers. The following possibilities of an order relation seem plausible:

(1) $a + bi < c + di$ if and only if $a < c$,
(2) $a + bi < c + di$ if and only if $a < c$ and $b \leq d$,
(3) $a + bi < c + di$ if and only if $|a + bi| < |c + di|$.

If we accept (1) as a definition of order, then $2 + 100i \not< 2 + 3i$, $2 + 3i \not< 2 + 100i$, and $2 + 100i \neq 2 + 3i$. Thus there would be no trichotomy.

If we accept (2) as a definition of order, then $2 + 5i \not< 3 + 4i$, $3 + 4i \not< 2 + 5i$, and $2 + 5i \neq 3 + 4i$. Thus there would be no trichotomy.

If we accept (3) as a definition of order, then $3 + 4i \not< 4 + 3i$, $4 + 3i \not< 3 + 4i$, and $3 + 4i \neq 4 + 3i$. Thus there would be no trichotomy.

From the above discussion we conjecture that there is no extension of the order relation from the real numbers to the complex numbers such that $(C, +, \times)$ is an ordered field. In fact, this conjecture can be proved but the proof is not included in this text.

In classical terminology any complex number of the form $0 + bi$, in which $b \neq 0$, is called a *pure imaginary number,* and any complex number of the form $a + bi$, in which $b \neq 0$ is called an *imaginary number.* Thus any nonzero complex number which is represented by a point on the Y-axis (in the complex plane) is a pure imaginary number, any complex number represented by a point not on the X-axis is an imaginary number, and any complex number represented by a point on the X-axis is a real number.

We summarize the complex number system with the following comments and figures. In Figure 6.4 we list some of the reasons for the invention of the various number systems. In Figure 6.5 we illustrate the set of complex numbers and its subsets.

Most mathematical models of physical problems have $(R_a, +, \times, <)$, $(R, +, \times, <)$, or $(C, +, \times)$ as their universe.

The universe of the mathematical model of a problem involving electric circuits of the RLC variety is $(C, +, \times)$. Hence there are extensive applications of imaginary numbers to physical problems.

$$C_0 \subset I \subset R_a \subset R \subset C$$

Number System	One Reason for Its Invention
C_0 (Counting numbers)	To count the elements of a set.
I (Integers)	To convert any open sentence of the type $x + 5 = 0$ to a true sentence by replacement of the variable.
R_a (Rationals)	To convert any open sentence of the type $2x + 3 = 0$ to a true sentence by replacement of the variable.
R (Reals)	To convert any open sentence of the type $x^2 - 2 = 0$ to a true sentence by replacement of the variable.
C (Complex numbers)	To convert any open sentence of the type $x^2 + 1 = 0$ to a true sentence by replacement of the variable.

FIGURE 6.4

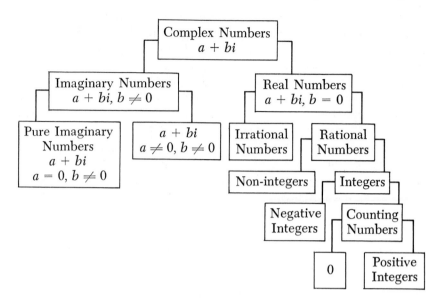

Exercise 6.5

I. Represent geometrically each of the following complex numbers.

(1) $2 + 3i$ (11) $0 + {}^-3i$
(2) $3 + 2i$ (12) ${}^-4i$
(3) ${}^-4 + 3i$ (13) $6i$
(4) $4 + {}^-3i$ (14) $0 + 5i$
(5) ${}^-4 + {}^-3i$ (15) $1 + i$
(6) ${}^-3 + {}^-4i$ (16) $1 + {}^-1i$
(7) ${}^-3 + 0i$ (17) ${}^-1 + {}^-1i$
(8) ${}^-3$ (18) ${}^-1 + i$
(9) 5 (19) i
(10) $5 + 0i$ (20) 0

II. Compute the absolute value of each complex number in Exercise I.

III. Write a short paper on the development of the complex numbers from the counting numbers.

CHAPTER 7

FINITE NUMBER SYSTEMS

7.1 Clock Arithmetic

In this text we began our study of the real number system $(R, +, \times)$ and learned that $(R, +, \times)$ is a field. We learned also that $(R_a, +, \times)$ is a subfield of $(R, +, \times)$. When we investigated $(I, +, \times)$, we discovered that $(I, +, \times)$ is not a field; in particular, property $F9$ fails. Similarly, since $F4$ and $F9$ fail in $(C_0, +, \times)$ we saw that $(C_0, +, \times)$ is not a field. As a matter of fact, we could have begun our study with $(C_0, +, \times)$ and successively extended this system to $(I, +, \times)$, $(R_a, +, \times)$, and finally to $(R, +, \times)$*. In this chapter we shall consider certain finite subsets of C_0, define the operations of addition and multiplication between numbers in *these subsets* to form finite *systems*, and then study the corresponding properties of these finite systems. We shall see that some finite number systems have all the properties of $(C_0, +, \times)$ and some do not. In fact, we shall discover that many of the finite number systems have all the field properties. At this time you should review the divisibility definitions and theorems listed in the appendix. In particular, you should review the definition of $a \mid b$, the definition of *greatest common divisor*, the definitions of *primes* and *composites*, theorems concerning primes divisors, the *division algorithm*, the *Euclidean algorithm*, and the *unique prime factorization theorem*.

To introduce finite number systems we consider *clock arithmetic*. In clock arithmetic the only numbers are 1, 2, 3, . . . , 12, which we call *clock numbers*. In the definition of addition, we are guided by the clock.

* Ohmer, Aucoin, and Cortez, *Elementary Contemporary Mathematics* (1964). New York: Blaisdell Publishing Company.

167

For example, if you have an appointment at 3:00 P.M. and you are 2 hours late, then you arrive for your appointment at 5:00 P.M. On the other hand, if you are 2 hours late for an 11:00 A.M. appointment, then you arrive at 1:00 P.M. Thus we define $a \oplus b$ so that $3 \oplus 2 = 5$ and $11 \oplus 2 = 1$. The binary operator $\oplus$, the operation of *clock addition*, and the *sum* $a \oplus b$ of any two clock numbers a and b are defined in Definition 1.

DEFINITION 1. The *sum* of any two clock numbers a and b is the number $a \oplus b$ defined as follows:

(a) $a \oplus b = a + b$ if and only if $a + b \le 12$,
(b) $a \oplus b = (a + b) - 12$ if and only if $12 < a + b$.

Observe from Definition 1 that the sum of any two clock numbers is a clock number.

From Definition 1, we may compute the sum of any two clock numbers a and b by visualizing an initial clock reading of a o'clock and then visualizing a terminal clock reading b hours later; that is, we begin at a o'clock and move the hour hand clockwise b numbers. The addition of 9 and 5 is illustrated in Figure 7.1.

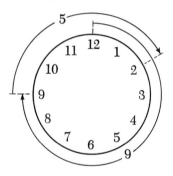

FIGURE 7.1

From Definition 1 (and Figure 7.1) we know that $9 \oplus 5 = 2$. From Definition 1, $5 \oplus 9 = (5 + 9) - 12 = 14 - 12 = 2$. In fact, if a and b are any clock numbers, then $a + b = b + a$ and hence $a \oplus b = b \oplus a$; that is, the commutative property for addition of clock numbers is true. Since the set of clock numbers is a finite set, we can list all of the addition facts in one table. The addition table is shown in Figure 7.2.

By Definition 1, the clock number system obeys the closure property for addition. Observe that the proof of the closure property for addition is contained also in Figure 7.2. In fact, although properties such as the commutative property and associative property for addition of clock numbers follow from Definition 1 and the corresponding properties for addition of counting numbers, we could prove these properties by actual *computation*. For example, to prove that $a \oplus b = b \oplus a$, for any clock numbers a and b, we could compute all 144 combinations of $a + b$. If the clock number system were infinite rather than finite, we would not be able to compute all possible combinations; we would have to derive each property *in general*, as in the real number system.

+	12	1	2	3	4	5	6	7	8	9	10	11
12	12	1	2	3	4	5	6	7	8	9	10	11
1	1	2	3	4	5	6	7	8	9	10	11	12
2	2	3	4	5	6	7	8	9	10	11	12	1
3	3	4	5	6	7	8	9	10	11	12	1	2
4	4	5	6	7	8	9	10	11	12	1	2	3
5	5	6	7	8	9	10	11	12	1	2	3	4
6	6	7	8	9	10	11	12	1	2	3	4	5
7	7	8	9	10	11	12	1	2	3	4	5	6
8	8	9	10	11	12	1	2	3	4	5	6	7
9	9	10	11	12	1	2	3	4	5	6	7	8
10	10	11	12	1	2	3	4	5	6	7	8	9
11	11	12	1	2	3	4	5	6	7	8	9	10

FIGURE 7.2

From Figure 7.2 we see that the identity for addition is 12; that is, for any clock number a, $a \oplus 12 = a$ and $12 \oplus a = a$. Of course, we could prove the identity property from Definition 1(b) as follows:

$$a \oplus 12 = (a + 12) - 12 = (a + 12) + {}^-12 = a + (12 + {}^-12)$$

$= a + 0 = a$, for any clock number a. Notice that the clock number system has a property that the counting number system does not have; namely, each clock number has a unique additive inverse which is a clock number. Since the additive identity is 12, the additive inverse of any clock number a is that unique clock number b such that $a \oplus b = 12$. Thus the additive inverse of 12 is 12, the additive inverse of 1 is 11, the additive inverse of 2 is 10, et cetera. Hence any open sentence of the form $a \oplus x = 12$, for any clock number a, can be converted to a true sentence by replacement of the variable x by a clock number. The fact that we could not convert any open sentence of the form $a + x = 0$, for any counting number a, to a true sentence by replacement of the variable x by a counting number led us to invent the negative integers. Consequently, although the *set* of clock numbers is a finite subset of the *set* of counting numbers, and the operators $\oplus$ and $+$ are related, the *system* of clock numbers has the above important property (that every clock number has a unique additive inverse) not possessed by the *system* of counting numbers.

We summarize this section by listing the properties of the clock number system considered in this section.

CLOSURE PROPERTY FOR ADDITION OF CLOCK NUMBERS
If a and b are any two clock numbers, then $a \oplus b$ is a unique clock number.

ASSOCIATIVE PROPERTY FOR ADDITION OF CLOCK NUMBERS
If a, b, and c are any clock numbers, then $(a \oplus b) \oplus c = a \oplus (b \oplus c)$.

IDENTITY PROPERTY FOR ADDITION OF CLOCK NUMBERS
If a and z are any clock numbers, then $a \oplus z = a$ if and only if $z = 12$.

INVERSE PROPERTY FOR ADDITION OF CLOCK NUMBERS
If a is any clock number, then there exists exactly one clock number a' (called the *additive inverse* of a) such that $a \oplus a' = 12$.

COMMUTATIVE PROPERTY FOR ADDITION OF CLOCK NUMBERS
If a and b are any clock numbers, then $a \oplus b = b \oplus a$.

Exercise 7.1

I. Verify the associative property for addition in each of the following.

(1) $a = 11$, $b = 1$, $c = 9$ (5) $a = 10$, $b = 4$, $c = 10$
(2) $a = 2$, $b = 8$, $c = 10$ (6) $a = 4$, $b = 12$, $c = 12$
(3) $a = 5$, $b = 10$, $c = 12$ (7) $a = 5$, $b = 5$, $c = 5$
(4) $a = 12$, $b = 4$, $c = 6$ (8) $a = 8$, $b = 7$, $c = 8$

II. Prove: If a, b, and c are any clock numbers such that $a + b + c \le 12$, then $(a \oplus b) \oplus c = a \oplus (b \oplus c)$.

III. Complete the following table.

Clock number	1	2	3	4	5	6	7	8	9	10	11	12
Additive inverse												

IV. Let the operation of addition of elements a and b of the set $A = \{0, 1, 2, 3\}$ be defined as follows:

$a \oplus b = a + b$ if and only if $a + b \leq 3$,
$a \oplus b = (a + b) - 4$ if and only if $3 < a + b$.

(1) Complete the addition table.

+	0	1	2	3
0				
1				
2				
3				

(2) By use of the addition table, prove that this finite system possesses the closure, identity, inverse, and commutative properties.

(3) Justify the associative property for 6 examples.

V. Convert each of the following open sentences to a true sentence by replacing the variable by a clock number.

(1) $x \oplus 11 = 5$ (6) $11 \oplus x = 1$
(2) $x \oplus 9 = 3$ (7) $12 \oplus t = t$
(3) $x \oplus 5 = 11$ (8) $u = u \oplus 12$
(4) $x \oplus 3 = 9$ (9) $4 \oplus 10 = x$
(5) $7 \oplus x = 1$ (10) $11 \oplus 5 = x$

VI. Convert each of the following open sentences to a true sentence by replacing the variable by an element of the set A of Exercise IV.

(1) $x \oplus 3 = 3$ (6) $0 \oplus x = 3$
(2) $x \oplus 3 = 1$ (7) $2 \oplus 3 = x$
(3) $2 \oplus x = 1$ (8) $x = 3 \oplus 1$
(4) $2 \oplus x = 2$ (9) $2 \oplus x = 0$
(5) $x \oplus 0 = 2$ (10) $x \oplus 3 = 0$

7.2 Finite Number Systems

Recall that the additive identity of the clock number system is 12 and the additive identity of the system of counting numbers is 0. We now consider another finite number system consisting of the 12 elements 0, 1, 2, . . . , 11 and an operation of addition similar to that of the clock numbers, and then we compare this finite number system with the clock number system. The binary operator $\oplus$, the operation *addition*, and the *sum* $a \oplus b$ of any two numbers of $\{0, 1, 2, . . . , 11\}$ are defined in Definition 2.

DEFINITION 2. The *sum* of any numbers a and b of $\{0, 1, 2, . . . , 11\}$ is the number $a \oplus b$ defined as follows:

(a) $a \oplus b = a + b$ if and only if $a + b \leq 11$,
(b) $a \oplus b = (a + b) - 12$ if and only if $11 < a + b$.

By Definition 2, the sum of any two numbers of $\{0, 1, 2, . . . , 11\}$ is a number of $\{0, 1, 2, . . . , 11\}$, as shown in the addition table in Figure 7.3.

$\oplus$	0	1	2	3	4	5	6	7	8	9	10	11
0	0	1	2	3	4	5	6	7	8	9	10	11
1	1	2	3	4	5	6	7	8	9	10	11	0
2	2	3	4	5	6	7	8	9	10	11	0	1
3	3	4	5	6	7	8	9	10	11	0	1	2
4	4	5	6	7	8	9	10	11	0	1	2	3
5	5	6	7	8	9	10	11	0	1	2	3	4
6	6	7	8	9	10	11	0	1	2	3	4	5
7	7	8	9	10	11	0	1	2	3	4	5	6
8	8	9	10	11	0	1	2	3	4	5	6	7
9	9	10	11	0	1	2	3	4	5	6	7	8
10	10	11	0	1	2	3	4	5	6	7	8	9
11	11	0	1	2	3	4	5	6	7	8	9	10

FIGURE 7.3

By comparing the addition table in Figure 7.3 with the addition table in Figure 7.2, we see that these two different number systems are *abstractly identical*; that is, they are identical except for notation. In fact, the only difference in notation is that 0 in the new system plays the role of 12 in the clock number system. Since the new system is abstractly identical with the old system, it obviously possesses the five properties enumerated in the last section.

We now consider another finite number system suggested by the set {Sunday, Monday, Tuesday, Wednesday, Thursday, Friday, Saturday}. For simplicity, we designate the days, in order, by 0, 1, 2, 3, 4, 5, 6 (called *calendar numbers*) as follows: 0 ↔ Sunday, 1 ↔ Monday, 2 ↔ Tuesday, 3 ↔ Wednesday, 4 ↔ Thursday, 5 ↔ Friday, 6 ↔ Saturday.

If you leave by car, on Friday, on a 4-day trip, when do you reach your destination? Looking at a calendar, you count 4 days from Friday; you reach your destination on Tuesday. You could count 4 days from 5 (for Friday): 6, 0, 1, 2. In this system $5 \oplus 4 = 2$. Similarly $2 \oplus 3 = 5$ and $5 \oplus 2 = 0$. Because of the above considerations, we define the binary operator $\oplus$, the operation of *addition*, and the *sum* of any two calendar numbers a and b as in Definition 3.

DEFINITION 3. The *sum* of any two calendar numbers a and b is the number $a \oplus b$ defined as follows:

(a) $a \oplus b = a + b$ if and only if $a + b \le 6$,
(b) $a \oplus b = (a + b) - 7$ if and only if $6 < a + b$.

According to Definition 3, the sum of any two calendar numbers is a unique calendar number, as shown in Figure 7.4.

$\oplus$	0	1	2	3	4	5	6
0	0	1	2	3	4	5	6
1	1	2	3	4	5	6	0
2	2	3	4	5	6	0	1
3	3	4	5	6	0	1	2
4	4	5	6	0	1	2	3
5	5	6	0	1	2	3	4
6	6	0	1	2	3	4	5

FIGURE 7.4

From Definition 3 (and Figure 7.4) we see that the calendar number system defined above possesses the closure property for addition. We now state the five properties of the preceding section, all of which the calendar number system possesses.

CLOSURE PROPERTY FOR ADDITION OF CALENDAR NUMBERS
If a and b are any calendar numbers, then $a \oplus b$ is a unique calendar number.

ASSOCIATIVE PROPERTY FOR ADDITION OF CALENDAR NUMBERS
If a, b, and c are any calendar numbers, then $(a \oplus b) \oplus c = a \oplus (b \oplus c)$.

IDENTITY PROPERTY FOR ADDITION OF CALENDAR NUMBERS
If a and z are any calendar numbers, then $a \oplus z = a$ if and only if $z = 0$.

INVERSE PROPERTY FOR ADDITION OF CALENDAR NUMBERS
If a is any calendar number, then there exists exactly one calendar number a' (called the *additive inverse* of a) such that $a \oplus a' = 0$.

COMMUTATIVE PROPERTY FOR ADDITION OF CALENDAR NUMBERS
If a and b are any calendar numbers, then $a \oplus b = b \oplus a$.

The proofs of all but the associative property follow immediately from Definition 3. We can prove the associative property by either using Definition 3 and considering the various cases, or by using the addition table in Figure 7.4. However, there are 7^3 sums $(a \oplus b) \oplus c$ and 7^3 sums $a \oplus (b \oplus c)$ to compute if we use the table. In the exercises you will *verify* the associative property for a few of these sums and will *prove* the identity property, inverse property, and commutative property.

Since the additive inverse of each calendar number is a calendar number, the open sentence $a \oplus x = 0$, for any calendar number a, may be converted to a true sentence by replacement of the variable x by a calendar number. For example, the open sentence $5 \oplus x = 0$ may be converted to a true sentence by replacement of the variable x by the calendar number 2; that is, in classical terminology, the *solution* of the *equation* $5 + x = 0$ is 2. Recall that no equation of the form $a + x = 0$, for any nonzero counting number a, has a root in the system of counting numbers. In fact, every equation $a \oplus x = b$, for any calendar numbers a and b, has a root which is a calendar number, but there are some equations $a + x = b$, for counting numbers a and b, which do not have roots.

However, since every integer has an additive inverse, we see that the equation $a + x = 0$, for any integer a, has a root which is an integer. Thus it appears that the calendar number system, which at first appeared to be more like the counting number system, is actually more like the system of integers. Does the system of integers possess the five properties of the calendar number system? In Chapter 1 we learned that the system of integers does possess these five properties. Although the calendar number system is a *finite* number system, it has these five properties in common with the *infinite* system of integers. In fact, the system of integers, the clock number system, and the calendar number system are three different number systems, which all possess these same five properties. Because many other systems, some from the physical and social sciences, also possess these same five properties, it is advantageous to study an *abstract* (rather than a specific) system which has these five properties. Then any theorem which is provable from *these five properties* is immediately available for application to any one of the particular systems. Thus it is unnecessary to prove the same theorem in all of these systems; it is sufficient to prove it *once* in the abstract system.

Any abstract system $(G, \oplus)$ which possesses the above-mentioned properties is given a special name.

DEFINITION 4. A system $(G, \oplus)$ is called a *commutative group* if and only if it possesses all of the following properties.

(a) If a and b are any elements of G, then $a \oplus b$ is a unique element of G (*closure property*).

(b) If a, b, and c are any elements of G, then $(a \oplus b) \oplus c = a \oplus (b \oplus c)$ (*associative property*).

(c) There exists a unique element i in G such that $a \oplus i = a$ for all a in G (*identity property*).

(d) If a is any element of G, then there exists a unique element a' in G such that $a \oplus a' = i$ (*inverse property*).

(e) If a and b are any elements of G, then $a \oplus b = b \oplus a$ (*commutative property*).

The following theorem, which states that the additive inverse of any sum is equal to the sum of the additive inverses, is an example of a theorem which may be proved from the definition of a commutative group. Observe that no properties other than the five properties of Definition 4 are used in the proof.

THEOREM 1.   If a and b are any elements of a commutative group $(G, \oplus)$, then $(a \oplus b)' = a' \oplus b'$.

Proof.
$$(a \oplus b) \oplus (a' \oplus b') = (b \oplus a) \oplus [a' \oplus b']$$
$$= [(b \oplus a) \oplus a'] \oplus b'$$
$$\text{(by the associative property)}$$
$$= [b \oplus (a \oplus a')] \oplus b'$$
$$= [b \oplus i] \oplus b'$$
$$= b \oplus b'$$
$$= i.$$

Thus $a' \oplus b'$ is the additive inverse of $a \oplus b$.

But $(a \oplus b)'$ is the additive inverse of $a \oplus b$.

Since the additive inverse is unique, it follows that $(a \oplus b)' = a' \oplus b'.\;/\!/$

According to the sign property for addition of integers $^-(a + b) = {}^-a + {}^-b$ for any integers a and b. This property is an immediate consequence of Theorem 1. If Theorem 1 had been available in Chapter 1 or in previous study concerning the integers, it would have been unnecessary to prove the sign property. Moreover, since Theorem 1 applies to *any* commutative group, it applies, in particular, to the clock number system and to the calendar number system, and, in fact, to every particular commutative group regardless of the binary operator and the number of elements in the group.

Exercise 7.2

I. Prove that the calendar number system possesses each of the following properties.

   (1) Identity property for addition
   (2) Inverse property for addition
   (3) Commutative property for addition

II. Verify the associative property for addition of calendar numbers in each of the following cases.

   (1) $a = 3, b = 1, c = 4$ (4) $a = 0, c = 5, c = 5$
   (2) $a = 1, b = 4, c = 5$ (5) $a = 6, b = 4, c = 4$
   (3) $a = 6, b = 0, c = 6$ (6) $a = 5, b = 5, c = 4$

III. Complete the following addition table so that the system will be commutative.

⊕	0	1	2	3	4
0	0	1	2	3	4
1		2	3	4	0
2			4	0	1
3				1	2
4					3

IV. (1) Complete the following addition table so that the system will be a commutative group. What is the identity of the group?

⊕	a	b	c
a	a	b	c
b		c	
c			b

(2) Complete the following table so that the system will be a commutative group. What is the identity of the group?

⊕	a	b	c	d
a	b		d	a
b	c			b
c		b		
d				d

V. Supply the reason for each step in the proof of Theorem 1.

7.3 Congruence Modulo m

In this and the following two sections we shall study a general method for generating a finite number system. First we define the *congruence relation modulo an integer m*.

DEFINITION 5. The integer a is said to be *congruent to* the integer b (modulo the integer m) if and only if m divides $a - b$. (Symbolically, $a \equiv b \pmod{m}$ if and only if $m \mid (a - b)$).

By definition of the relation *divides*, we see that $a \equiv b \pmod{m}$ if and only if there exists an integer k such that $a - b = km$. The following examples illustrate Definition 5.

Example 1. $47 \equiv 5 \pmod 7$ because $7 \mid (47 - 5)$; that is, $47 - 5$ $= 42 = 6(7)$. *Note.* $a = 47$, $b = 5$, $m = 7$, and $k = 6$.

Example 2. $47 \equiv 11 \pmod{12}$ because $12 \mid (47 - 11)$; that is, $47 - 11$ $= 36 = 3(12)$. *Note.* $a = 47$, $b = 11$, $m = 12$, and $k = 3$.

Example 3. $15 \equiv 1 \pmod 2$ because $2 \mid (15 - 1)$; that is, $15 - 1$ $= 14 = 7(2)$. *Note.* $a = 15$, $b = 1$, $m = 2$, and $k = 7$.

Example 4. $15 \equiv 1 \pmod 7$ because $7 \mid (15 - 1)$; that is, $15 - 1$ $= 14 = 2(7)$. *Note.* $a = 15$, $b = 1$, $m = 7$, and $k = 2$.

Example 5. $5 \equiv 47 \pmod 7$ because $7 \mid (5 - 47)$; that is, $5 - 47$ $= {}^-42 = {}^-6(7)$. *Note.* $a = 5$, $b = 47$, $m = 7$, and $k = {}^-6$.

Example 6. $5 \equiv 5 \pmod 7$ because $7 \mid (5 - 5)$; that is, $5 - 5 = 0$ $= 0(7)$. *Note.* $a = 5$, $b = 5$, $m = 7$, and $k = 0$.

As in any relation, we question whether congruence mod m is an equivalence relation. Examples 1 and 5 lead us to suspect that congruence mod m obeys the symmetric property, and Example 6 leads us to conjecture that congruence mod m obeys the reflexive property. The following theorem assures us that congruence mod m is an equivalence relation.

THEOREM 2. The relation *congruence mod m* defined on I is an equivalence relation. That is,

(a) $a \equiv a \pmod m$ (reflexive property);
(b) If $a \equiv b \pmod m$, then $b \equiv a \pmod m$ (symmetric property);
(c) If $a \equiv b \pmod m$ and $b \equiv c \pmod m$, then $a \equiv c \pmod m$ (transitive property).

Proof.   (a) $a = a$
$a - a = 0$
$a - a = 0(m)$
$a \equiv a \pmod m$

(b) Let $a \equiv b \pmod m$.
    Then $m \mid (a - b)$.
    Hence $m \mid (b - a)$.
    Thus $b \equiv a \pmod m$.

(c) Let $a \equiv b \pmod m$ and $b \equiv c \pmod m$.
    Then $m \mid (a - b)$ and $m \mid (b - c)$.
    Thus $m \mid [(a - b) + (b - c)]$
    Hence $m \mid (a - c)$.
    Thus $a \equiv c \pmod m$.

Consequently, *congruence mod* m on the set of integers is an equivalence relation. //

Recall that an equivalence relation on a set S separates the elements of S into mutually exclusive subsets (called *equivalence classes*) of S as follows:

(1) Every element of S is in exactly one of the subsets;
(2) Any two elements which are in the same subset are related;
(3) No two elements which are in different subsets are related.

Since congruence mod m (and, in particular, congruence mod 7) on the set of integers is an equivalence relation, we know that congruence mod 7 separates the set of integers into mutually exclusive subsets (equivalence classes) as shown in Figure 7.5.

.	.	.	.	.	.	.
.	.	.	.	.	.	.
.	.	.	.	.	.	.
-14	-13	-12	-11	-10	-9	-8
-7	-6	-5	-4	-3	-2	-1
0	1	2	3	4	5	6
7	8	9	10	11	12	13
14	15	16	17	18	19	20
.	.	.	.	.	.	.
.	.	.	.	.	.	.
.	.	.	.	.	.	.

FIGURE 7.5

Similarly, congruence mod 4 separates the set of integers into equivalence classes as shown in Figure 7.6.

We shall employ the symbol a_7 to represent the equivalence class to which a belongs (mod 7). That is, $a_7 = \{x : x \equiv a \pmod 7\}$. Similarly, $a_4 = \{x : x \equiv a \pmod 4\}$. In general, $a_m = \{x : x \equiv a \pmod m\}$.

FIGURE 7.6

Thus the symbols 0_7, 1_7, 2_7, . . . , 6_7 represent the equivalence classes (mod 7) to which 0, 1, 2, . . . , 6, respectively, belong. Similarly, 0_4, 1_4, 2_4, 3_4 represent the equivalence classes (mod 4) to which 0, 1, 2, 3, respectively, belong. Similar notation is used for the equivalence classes (mod any integer m). Thus we refer to the equivalence classes (mod m) as 0_m, 1_m, 2_m, . . . , $(m-1)_m$. However, you should realize that there are many other representations for a given equivalence class. For example, $10_4 = 6_4 = 2_4$, and $8_4 = 4_4 = 0_4$. In the following section we define the operations of addition and multiplication of equivalence classes (mod m).

Exercise 7.3

I. Label each of the following sentences as true or false.

(1) $65 \equiv 13 \pmod 5$ (6) $66 \equiv {}^-28 \pmod 2$
(2) $72 \equiv 12 \pmod 7$ (7) $27 \equiv 6 \pmod 3$
(3) $65 \equiv 13 \pmod{26}$ (8) $36 \equiv 12 \pmod 4$
(4) $72 \equiv 12 \pmod 5$ (9) ${}^-183 \equiv 6 \pmod 5$
(5) $79 \equiv {}^-17 \pmod 2$ (10) ${}^-178 \equiv 7 \pmod 7$

II. Separate the set of integers from $^-20$ to 20 into equivalence classes

(1) mod 5   (7) mod 10
(2) mod 7   (8) mod 8
(3) mod 6   (9) mod 15
(4) mod 4   (10) mod 20
(5) mod 2   (11) mod 1
(6) mod 3   (12) mod 0

III. Retrace the proof of Theorem 2 for the special case

(1) $m = 5$
(2) $m = 7$

IV. Convert each of the following open sentences to a true sentence by three different replacements of the variable.

(1) $x \equiv 7 \pmod 3$

(2) $x \equiv 3 \pmod 7$

(3) $x + 4 \equiv 6 \pmod 5$

(4) $x + 5 \equiv 4 \pmod 6$

(5) $x + 11 \equiv 11 \pmod 4$

(6) $x + 11 \equiv 11 \pmod{11}$

(7) $x + {}^-1 \equiv {}^-5 \pmod 3$

(8) $x + {}^-3 \equiv {}^-5 \pmod 1$

(9) $x + 10 \equiv 9 \pmod 2$

(10) $x + 9 \equiv 10 \pmod 2$

V. How are the three replacements in each part of Exercise IV related to each other?

VI. Give five representations of each of the following equivalence classes.

(1) 0_7

(2) 4_7

(3) 3_4

(4) 11_{12}

(5) $^-6_9$

(6) $^-3_5$

(7) 8_5

(8) 10_{10}

(9) 102_2

(10) 999_3

7.4 Addition and Multiplication of Equivalence Classes

If a, b, c, and d are any integers such that $a = b$ and $c = d$, then $a + c = b + d$. Is there a similar theorem for congruences? That is, if a, b, c, d, and m are any integers such that $a \equiv b \pmod m$ and $c \equiv d \pmod m$ can we conclude that $a + c \equiv b + d \pmod m$? The following examples suggest that we can.

Example 1. $25 \equiv 13 \pmod 3$ and $16 \equiv 1 \pmod 3$.
Is $25 + 16 \equiv 13 + 1 \pmod 3$?
$(25 + 16) - (13 + 1) = 27 = 9(3)$.
Hence $25 + 16 \equiv 13 + 1 \pmod 3$.

Example 2. $83 \equiv 28 \pmod 5$ and $71 \equiv 56 \pmod 5$.
Is $83 + 71 \equiv (28 + 56) \pmod 5$?
$(83 + 71) - (28 + 56) = 70 = 14(5)$.
Hence $83 + 71 \equiv 28 + 56 \pmod 5$.

The following theorem assures us that the above conjecture is true.

THEOREM 3.   If a, b, c, d, and m are any integers such that $a \equiv b \pmod m$ and $c \equiv d \pmod m$, then $a + c \equiv b + d \pmod m$.

Proof.   Let $a \equiv b \pmod{m}$ and $c \equiv d \pmod{m}$.

Then $m \mid (a - b)$ and $m \mid (c - d)$ (by Definition 5).

Hence $m \mid [(a - b) + (c - d)]$.

Thus $m \mid [(a + c) - (b + d)]$.

Hence $a + c \equiv b + d \pmod{m}$ (by Definition 5).//

It follows immediately from Theorem 3 that, if $a \equiv b \pmod{m}$, then $a + c \equiv b + c \pmod{m}$.

If a, b, c, and d are any integers such that $a = b$ and $c = d$, then $ac = bd$. Proceeding as above, we state and prove the following theorem.

THEOREM 4.   If a, b, c, d, and m are any integers such that $a \equiv b \pmod{m}$ and $c \equiv d \pmod{m}$, then $ac \equiv bd \pmod{m}$.

Proof.   Let $a \equiv b \pmod{m}$ and $c \equiv d \pmod{m}$.

Then $m \mid (a - b)$ and $m \mid (c - d)$.

Thus $a - b = k_1 m$ and $c - d = k_2 m$, for some integers k_1 and k_2.

$(a - b)c = k_1 mc$ and $b(c - d) = bk_2 m$

$ac - bc = k_1 mc$ and $bc - bd = k_2 mb$

$(ac - bc) + (bc - bd) = k_1 mc + k_2 mb$

$(ac - bd) = (k_1 c + k_2 b)m$

$ac - bd = km$, where $k = k_1 c + k_2 b$

$m \mid (ac - bd)$

Thus $ac \equiv bd \pmod{m}$.//

It follows immediately from Theorem 4 that, if $a \equiv b \pmod{m}$, then $ac \equiv bc \pmod{m}$.

By Theorem 3, if a and b are in the same equivalence class, and c and d are in the same equivalence class, then $a + c$ and $b + d$ are in the same equivalence class. Now we define the sum of two *equivalence classes*.

DEFINITION 6.   The *sum* of the equivalence class a_m and the equivalence class c_m is the equivalence class $(a + c)_m$; that is, $a_m \oplus c_m = (a + c)_m$.

Because every equivalence class has many representations, we could not be certain that the sum does not depend on the particular representation used for each equivalence class if it were not for Theorem 3.

The following theorem assures us that the sum defined in Definition 6 is well-defined.

THEOREM 5. If a_m, b_m, c_m, and d_m are equivalence classes (modulo m), and $a_m = b_m$ and $c_m = d_m$, then $a_m \oplus c_m = b_m \oplus d_m$.

Proof. Let $a_m = b_m$ and $c_m = d_m$.

Thus a and b belong to the same equivalence class, and c and d belong to the same equivalence class.

Then $a \equiv b \pmod{m}$ and $c \equiv d \pmod{m}$.

Hence $a + c \equiv b + d \pmod{m}$ (by Theorem 3).

Thus $(a + c)_m = (b + d)_m$.

But $a_m \oplus c_m = (a + c)_m$ and $b_m \oplus d_m = (b + d)_m$
                    (by Definition 6).

Hence $a_m \oplus c_m = b_m \oplus d_m$.//

Thus the sum of any two equivalence classes of integers modulo m is well-defined.

The binary operator $\odot$, or $\otimes$, the binary operation *multiplication*, and the *product* of two equivalence classes is given in Definition 7.

DEFINITION 7. The *product* of the equivalence class a_m and the equivalence class c_m is the equivalence class $(a \times c)_m$; that is, $a_m \otimes c_m = (a \times c)_m$.

As in the sum of two equivalence classes, we want to be certain that the product does not depend on the particular representation of each equivalence class. The following theorem assures us that the product is well-defined.

THEOREM 6. If a_m, b_m, c_m, and d_m are equivalence classes (modulo m), and $a_m = b_m$ and $c_m = d_m$, then $a_m \odot c_m = b_m \odot d_m$.

Proof. Similar to proof of Theorem 5, and based on Theorem 4.//

The following examples illustrate the computation of the sum and of the product of two equivalence classes.

Example 3. Compute the sum of the equivalence classes 5_7 and 6_7.

$5_7 \oplus 6_7 = (5 + 6)_7 = 11_7$.

Since $11 \equiv 4 \pmod 7$, it follows that $11_7 = 4_7$.

Hence $5_7 \oplus 6_7 = 4_7$.

Example 4.   Compute the sum of the equivalence classes 11_{12} and 8_{12}.

$11_{12} \oplus 8_{12} = (11 + 8)_{12} = 19_{12}$.
Since $19 \equiv 7 \pmod{12}$, it follows that $19_{12} = 7_{12}$.
Hence $11_{12} \oplus 8_{12} = 7_{12}$.

Example 5.   Compute the product of the equivalence classes 5_7 and 6_7.

$5_7 \otimes 6_7 = (5 \times 6)_7 = 30_7$.
Since $30 \equiv 2 \pmod{7}$, it follows that $30_7 = 2_7$.
Hence $5_7 \otimes 6_7 = 2_7$.

Example 6.   Compute the product of the equivalence classes 8_{12} and 6_{12}.

$8_{12} \otimes 6_{12} = (8 \times 6)_{12} = 48_{12}$.
Since $48 \equiv 0 \pmod{12}$, it follows that $48_{12} = 0_{12}$.
Hence $8_{12} \otimes 6_{12} = 0_{12}$.

Example 7.   Compute $4_7 \otimes (3_7 \oplus 5_7)$.

$$\begin{aligned}
4_7 \otimes (3_7 \oplus 5_7) &= 4_7 \otimes (3 + 5)_7 \\
&= 4_7 \otimes 8_7 \\
&= 4_7 \otimes 1_7 \\
&= (4 \times 1)_7 \\
&= 4_7.
\end{aligned}$$

Example 8.   Compute $(4_7 \otimes 3_7) \oplus (4_7 \otimes 5_7)$.

$$\begin{aligned}
(4_7 \otimes 3_7) \oplus (4_7 \otimes 5_7) &= (4 \times 3)_7 \oplus (4 \times 5)_7 \\
&= 12_7 \oplus 20_7 \\
&= 5_7 \oplus 6_7 \\
&= (5 + 6)_7 \\
&= 11_7 \\
&= 4_7.
\end{aligned}$$

Exercise 7.4

I. Compute each of the following sums.

(1) $3_7 \oplus 2_7$ (6) $4_6 \oplus 3_6$
(2) $4_7 \oplus 2_7$ (7) $11_{12} \oplus 10_{12}$
(3) $6_7 \oplus 1_7$ (8) $8_{12} \oplus 9_{12}$
(4) $4_7 \oplus 3_7$ (9) $100_4 \oplus 72_4$
(5) $4_5 \oplus 3_5$ (10) $32_6 \oplus 72_6$

II. Compute each of the following products.

(1) $3_7 \otimes 2_7$ (6) $0_8 \otimes 3_8$

(2) $4_7 \otimes 2_7$ (7) $3_7 \otimes 0_7$

(3) $11_{12} \otimes 10_{12}$ (8) $5_{10} \otimes 6_{10}$

(4) $9_{12} \otimes 8_{12}$ (9) $5_{10} \otimes 8_{10}$

(5) $4_8 \otimes 6_8$ (10) $5_{11} \otimes 8_{11}$

III. Compute each of the following.

(1) $3_5 \otimes (4_5 \oplus 2_5)$

(2) $3_7 \otimes (4_7 \oplus 2_7)$

(3) $(3_5 \odot 4_5) \oplus (3_5 \odot 2_5)$

(4) $(3_7 \odot 4_7) \oplus (3_7 \odot 2_7)$

(5) $3_6 \otimes (4_6 \oplus 2_6)$

(6) $4_8 \otimes (5_8 \oplus 3_8)$

(7) $(3_6 \otimes 4_6) \oplus (3_6 \times 2_6)$

(8) $(4_8 \otimes 5_8) \oplus (4_8 \times 3_8)$

(9) $(6_{12} \oplus 3_{12}) \oplus 2_{12}$

(10) $6_{12} \oplus (3_{12} \oplus 2_{12})$

IV. Prove Theorem 6.

7.5   Properties of Equivalence Classes

In the preceding section we defined addition and multiplication of equivalence classes. In this section we study the important properties of any system of equivalence classes modulo any integer m. In addition, we shall compare the properties of any system of equivalence classes modulo any prime p with those of any system of equivalence classes modulo any composite c. One reason we study these systems is to gain a better understanding of the systems of counting numbers, integers, rationals, and reals. This is analogous to the study of a foreign language; after one has studied a foreign language, he has a better understanding of his native language. Another reason we study these systems is that they occasionally serve as mathematical models of physical problems.

Before we state and prove the properties of a given system of equivalence classes, we shall simplify the notation. Recall that $a_m \oplus b_m$ $= c_m$ if and only if $a + b \equiv c \pmod{m}$. For this reason we write $a_m + b_m = c_m$ to mean that $a_m \oplus b_m = c_m$, and when no ambiguity results, we write $a + b = c$ to mean $a_m \oplus b_m = c_m$. For example, in the addition table mod 7 we write $5 + 6 = 4$ to mean $5_7 \oplus 6_7 = 4_7$. Frequently we shall refer to the *equivalence classes* modulo m as the *integers* modulo m. For example, we shall refer to the equivalence classes modulo 3 as the integers modulo 3.

Let m be any integer and consider the system of equivalence classes modulo m. We shall prove that the system $(I_m, +)$ of equivalence classes mod m is a commutative group; that is, the system $(I_m, +)$ possesses the following properties.

(1) If a_m and b_m are any elements of I_m, then $a_m + b_m$ is a unique element of I_m (closure property for addition).

(2) If a_m, b_m, and c_m are any elements of I_m, then $(a_m + b_m) + c_m = a_m + (b_m + c_m)$ (associative property for addition).

(3) There exists a unique element 0_m of I_m such that $a_m + 0_m = a_m$ for all a_m in I_m (identity property for addition).

(4) If a_m is any element of I_m, then there exists a unique element a_m' of I_m such that $a_m + a_m' = 0_m$ (inverse property for addition).

(5) If a_m and b_m are any elements of I_m, then $a_m + b_m = b_m + a_m$ (commutative property for addition).

It follows immediately from Definition 6 that the sum of any two equivalence classes is a *unique* equivalence class; that is, the closure property for addition of equivalence classes is true.

Since $(a + b) + c \equiv a + (b + c)$ (mod m) for any integers a, b, c, it follows that $(a_m + b_m) + c_m = a_m + (b_m + c_m)$ for any equivalence classes a_m, b_m and c_m. Hence the associative property for addition of equivalence classes is true.

Since $a + 0 \equiv a$ (mod m), for any integer a, it follows that $a_m + 0_m = a_m$ for any equivalence class a_m.

To prove that the class 0_m is unique, we let z_m be an equivalence class mod m such that $a_m + z_m = a_m$.

Then $a + z \equiv a$ (mod m).

By Definition 5, $m \mid (a + z) - a$; that is, $m \mid z - 0$.

By Definition 5, $z \equiv 0$ (mod m).

Thus $z_m = 0_m$.

Hence there exists a unique equivalence class 0_m such that $a_m + 0_m = a_m$ for any equivalence class a_m. Thus the identity property for addition of equivalence classes is true.

If a is any integer, then $a + (m - a) \equiv 0$ (mod m). Thus $a_m + (m - a)_m = 0_m$ for any equivalence class a_m.

To prove that the equivalence class $(m - a)_m$ is unique, we let q_m be an equivalence class such that $a_m + q_m = 0_m$.

Then $a + q \equiv 0$ (mod m).

By Definition 5, $a + q = km$, for some integer k.

Hence $a + q = m + (k - 1)m$.

$q + \bar{m} + a = (k-1)m,$

$q - (m-a) = (k-1)m,$

$q \equiv (m-a) \pmod{m}.$

Thus $q_m = (m-a)_m$; that is, the equivalence class $(m-a)_m$ is unique.

Hence if a_m is any equivalence class mod m, then there exists a unique equivalence class $(m-a)_m$ such that $a_m + (m-a)_m = 0_m$. Thus the inverse property for addition of equivalence classes is true.

Since $a + b \equiv b + a \pmod{m}$ for any integers a and b, it follows that $a_m + b_m = b_m + a_m$ for any equivalence classes a_m and b_m containing a and b, respectively. Hence the commutative property for addition of equivalence classes is true.

Thus every system of equivalence classes modulo any integer m, with operation addition, is a commutative group.

We shall follow the customary procedure of designating an equivalence class by the smallest counting number in the class. For example, if $m = 7$, we designate the 7 equivalence classes by 0_7, 1_7, 2_7, 3_7, 4_7, 5_7, 6_7 or simply by 0, 1, 2, 3, 4, 5, 6, whenever there is no ambiguity. Then we may write the addition table as shown in Figure 7.7.

As we have already proved that the system $(I_m, +)$, for any integer m, is a commutative group, we know that the system $(I_7, +)$ is a commutative group. Observe that the identity element is 0_7 and that the inverse of any element a_7 is $(7-a)_7$. The system $(I_7, +)$ is abstractly identical with the calendar number system of Figure 7.4. The advantage of the present development is that we can generate a finite system consisting of any desired number of elements and we know, in advance, that this system is a commutative group with operation addition.

+	0	1	2	3	4	5	6
0	0	1	2	3	4	5	6
1	1	2	3	4	5	6	0
2	2	3	4	5	6	0	1
3	3	4	5	6	0	1	2
4	4	5	6	0	1	2	3
5	5	6	0	1	2	3	4
6	6	0	1	2	3	4	5

FIGURE 7.7

The system $(I_m, +)$, for any integer m, is a commutative group Recall that $a_m \otimes b_m = c_m$ if and only if $ab \equiv c \pmod{m}$. For this reason, we shall write $a_m \times b_m$, $a_m \cdot b_m$, or $a_m b_m$ to mean $a_m \otimes b_m$, and whenever there is no ambiguity, we shall write simply ab to mean $a_m \otimes b_m$. Since we have defined multiplication of equivalence classes modulo m, we might suspect that the system $(I_m, +, \times)$ is a field. In order to decide whether or not $(I_m, +, \times)$ is a field, we must check each of the 11 field properties. As we have already proved that the system $(I_m, +, \times)$ possesses the first five of the field properties (the five properties of a commutative group with the operation addition), we must check the remaining properties $F6$ through $F11$. We can prove that, for any integer m, the system $(I_m, +, \times)$ *possesses* not only properties $F1$ through $F5$ but also the following properties.

F6. If a_m and b_m are any elements of I_m, then $a_m \times b_m$ is a unique element of I_m (closure property for multiplication).

F7. If a_m, b_m, and c_m are any elements of I_m, then $(a_m \times b_m) \times c_m = a_m \times (b_m \times c_m)$ (associative property for multiplication).

F8. There exists a unique element 1_m of I_m such that $a_m \times 1_m = a_m$ for all a_m in I_m (identity property for multiplication).

F10. If a_m and b_m are any elements of I_m, then $a_m \times b_m = b_m \times a_m$ (commutative property for multiplication).

F11. If a_m, b_m, and c_m are any elements of I_m, then $a_m \times (b_m + c_m) = a_m \times b_m + a_m \times c_m$ (distributive property).

As the proofs of $F6$, $F7$, $F8$, and $F10$ are similar to the proofs of $F1$, $F2$, $F3$, and $F5$, respectively, they are assigned to you in the exercises.

Since $a(b + c) \equiv ab + ac \pmod{m}$ for any integers a, b, and c, it follows that $a_m(b_m + c_m) = a_m b_m + a_m c_m$ for any equivalence classes a_m, b_m, and c_m. Hence the distributive property is true.

Hence the system $(I_m, +, \times)$, for any integer m, possesses all field properties except $F9$. For example, the system $(I_4, +, \times)$ possesses all field properties except $F9$. Why does $(I_4, +, \times)$ not have the property $F9$? To answer this question, we consider the elements 0_4, 1_4, 2_4, 3_4 of $(I_4, +, \times)$ and show that the element 2_4 does not have a multiplicative inverse. If 2_4 has a multiplicative inverse b_4, then $2_4 b_4 = 1_4$. However, since $2_4 \times 0_4 = 0_4$, $2_4 \times 1_4 = 2_4$, $2_4 \times 2_4 = 0_4$, and $2_4 \times 3_4 = 2_4$, we see that there is no element b_4 such that $2_4 b_4 = 1_4$. Hence 2_4 has no multiplicative inverse. In the next section we prove that $(I_m, +, \times)$ possesses property $F9$ if and only if m is a prime. That is, if m is a prime, then $(I_m, +, \times)$ does possess $F9$ and is, therefore, a field; and inversely, if m is not a prime, then $(I_m, +, \times)$ does not possess $F9$.

Exercise 7.5

I. Prove that each of the following systems possesses field property $F9$, and exhibit the multiplicative inverse of each nonzero element.

(1) $(I_2, +, \times)$ (4) $(I_7, +, \times)$

(2) $(I_3, +, \times)$ (5) $(I_{11}, +, \times)$

(3) $(I_5, +, \times)$ (6) $(I_{13}, +, \times)$

II. Prove that each of the following systems does *not* possess field property $F9$, and exhibit all nonzero elements which do not have multiplicative inverses.

(1) $(I_6, +, \times)$ (4) $(I_{10}, +, \times)$

(2) $(I_8, +, \times)$ (5) $(I_{12}, +, \times)$

(3) $(I_9, +, \times)$ (6) $(I_{14}, +, \times)$

III. Determine which of the following systems is a commutative group with operation addition.

(1) $\{0, 3, 6\}$ (mod 7)   (5) $\{0, 2\}$ (mod 3)

(2) $\{0, 2, 4, 6\}$ (mod 7)   (6) $\{0, 3\}$ (mod 4)

(3) $\{0, 2, 4\}$ (mod 6)   (7) $\{0, 2, 4, 6\}$ (mod 8)

(4) $\{0, 3\}$ (mod 6)   (8) $\{0, 5, 10\}$ (mod 15)

IV. (1) Prove that *congruence mod* 0 is equality and hence defines the system of integers.

(2) Prove that *congruence mod* 1 yields a single equivalence class which contains all integers.

(3) Prove that *congruence mod* 2 separates the integers into two equivalence classes—one consisting of the odd integers and the other consisting of the even integers.

(4) Prove property $F6$ in the system $(I_m, +, \times)$.

(5) Prove property $F7$ in the system $(I_m, +, \times)$.

(6) Prove property $F8$ in the system $(I_m, +, \times)$.

(7) Prove property $F10$ in the system $(I_m, +, \times)$.

7.6   Properties of the System of Integers Modulo a Prime

Recall that the system $(I, +, \times)$ of integers possesses all field properties except $F9$, and recall also that the system $(I_m, +, \times)$, for any composite integer m, possesses all field properties except $F9$. Do all of the properties of $(I, +, \times)$ follow from *F1–F8*, *F10*, *F11*? If they do, then for every property of $(I, +, \times)$ there is a corresponding property of $(I_m, +, \times)$. For example, under this assumption, since $(I, +, \times)$ has the multiplication property of 0, then the system $(I_m, +, \times)$ must also have this property. However, we shall prove that $(I_m, +, \times)$ does not have the multiplication property of 0. As a consequence, we shall see that the multiplication property of zero does not follow from the properties *F1–F8*, *F10*, *F11*.

THEOREM 7.   If m is any composite number, then the system $(I_m, +, \times)$ does not possess the multiplication property of 0.

Proof.   Let m be any composite number.

Then there exist integers a and b such that $1 < a < m$, $1 < b < m$, and $ab = m$.

Then $ab \equiv 0 \pmod{m}$.

Hence $a_m \times b_m = 0_m$; that is, the product of the two nonzero equivalence classes a_m and b_m is equal to the equivalence class 0_m.

Consequently, $(I_m, +, \times)$ does not possess the multiplication property of 0. //

For example, consider the equivalence classes mod 6. Although $2_6 \neq 0_6$ and $3_6, \neq 0_6$, we see that $2_6 \times 3_6 = 0_6$. In $(I, +, \times)$, $(ab = 0) \rightleftarrows (a = 0 \lor b = 0)$. However, in $(I_m, +, \times)$, the sentence $(a_m b_m = 0_m) \rightleftarrows (a_m = 0_m \lor b_m = 0_m)$ *is a false sentence*, provided m is a composite number.

Recall the cancellation property for multiplication of integers: if a, b, and c are any integers such that $a \neq 0$ and $ab = ac$, then $b = c$. If m is a composite, is the cancellation property for multiplication true in $(I_m, +, \times)$? To answer this question, we observe that $5_{10} \times 2_{10} = 5_{10} \times 4_{10}$ and $5_{10} \neq 0_{10}$, but $2_{10} \neq 4_{10}$.

The following theorem assures us that $(I_m, +, \times)$, for any composite m, does not possess the cancellation property for multiplication.

THEOREM 8.   If m is any composite number, then the system $(I_m, +, \times)$ does not possess the cancellation property for multiplication.

Proof.   Follows from Theorem 7. //

We know that the system $(I_m, +, \times)$ does not possess property $F9$ if m is composite. Now we wish to prove that $(I_m, +, \times)$ does possess property $F9$ if m is a prime p. That is, we wish to prove that every equation of the form $a_p x_p = 1_p$, for any $a_p \neq 0_p$, has a unique solution. The following examples illustrate the method of proof.

Example 1.   Solve the equation $6_7 x_7 = 1_7$.

Of course, we can solve the given equation by actually replacing the variable x_7 by each of the equivalence classes 0_7, 1_7, 2_7, 3_7, 4_7, 5_7, 6_7. By this method, we see that $6_7 \times 6_7 = 1_7$ and hence that the equation $6_7\, x_7 = 1_7$ has the unique solution 6_7; that is, the multiplicative inverse of 6_7 is 6_7.

Example 2.   Solve the equation $4_{11} x_{11} = 1_{11}$.

Replacing the variable successively by 1_{11}, 2_{11}, 3_{11}, ... , 10_{11}, we see that $4_{11} \times 3_{11} = 1_{11}$ and, moreover, that 3_{11} is the only solution.

Thus if $4 \times 3 \equiv 1 \pmod{11}$ and, moreover, if $4 \times s \equiv 1 \pmod{11}$, then $s \equiv 3 \pmod{11}$. More generally, if $4r \equiv 1 \pmod{11}$ and $4s \equiv 1 \pmod{11}$, then $4r \equiv 4s \pmod{11}$. Moreover, if $4r \equiv 4s \pmod{11}$, then $r \equiv s \pmod{11}$. Thus we are assured that the congruence $4x \equiv 1 \pmod{11}$ has a unique solution in the set $\{0, 1, 2, 3, 4, 5, 6, 7, 8, 9, 10\}$.

THEOREM 9.   If p is any prime and a is any positive integer less than p, then there exists a unique positive integer $b < p$ such that $ab \equiv 1 \pmod{p}$.

Proof.   Let p be a prime, let a be a positive integer less than p, and let $ar \equiv as \pmod{p}$.
Then $(p, a) = 1$ and $p \mid (ar - as)$.
Thus $p \mid a(r - s)$.
But $p \nmid a$.
Hence $p \mid (r - s)$.
Thus $r \equiv s \pmod{p}$ (by Definition 5).
Hence $ar \equiv as \pmod{p} \rightarrow r \equiv s \pmod{p}$.
Conversely, $r \equiv s \pmod{p} \rightarrow ar \equiv as \pmod{p}$ (by Theorem 4).

Hence $ar \equiv as \pmod{p} \rightleftarrows r \equiv s \pmod{p}$.

Now $a \in \{0, 1, 2, \ldots, p - 1\}$.

Let $r \in \{0, 1, 2, \ldots, p - 1\}$.

Thus r is one of p distinct elements less than p.

Hence ar is congruent to one of p distinct elements less than p.

For exactly one choice b of r, ab must be congruent to 1; that is, $ab \equiv 1 \pmod{p}$ for some $b \in \{0, 1, 2, \ldots, p - 1\}$.//

By Theorem 9, if p is a prime and a_p is any equivalence class, then there exists a unique equivalence class b_p such that $a_p b_p = 1_p$. That is, if p is any prime, then $(I_p, +, \times)$ possesses field property F9. Since $(I_p, +, \times)$ possesses all other field properties, we see that $(I_p, +, \times)$ is a field. For reference, we state this result as a theorem.

THEOREM 10.   If p is any prime, then $(I_p, +, \times)$ is a field.

Proof.   Follows from Theorem 9 and previous properties.//

Since $(I_p, +, \times)$ is a field, we can solve any equation of the form $a_p x_p = b_p$. For example, to solve the equation $3_7 x_7 = 4_7$, we multiply both sides by 5_7 (the multiplicative inverse of 3_7). Thus $5_7(3_7 x_7) = 5_7(4_7)$; that is, $x_7 = 6_7$. You should realize that this means that the product of the equivalence class containing 3 and the equivalence class containing 6 is the equivalence class containing 4. In general, we solve $a_p x_p = b_p$ by multiplying both members by the multiplicative inverse, $a^\#{}_p$, of a_p as follows:

$a^\#{}_p(a_p x_p) = a^\#{}_p b_p,$

$x_p = a_p b_p.$

In summary we observe the following:

In $(I, +, \times)$, every equation $a + x = b$ has a solution.

In $(I_m, +, \times)$ every equation $a_m + x_m = b_m$ has a solution.

In $(I, +, \times)$, not every equation $ax = b$ has a solution (even if $a \neq 0$).

In $(I_m, +, \times)$, not every equation $a_m x_m = b_m$ has a solution (even if $a_m \neq 0_m$).

In $(F, +, \times)$, every equation $ax = b$ has a solution if $a \neq 0$.

In $(I_p, +, \times)$, every equation $a_p x_p = b_p$ has a solution if $a_p \neq 0_p$.

Exercise 7.6

I. Solve each of the following congruences.

(1) $2x \equiv 1 \pmod 3$ (6) $5x \equiv 1 \pmod{17}$

(2) $2x \equiv 1 \pmod 5$ (7) $10x \equiv 3 \pmod{17}$

(3) $3x \equiv 1 \pmod 5$ (8) $8x \equiv 3 \pmod{17}$

(4) $4x \equiv 1 \pmod 5$ (9) $4x \equiv 10 \pmod{11}$

(5) $6x \equiv 1 \pmod{17}$ (10) $6x \equiv 10 \pmod{11}$

II. Solve each of the following equations.

(1) $2_3 x_3 = 1_3$ (6) $3_{11} x_{11} = 2_{11}$

(2) $2_5 x_5 = 1_5$ (7) $9_{11} x_{11} = 10_{11}$

(3) $8_{17} x_{17} = 4_{17}$ (8) $10_{11} x_{11} = 9_{11}$

(4) $8_{17} x_{17} = 6_{17}$ (9) $3_{13} x_{13} = 11_{13}$

(5) $2_{11} x_{11} = 3_{11}$ (10) $4_{13} x_{13} = 11_{13}$

III. Discuss the difference between the *congruence* $ax \equiv b \pmod p$ and the *equation* $a_p x_p = b_p$.

IV. Illustrate Theorem 8 in each of the following.

(1) $(I_8, +, \times)$ (6) $(I_{15}, +, \times)$

(2) $(I_6, +, \times)$ (7) $(I_{21}, +, \times)$

(3) $(I_9, +, \times)$ (8) $(I_{25}, +, \times)$

(4) $(I_{10}, +, \times)$ (9) $(I_{49}, +, \times)$

(5) $(I_{14}, +, \times)$ (10) $(I_{81}, +, \times)$

7.7 Applications

In this section we study some of the applications of modular number systems. One of the applications is to a well-known divisibility test which states that an integer is divisible by 9 if and only if the sum of its digits is divisible by 9. The following examples illustrate the test.

Example 1.   Does $9 \mid 603$?

$9 \mid (6 + 0 + 3)$.

Hence $9 \mid 603$.

Example 2.   Does $9 \mid 654{,}327$?

$9 \mid (6 + 5 + 4 + 3 + 2 + 7)$.

Hence $9 \mid 654{,}327$.

Example 3.   Does $9 \mid 754{,}327$?

$9 \nmid (7 + 5 + 4 + 3 + 2 + 7)$

Hence $9 \nmid 754{,}327$.

Why does this test work? Before we answer this question in general, we shall analyze the test for the integer 567.

$$567 = 5(10^2) + 6(10) + 7(1)$$

$$7(1) \equiv 7 \pmod 9$$

$$10 \equiv 1 \pmod 9$$

$$6(10) \equiv 6 \pmod 9 \quad \text{(by Theorem 4)}$$

$$10(10) \equiv 1(1) \pmod 9 \quad \text{(by Theorem 4)}$$

$$5(10^2) \equiv 5 \pmod 9 \quad \text{(by Theorem 4)}$$

$$5(10^2) + 6(10) + 7(1) \equiv 5 + 6 + 7 \pmod 9 \quad \text{(by Theorem 3)}$$

Hence $567 \equiv 5 + 6 + 7 \pmod 9$

If $567 \equiv 0 \pmod 9$, then $5 + 6 + 7 \equiv 0 \pmod 9$ (by transitive property for $\equiv$)

Conversely, if $5 + 6 + 7 \equiv 0 \pmod 9$, then $567 \equiv 0 \pmod 9$ (by transitive property for $\equiv$)

Hence if $9 \mid 567$, then $9 \mid (5 + 6 + 7)$.

Conversely, if $9 \mid (5 + 6 + 7)$, then $9 \mid 567$.

Consequently $9 \mid 567 \rightleftarrows 9 \mid (5 + 6 + 7)$.

We now state a preliminary theorem which will enable us to give the general proof of the test.

THEOREM 11.   If a and k are any counting numbers, then $a \times 10^k \equiv a \pmod 9$.

Proof. $10 \equiv 1 \pmod 9$
$10 \times 10 \equiv 1 \times 1 \pmod 9$
$10 \times 10 \times 10 \equiv 1 \times 1 \times 1 \pmod 9$

$$\underbrace{10 \times 10 \times 10 \times \ldots \times 10}_{k\text{-factors}} \equiv \underbrace{1 \times 1 \times 1 \times \ldots \times 1}_{k\text{-factors}} \pmod 9$$

$10^k \equiv 1 \pmod 9$
However $a \equiv a \pmod 9$
Hence $a \times 10^k \equiv a \pmod 9$. $/\!/$

We now state and prove the general theorem that any integer is divisible by 9 if and only if the sum of its digits is divisible by 9.

THEOREM 12. The integer $a_k(10^k) + a_{k-1}(10^{k-1}) + \ldots + a_1(10^1) + a_0(1)$ is divisible by 9 if and only if $(a_k + a_{k-1} + \ldots + a_1 + a_0)$ is divisible by 9.

Proof. $a_0(1) \equiv a_0 \pmod 9$

$a_1(10^1) \equiv a_1 \pmod 9$ (by Theorem 11)

$a_2(10^2) \equiv a_2 \pmod 9$ (by Theorem 11)

.
.
.

$a_{k-1}(10^{k-1}) \equiv a_{k-1} \pmod 9$ (by Theorem 11)

$a_k(10^k) \equiv a_k \pmod 9$ (by Theorem 11)

Hence $a_k(10^k) + a_{k-1}(10^{k-1}) + \ldots + a_1(10^1) + a_0(1)$
$\equiv a_k + a_{k-1} + \ldots + a_1 + a_0 \pmod 9$ (by Theorem 3).
Thus $a_k(10^k) + a_{k-1}(10^{k-1}) + \ldots + a_1(10^1) + a_0(1) \equiv 0$
$\pmod 9 \rightleftarrows a_k + a_{k-1} + \ldots + a_1 + a_0 \equiv 0 \pmod 9$
(by transitive property for $\equiv$).
Consequently, $9 \mid [a_k(10^k) + a_{k-1}(10^{k-1}) + \ldots + a_1(10^1)$
$+ a_0(1)]$ if and only if $9 \mid [a_k + a_{k-1} + \ldots + a_1 + a_0].\mathbin{/\!/}$

A second application of modular number systems is to a well-known addition check called *casting out nines*. According to this check, we may check the sum of integers by adding the digits of each integer, casting out nines, adding the remainders, casting out nines, and so on until a remainder less than 9 is obtained. Then we add the digits of the sum, cast out nines, and retain the remainder. If the arithmetic contains no errors, the latter remainder is equal to the remainder after nines have been cast from the sum of the remainders. The following example illustrates the method of casting out nines.

Example 4. Compute the following sum and check by casting out nines.

$547 \rightarrow 5 + 4 + 7 = 1(9) + 7 \equiv 7$
$(\bmod 9) \rightarrow 7 \mid 7 + 8 + 3$
$89 \rightarrow 8 + 9 = 1(9) + 8 \equiv 8 (\bmod 9) \rightarrow 8 \} = 2(9) + 0 \equiv \textcircled{0}$
$930 \rightarrow 9 + 3 + 0 = 1(9) + 3 \equiv 3$ $(\bmod 9)$
$(\bmod 9) \rightarrow 3$
$1566 \rightarrow 1 + 5 + 6 + 6 = 2(9) + 0 \equiv 0 (\bmod 9) \rightarrow \textcircled{0}$
Hence the computed sum is probably correct. If the computed sum is incorrect, the error in the computed sum is a multiple of 9.
Observe that $547 \equiv 7 \pmod 9$, $89 \equiv 8 \pmod 9$, and $930 \equiv 3 \pmod 9$.

Hence $547 + 89 + 930 \equiv 7 + 8 + 3 \pmod 9$. That is, $1566 \equiv 18$ (mod 9). Consequently, when 1566 is divided by 9, it leaves the same remainder as 18 does when it is divided by 9. We see, then, that checking addition by casting out nines is based on Theorem 12 and the fact that $a \equiv r \pmod 9$ and $b \equiv s \pmod 9 \rightarrow a + b \equiv r + s \pmod 9$.

We usually abbreviate the procedure for casting out nines as in the following example.

Example 5.   Compute the following sum and check by casting out nines.

$$9877 \rightarrow 9 + 8 + 7 + 7 \rightarrow 4$$
$$5746 \rightarrow 5 + 7 + 4 + 6 \rightarrow 4$$
$$8097 \rightarrow 8 + 0 + 9 + 7 \rightarrow 6 \quad \rightarrow 4 + 4 + 6 + 5 \rightarrow ①$$
$$1202 \rightarrow 1 + 2 + 0 + 2 \rightarrow 5$$
$$\overline{24922 \rightarrow 2 + 4 + 9 + 2 + 2 \rightarrow ①}$$

Hence the computed sum is probably correct.

The checking of multiplication by casting out nines is based on Theorem 12 and the fact that $a \equiv r \pmod 9$ and $b \equiv s \pmod 9$ $\rightarrow ab \equiv rs \pmod 9$. The following example illustrates the method.

Example 6.   Compute the product of 678 and 83, and check by casting out nines.

$$678 \rightarrow 6 + 7 + 8 \rightarrow 3 \quad \rightarrow 3 \times 2 \rightarrow ⑥$$
$$83 \rightarrow 8 + 3 \rightarrow 2$$
$$\overline{2034}$$
$$5424$$
$$\overline{56274 \rightarrow 5 + 6 + 2 + 7 + 4 \rightarrow ⑥}$$

Another computational check is called *casting out elevens*. This check is based on the fact that $10 \equiv {}^-1 \pmod{11}$. If the numeration system is the base five numeration system, the corresponding checks are *casting out fours* and *casting out sixes*, respectively.

Exercise 7.7

I. Determine which of the following are divisible by 9.

(1) 27,638   (4) 93,645
(2) 78,362   (5) 26,893
(3) 85,419   (6) 37,894

(7) 173,287   (9) 654,723

(8) 771,382   (10) 465,372

II. Compute $a + b$ in each of the following, and check by casting out nines.

(1) $a = 673, b = 93$ (4) $a = 583, b = 768$

(2) $a = 795, b = 88$ (5) $a = 6359, b = 7286$

(3) $a = 876, b = 538$ (6) $a = 9365, b = 2876$

III. Compute $a - b$ in each part of Exercise II and check by casting out nines.

IV. Compute ab in each part of Exercise II and check by casting out nines.

V. Devise a method of checking long division by casting out nines. (*Hint.* Recall that $a = bq + r$ and, consequently, $a - r = bq$.)

VI. Compute q and r and check each of the following long divisions.

(1) $23 \overline{)653}$ (4) $68 \overline{)9630}$

(2) $32 \overline{)536}$ (5) $837 \overline{)29,367}$

(3) $73 \overline{)6390}$ (6) $783 \overline{)37,926}$

VII. (1) Devise a check for divisibility by 11.

(2) Devise a method for checking addition by casting out elevens.

(3) Devise a method for checking multiplication by casting out elevens.

(4) Devise a method for checking division by casting out elevens.

VIII. Check each sum in Exercise II by casting out elevens.

IX. Check each product in Exercise IV by casting out elevens.

X. Check each division in Exercise VI by casting out elevens.

XI. In base b ($2 \le b$), the corresponding checks are casting out $b - 1$ and casting out $b + 1$. Compute each of the following sums and check (the subscript indicates the *base*).

(1) $627_8 + 533_8$ (4) $344_5 + 232_5$

(2) $375_8 + 643_8$ (5) $t0te_{12} + t39_{12}$

(3) $413_5 + 342_5$ (6) $tete_{12} + 931_{12}$

7.8 Applications (*continued*)

A third application of modular number systems and the congruence relation is to the solution of a certain type of equation called a *linear Diophantine equation,* named for the Greek mathematician Diophantos who lived in Alexandria during the middle of the third century A.D. Any

equation of the form $ax + my = b$ (or $mx + ay = b$) in two variables
x and y is called a *linear Diophantine equation* in two variables if and
only if the universe (of each variable) is the set of integers. Thus the
solution set of a linear Diophantine equation is a subset of $I \times I$; that is,
the solution set is a set of ordered pairs of integers. The numbers a, b,
and m are integers; a and m are called *coefficients* of the variables x
and y.

Example 1.   Solve the linear Diophantine equation $7x + 16y = 40$;
that is, compute $\{(x, y): x \in I \land y \in I \land 7x + 16y = 40\}$.

$7x + 16y = 40$ ($x \in I$ and $y \in I$)
$16y - 40 = 7(^-x)$
$16y \equiv 40 \pmod{7}$
$2y \equiv 5 \pmod{7}$
Since 7 is a prime, we know that 2 has a multiplicative inverse. By inspection, we see that the inverse of 2 is 4.
$4(2y) \equiv 4(5) \pmod{7}$
$y \equiv 6 \pmod{7}$
$y = 6 + 7k$ ($k \in I$)
$7x + 16y = 40$ ($x \in I$ and $y \in I$)
$7x + 16(6 + 7k) = 40$
$7x + 96 + 16(7k) = 40$
$7x = ^-56 - (16k)7$
$x = ^-8 - 16k$ ($k \in I$)
$y = 6 + 7k$ ($k \in I$)
For any integer k, the integers x and y given by $x = ^-8 - 16k$ and $y = 6 + 7k$ satisfy the given linear Diophantine equation; that is, $\{(x, y): 7x + 16y = 40 \land x \in I \land y \in I\} = \{(x, y): (x = ^-8 - 16k) \land (y = 6 + 7k) \land (k \in I)\}$.
The accompanying table exhibits some of the pairs (x, y)
which satisfy the given equation.

k	x	y
-2	24	-8
-1	8	-1
0	-8	6
1	-24	13
2	-40	20

The following example illustrates the type of problem which can be solved by means of a linear Diophantine equation.

Example 2. An electrical appliance dealer placed an order for some transistor radios at $31 each and for some cheaper ones at $28 each. The total order amounted to $1460. How many of each type did he order?

Let x represent the number of $28 radios and let y represent the number of $31 radios.

Then $28x + 31y = 1460$ ($x \in C_0$ and $y \in C_0$)

$28x - 1460 = 31(-y)$

$28x \equiv 1460 \pmod{31}$

$28x \equiv 3 \pmod{31}$

Since 31 is a prime, we know that 28 has a multiplicative inverse.

By inspection we compute the inverse to be 10.

Hence $10(28x) \equiv 10(3) \pmod{31}$

$x \equiv 30 \pmod{31}$

$x - 30 = 31k$

$x = 30 + 31k$

$28x + 31y = 1460$ ($x \in C_0$ and $y \in C_0$)

$28(30 + 31k) + 31y = 1460$

$840 + 28(31)k + 31y = 1460$

$31y = 620 - (28k)(31)$

$y = 20 - 28k$ ($k \le 0$, since $y \in C_0$)

$x = 30 + 31k$ ($0 \le k$, since $x \in C_0$)

Hence $k = 0$.

Thus $x = 30$ and $y = 20$.

Hence the dealer ordered 20 radios at $31 each and 30 radios at $28 each.

The essential point in Examples 1 and 2 is that one of the coefficients is an odd prime and the other coefficient is different from it. In Example 1, the coefficient of x is 7; in Example 2, the coefficient of y is 31. The procedure in the above examples can be used whenever one of the coefficients is an odd prime and the two coefficients are not equal. Is there a procedure which can be used when neither coefficient is prime? To answer this question, we consider the general Diophantine equation $ax + my = b$, in which $(a, m, b) = 1$; that is, the greatest common divisor of a, m, and b is equal to 1. If a, m, and b have a common factor larger than 1, we first divide by this common factor and consider the resulting equation. For example, in lieu of $75x + 20y = 50$, we write $15x + 4y = 10$.

The following example illustrates the fact that a linear Diophantine equation may be solvable even if neither coefficient is prime.

Example 3.   Solve the linear Diophantine equation $15x + 4y = 10$.

$15x + 4y = 10$ $(x \in I, y \in I)$
$15x - 10 = 4(^-y)$
$15x \equiv 10 \pmod 4$
$3x \equiv 2 \pmod 4$
To solve this congruence for x, we need to compute a multiplicative inverse of 3 $\pmod 4$, if one exists.
By inspection, we see that a multiplicative inverse of 3 is 3; that is, $3(3) \equiv 1 \pmod 4$.
$3(3x) \equiv (3)(2) \pmod 4$
$x \equiv 6 \pmod 4$
$x \equiv 2 \pmod 4$
$x = 2 + 4k$ $(k \in I)$
$15x + 4y = 10$ $(x \in I, y \in I)$
$15(2 + 4k) + 4y = 10$
$30 + 15(4k) + 4y = 10$
$4y = ^-20 - 15(4)k$
$y = ^-5 - 15k$ $(k \in I)$
For any integer k,
$x = 2 + 4k$,
$y = ^-5 - 15k$.

The above example illustrates an important point in the solution of a linear Diophantine equation. Although 4 (the modulus) is not prime, 3 has a multiplicative inverse. If 3 had no multiplicative inverse $\pmod 4$, the above procedure would have failed. We have already learned that every integer $a \not\equiv 0 \pmod p$ has a multiplicative inverse $\pmod p$; however, we have learned that this is not true if the modulus is composite. Under what conditions can we be assured that an integer $a \not\equiv 0 \pmod m$, for an integer m, has a multiplicative inverse? The following theorem answers this question.

THEOREM 13.   If a and m are any integers and $(a, m) = 1$, then there is an integer $a^{\#}$ such that $a^{\#} \times a \equiv 1 \pmod m$.

Proof.   Similar to the proof of Theorem 9.//

THEOREM 14.   (a) If $(a, m) = 1$, then the solution set of the linear Diophantine equation $ax + my = b$ is infinite.

(b) If $(a, m) \neq 1$, and $(a, m, b) = 1$, then the solution set of the linear Diophantine equation $ax + my = b$ is empty.

Proof. (a) Let $ax + my = b$ and $(a, m) = 1$.

Then $ax \equiv b \pmod{m}$, and $(a, m) = 1$.

Hence there exists $a^\#$ such that $a^\# a \equiv 1 \pmod{m}$ (by Theorem 13).

$a^\# ax \equiv a^\# b \pmod{m}$

$x \equiv a^\# b \pmod{m}$

$x = a^\# b + km \ (k \in I)$

$ax + my = b$

$a(a^\# b + km) + my = b$

$aa^\# b + akm + my = b$

$my = b - aa^\# b - akm$

$y = b [(1 - aa^\#)/m] - ak$

Since $1 - aa^\# \equiv 0 \pmod{m}$, it follows that $(1 - aa^\#)/m$ is an integer v.

Hence $y = bv - ak$.

Thus $\{(x, y): ax + my = b \wedge (a, m) = 1 \wedge x \in I \wedge y \in I\} = \{(x, y): x = a^\# b + km \wedge y = bv - ak \wedge k \in I\}$.

(b) Let $(a, m) \neq 1$ and $(a, m, b) = 1$.

Then $(a, m) = d \neq 1$, and $a = a_1 d$, and $m = m_1 d$ for some integers a_1 and m_1.

Assume that there exists a pair of integers x and y such that $ax + my = b$.

Then $a_1 dx + m_1 dy = b$; that is, $d(a_1 x + m_1 y) = b$.

Hence $d \mid b$.

But $(a, m, b) = 1$.

Hence $d \nmid b$.

Thus $d \nmid b \wedge d \mid b$.

Hence there are no integers x and y such that $ax + my = b$; that is, $\{(x, y): ax + my = b \wedge (a, m) \neq 1 \wedge (a, b, m) = 1 \wedge U = I\} = \phi.//$

Example 4. Carol has \$5.42 worth of stamps in 4 cent stamps and 15 cent stamps. What are the possible combinations of 4 cent stamps and 15 cent stamps? Let x represent the number of 4 cent stamps and y represent the number of 15 cent stamps.

Then $4x + 15y = 542$

Thus $15y - 542 = 4(^-x)$

$15y \equiv 542 \pmod 4$

$3y \equiv 2 \pmod 4$

$3(3y) \equiv 3(2) \pmod 4$

$y \equiv 6 \pmod 4$

$y \equiv 2 \pmod 4$

$y = 2 + 4k \ (k \in C_0)$

$4x + 15y = 542$

$4x + 15(2 + 4k) = 542$

$4x + 30 + 15(4k) = 542$

$4x = 512 - 15(4k)$

$x = 128 - 15k$

$y = 2 + 4k$

Since x cannot be negative, we see that $k \leq 8$. Since y cannot be negative, we see that $0 \leq k$.

Hence $0 \leq k \leq 8$.

The results are shown in the accompanying table.

k	No. of 4 cent stamps	No. of 15 cent stamps
0	128	2
1	113	6
2	98	10
3	83	14
4	68	18
5	53	22
6	38	26
7	23	30
8	8	34

We have seen that a multiplicative inverse $a^\#$ of a exists whenever $(a, m) = 1$. If m is small, it is easy to compute $a^\#$ by inspection. If m is large, it may be easier to apply the Euclidean algorithm, as in the following example.

Example 5.   Solve the congruence $24x \equiv 1 \pmod{35}$.

$$35 = 24(1) + 11$$
$$24 = 11(2) + 2$$
$$11 = 2(5) + 1$$
$$1 = 11 - 2(5)$$

$$11 = 35 - 24(1)$$
$$2 = 24 - 11(2)$$
$$1 = 11 - 2(5)$$

$$= 11 - [24 - 11(2)](5)$$
$$= 11 - 5(24) + 11(10)$$
$$= 11(11) - 5(24)$$
$$= 11[35 - 24(1)] - 5(24)$$
$$= 11(35) - 11(24) - 5(24)$$
$$= 11(35) - 16(24)$$
$$1 = 11(35) + {}^{-}16(24)$$
$$24({}^{-}16) - 1 = {}^{-}11(35)$$
$$24({}^{-}16) \equiv 1 \pmod{35}$$

Thus $^{-}16$ is a solution of $24x \equiv 1 \pmod{35}$.

But $^{-}16 \equiv 19 \pmod{35}$.

Hence 19 is a solution of the congruence $24x \equiv 1 \pmod{35}$.

Consequently 19 is a multiplicative inverse of 24 $\pmod{35}$.

Occasionally we wish to solve a *system* of congruences. Usually we are not interested in the complete solution but only in a particular solution. The following example illustrates a method by which some solutions may be computed.

Example 6.   Solve the system $\begin{bmatrix} x \equiv 1 \pmod{4} \\ x \equiv 4 \pmod{7} \\ x \equiv 7 \pmod{9} \end{bmatrix}$ for $0 \le x \le 40$; that is, compute the solution set, $\{x: x \equiv 1 \pmod{4} \land x \equiv 4 \pmod{7} \land x \equiv 7 \pmod{9} \land 0 \le x \le 40\}$.

The solution set is equal to $\{x: x \equiv 1 \pmod{4}\} \cap \{x: x \equiv 4 \pmod{7}\} \cap \{x: x \equiv 7 \pmod{9}\} \cap \{x: 0 \le x \le 40\}$.

Now $\{x: x \equiv 1 \pmod{4} \land 0 \le x \le 40\} = \{1, 5, 9, 13, 17, 21, 25, 29, 33, 37\}$.

$\{x: x \equiv 4 \pmod{7} \land 0 \le x \le 40\} = \{4, 11, 18, 25, 32, 39\}$.

$\{x: x \equiv 7 \pmod{9} \land 0 \le x \le 40\} = \{7, 16, 25, 34\}$.

Hence the solution of the system is 25; that is, $\{x: x \equiv 1 \pmod{4} \land x \equiv 4 \pmod{7} \land x \equiv 7 \pmod{9} \land 0 \le x \le 40\} = \{25\}$.

The following example illustrates an application of systems of congruences.

Example 7.   The driver of a sightseers' bus takes his passengers into a small shop which has only 4 rows of seats and notices that the sightseers exactly fill all seats. At the lunch stop, they fill 5 tables and one person sits at the counter. At the third and final stop, they occupy 7 rows of chairs and one person stands. The bus accommodates 50 passengers. How many persons did the driver take on the tour?

Let x represent the number of sightseers.

Then $\begin{bmatrix} x \equiv 0 \pmod 4 \\ x \equiv 1 \pmod 5 \\ x \equiv 1 \pmod 7 \\ 0 \leq x \leq 50 \end{bmatrix}$

The solution set is $\{x: x \equiv 0 \pmod 4\} \cap \{x: x \equiv 1 \pmod 5\} \cap \{x: x \equiv 1 \pmod 7\} \cap \{x: 0 \leq x \leq 50\}$.

Now $\{x: x \equiv 0 \pmod 4 \wedge 0 \leq x \leq 50\} = \{0, 4, 8, 12, 16, 20, 24, 28, 32, 36, 40, 44, 48\}$.

$\{x: x \equiv 1 \pmod 5 \wedge 0 \leq x \leq 50\} = \{1, 6, 11, 16, 21, 26, 31, 36, 41, 46\}$.

$\{x: x \equiv 1 \pmod 7 \wedge 0 \leq x \leq 50\} = \{1, 8, 15, 22, 29, 36, 43\}$.

Hence the solution of the system is 36; that is, the number of passengers is 36.

We have considered only some elementary topics of congruences and their applications. The standard texts on number theory include more advanced topics and general theorems. For example, the conditions under which any system of linear congruences has a solution are stated in a general theorem, called the *Chinese Remainder Theorem*. This theorem also prescribes the general procedure for solving the system. In the exercises you will have an opportunity to test your skill on some of the simpler applications.

Exercise 7.8

I. Solve each of the following linear Diophantine equations.

(1) $x + 3y = {}^-21$ (4) $7x - 6y = {}^-25$

(2) $3x + y = 21$ (5) $9x - 8y = 10$

(3) $5x - 6y = 20$ (6) $10x - 9y = 10$

II. Compute the solution set of each of the following systems.

(1) $\begin{bmatrix} x \equiv 2 \pmod{3} \\ x \equiv 3 \pmod{5} \\ x \equiv 1 \pmod{4} \\ 0 \le x \le 30 \end{bmatrix}$
     (3) $\begin{bmatrix} 2x \equiv 3 \pmod{5} \\ 5x - 3 \equiv 2 \pmod{4} \\ 0 \le x \le 100 \end{bmatrix}$

(2) $\begin{bmatrix} x \equiv 1 \pmod{3} \\ x \equiv 2 \pmod{5} \\ x \equiv 3 \pmod{4} \\ 0 \le x \le 30 \end{bmatrix}$
     (4) $\begin{bmatrix} 3x \equiv 2 \pmod{7} \\ 3x - 5 \equiv 4 \pmod{8} \\ 0 \le x \le 100 \end{bmatrix}$

III. Formulate a mathematical model of each of the following problems and solve.

(1) Rene has $5.12 worth of 4 cent stamps and 15 cent stamps. What are the possible combinations of 4 cent stamps and 15 cent stamps?

(2) James has $7.25 worth of 5 cent stamps and 8 cent stamps. What are the possible combinations of 5 cent stamps and 8 cent stamps?

(3) Joe asked his mathematics professor for his grade on the last test. The professor told Joe, "If you divide your grade by 3, the remainder is 2; if you divide your grade by 13, the remainder is 1; and if you divide your grade by 5, the remainder is 2. What was Joe's grade on the test? (Assume that the total possible score is 100.)

(4) A stock clerk who is assigned to stacking boxes stacks the boxes in three stacks. When the manager notices that the stacks are too high, he orders the clerk to restack the boxes in more stacks. The clerk then restacks the boxes into 7 stacks, with two boxes left over. The manager then tells the clerk that the new arrangement is taking up too much floor space. So the clerk restacks once more, this time into 5 stacks. Later the manager wants to know how many boxes the clerk has stacked. Not wishing to leave his air-conditioned office to count them himself or to ask the unreliable clerk to count them, he decides to compute the number of boxes. How many boxes are there?

IV. Prove Theorem 13.

CHAPTER 8

ALGEBRAIC STRUCTURES

8.1 Groups

Recall from Chapter 7 that the system $(I, +)$ and the system $(I_m, +)$ are commutative groups. In Definition 4 of Chapter 7, we required that the identity element of the group be *unique* and that the inverse of each element be *unique*. The following definition of *commutative group* is less restrictive than Definition 4 of Chapter 7.

DEFINITION 1. A system $(G, \odot)$ is called a *commutative group* if and only if it possesses all of the following properties:

(a) If a and b are any elements of G, then $a \odot b$ is a unique element of G (closure property).

(b) If a, b, and c are any elements of G, then $(a \odot b) \odot c = a \odot (b \odot c)$ (associative property).

(c) There exists an element i in G such that $a \odot i = a$ for all a in G (identity property).

(d) If a is any element of G, then there exists an element a' in G such that $a \odot a' = i$ (inverse property).

(e) If a and b are any elements of G, then $a \odot b = b \odot a$ (commutative property)

Notice the difference between the above definition and Definition 4 of Chapter 7. There is no requirement that G shall have a *unique* identity, and there is no requirement in the above definition that each element

206

shall have a *unique* inverse. In fact, according to Definition 1, it appears possible that G may have more than one identity and that each element may have more than one inverse. If there is actually more than one identity or if some element actually has more than one inverse, then Definition 1 does not agree with the previous definition of commutative group. The following theorems assert that there is only one identity in G and that each element of G has only one inverse. Consequently Definition 1 of this section is equivalent to Definition 4 of Chapter 7.

THEOREM 1. The identity element i of any commutative group $(G, \odot)$ is unique.

Proof. Assume that i and u are both identities in G.
Then $a \odot i = a$ and $a \odot u = a$ for all a in G.
Thus $a \odot u = a \odot i$.

$a' \odot (a \odot u) = a' \odot (a \odot i)$	(by closure property)
$(a' \odot a) \odot u = (a' \odot a) \odot i$	(by associative property)
$(a \odot a') \odot u = (a \odot a') \odot i$	(by commutative property)
$i \odot u = i \odot i$	(by inverse property)
$u \odot i = i \odot i$	(by commutative property)
$u = i$	(by identity property)

Hence there is exactly one identity element in G.

THEOREM 2. Each element a of any commutative group $(G, \odot)$ has a unique inverse.

Proof. Let $a \in G$.
Assume that a' and a'' are both inverses of a.
Then $a \odot a' = i$ and $a \odot a'' = i$.
Thus $a \odot a' = a \odot a''$

$a' \odot (a \odot a') = a' \odot (a \odot a'')$	(by closure property)
$(a' \odot a) \odot a' = (a' \odot a) \odot a''$	(by associative property)
$(a \odot a') \odot a' = (a \odot a') \odot a''$	(by commutative property)
$i \odot a' = i \odot a''$	(by inverse property)
$a' \odot i = a'' \odot i$	(by commutative property)
$a' = a''$	(by identity property)

Hence each element a of $(G, \odot)$ has exactly one inverse a' in $(G, \odot)$.

When we developed the integers $(I, +)$* and proved that $a + 0 = a$ for every integer a, we also proved that 0 is the only integer with this property; i.e., we proved that the identity is unique. Similarly, in Chapter 7 when we developed $(I_m, +)$ and proved that $a_m + 0_m = a_m$ for every equivalence class a_m, we also proved that 0_m is the only equivalence class with this property. If Definition 1 and Theorem 1 had been available to us then, it would not have been necessary to prove the uniqueness in each case. If Theorem 2 had been available to us then, it would not have been necessary to prove the uniqueness of the inverse of any integer or of any equivalence class. Consequently, studying an abstract system has very definite advantages.

Recall that the rational number system $(R_a, +, \times)$ is a field and hence $(R_a, +)$ is a commutative group. Again, if Definition 1, Theorem 1, and Theorem 2 had been available when we developed the rational number system,* it would have been unnecessary to prove the uniqueness of the identity and the inverses.

Is $(C_0, +)$ a commutative group? Since $(C_0, +)$ does not possess the inverse property, we see that it is not a commutative group. For example, the element 3 does not have an inverse. In fact, we invented the set of integers because of this defect of $(C_0, +)$.*

There are abstract systems which possess the closure property, associative property, identity property, and inverse property, but not the commutative property. For this reason, mathematicians study a more general system known as a *group*.

DEFINITION 2. A system $(G, \odot)$ is called a *group* if and only if it possesses all of the following properties:

(a) If a and b are any elements of G, then $a \odot b$ is a unique element of G (closure property).

(b) If a, b, and c are any elements of G, then $(a \odot b) \odot c = a \odot (b \odot c)$ (associative property).

(c) There exists an element i of G such that $a \odot i = a$ for all a in G (identity property).

(d) If a is any element of G, then there exists an element a' of G such that $a \odot a' = i$ (inverse property).

Later we shall study a particular system, known as a *permutation group*, which is not commutative. The remainder of this section will be concerned with some general theorems and comments about groups.

---

* Ohmer, Aucoin, and Cortez, *Elementary Contemporary Mathematics* (1964). New York: Blaisdell Publishing Company.

The following theorems are stated without proof.

THEOREM 3.   If a is any element of G, then $i \odot a = a \odot i = a$.

THEOREM 4.   If a is any element of G and a' is an inverse of a, then $a' \odot a = a \odot a' = i$.

THEOREM 5.   The identity element i of Definition 2 is unique.

THEOREM 6.   Each element a of any group G has a unique inverse.

Henceforth when we refer to the *identity property*, we mean $i \odot a = a \odot i = a$, and when we refer to the *inverse property* we mean $a' \odot a = a \odot a' = i$.

A group is a beautiful example of a mathematical system which is interesting to pure mathematicians for its own sake. Perhaps it seems to you that no important theory can be developed from such a simple system as a group. However, many interesting and important theorems in modern mathematics have resulted from the study of groups. In fact, group theory has been applied to geometry, nuclear physics, chemistry, thermodynamics, and other fields. This is a frequent occurrence in mathematics: mathematicians develop abstract theory for its own elegance; later, the theory is applied to physical problems and society is advanced thereby.

Several famous mathematicians (Legendre, Abel, and Galois) were responsible for the origin and the preliminary developments of group theory. One of the main problems which occupied the attention of mathematicians during their lives was that of deriving a formula in terms of the coefficients (similar to the quadratic formula) for computing the roots of the equation $a_0 + a_1 x + a_2 x^2 + \ldots + a_m x^m = 0$ for any positive integer m. Instead of trying to derive such a formula, the above-named mathematicians tried to prove that no such formula exists if $5 \leq m$. They showed great ingenuity when they focused their attention on the *abstract* structure rather than the particular aspects of the number system. The formidable result, credited to Galois, is that no formula exists for solving the equation $a_0 + a_1 x + a_2 x^2 + \ldots + a_m x^m = 0$ for $5 \leq m$. These mathematicians developed the fundamentals of group theory as the principal tool in the solution of this problem. Later mathematicians extended the theory for its own beauty.

Exercise 8.1

I. Let $S = \{a + b\sqrt{3}: a \in R \wedge b \in R\}$.
    Prove that $(S, +)$ is a commutative group.

II. Prove that $(C, +)$ is a commutative group.

III. Determine whether each of the following systems is a group; if it is a group, determine whether it is a commutative group.

(1)

$\odot$	i	a	b	c
i	i	a	b	c
a	a	b	c	i
b	b	c	i	a
c	c	i	a	b

(4)

$\odot$	i	a	b	c
i	i	a	b	c
a	a	i	c	b
b	b	c	i	a
c	c	b	a	i

(2)

$\odot$	a	b	c	d
a	a	b	c	d
b	b	c	d	a
c	c	d	a	b
d	d	a	b	c

(5)

$\odot$	a	b	c	d
a	a	b	c	d
b	b	a	d	c
c	c	d	a	b
d	d	c	b	a

(3)

$\odot$	a	b	c	d
a	a	b	c	d
b	b	a	c	d
c	c	d	a	c
d	d	a	b	c

(6)

$\odot$	a	b	c	d
a	b	c	a	d
b	c	a	d	b
c	a	d	b	c
d	d	a	c	b

IV. (1) Prove: if a and b are any elements of a group, then $(a \odot b)' = b' \odot a'$.

(2) Prove: if a, b, and c are any elements of a group, then $(a \odot b \odot c)' = c' \odot b' \odot a'$. [Because of the associative property, $a \odot b \odot c = (a \odot b) \odot c = a \odot (b \odot c)$].

8.2   Permutations

In the preceding section we defined *group* and remarked that not every group is commutative. In this section we shall give an example of a noncommutative group, called a *permutation group*. We have already mentioned the advantages of studying abstract systems. Frequently when the mathematical model of a physical problem involves a group $(G, \odot)$ the elements of G are not numbers, and the group operator $\odot$ is not one of the familiar operators. The permutation group is a simple example of such a group.

A teacher sends three pupils p_1, p_2, and p_3 to the board to work an arithmetic problem. These three pupils occupy their usual seats. We indicate this fact by writing $\left(\begin{smallmatrix} p_1p_2p_3 \\ p_1p_2p_3 \end{smallmatrix}\right)$; i.e., pupil p_1 occupies his own seat, pupil p_2 occupies his own seat, and pupil p_3 occupies his own seat. When they complete their work at the board, they return to their seats. However, p_2 now occupies p_3's seat, and p_3 now occupies p_2's seat. We indicate this new position by $\left(\begin{smallmatrix} p_1p_2p_3 \\ p_1p_3p_2 \end{smallmatrix}\right)$. The teacher then begins to wonder how many different seating arrangements of p_1, p_2, and p_3 there are. Consequently she calls the class's attention to the new seating arrangement, writes the symbols $\left(\begin{smallmatrix} p_1p_2p_3 \\ p_1p_2p_3 \end{smallmatrix}\right)$ and $\left(\begin{smallmatrix} p_1p_2p_3 \\ p_1p_3p_2 \end{smallmatrix}\right)$ on the board, and explains that the first symbol represents the first (original) seating arrangement of the three pupils and the second symbol represents the second (new) seating arrangement. Then she invites the class to write the symbols for other seating arrangements. One pupil writes $\left(\begin{smallmatrix} p_1p_2p_3 \\ p_3p_2p_1 \end{smallmatrix}\right)$, and another writes $\left(\begin{smallmatrix} p_1p_2p_3 \\ p_2p_1p_3 \end{smallmatrix}\right)$. Finally one pupil writes $\left(\begin{smallmatrix} p_1p_2p_3 \\ p_2p_3p_1 \end{smallmatrix}\right)$ and $\left(\begin{smallmatrix} p_1p_2p_3 \\ p_3p_1p_2 \end{smallmatrix}\right)$ and then says that there are no more arrangements. When the teacher and other pupils agree that these are the only six arrangements, she writes them all on the board, calls them *permutations*, and simplifies the notation as follows:

$$i = \left(\begin{smallmatrix} 1 & 2 & 3 \\ 1 & 2 & 3 \end{smallmatrix}\right), \ a = \left(\begin{smallmatrix} 1 & 2 & 3 \\ 1 & 3 & 2 \end{smallmatrix}\right), \ b = \left(\begin{smallmatrix} 1 & 2 & 3 \\ 3 & 2 & 1 \end{smallmatrix}\right), \ c = \left(\begin{smallmatrix} 1 & 2 & 3 \\ 2 & 1 & 3 \end{smallmatrix}\right), \ d = \left(\begin{smallmatrix} 1 & 2 & 3 \\ 2 & 3 & 1 \end{smallmatrix}\right), \ e = \left(\begin{smallmatrix} 1 & 2 & 3 \\ 3 & 1 & 2 \end{smallmatrix}\right).$$

Then she explains that $\left(\begin{smallmatrix} 1 & 2 & 3 \\ 1 & 3 & 2 \end{smallmatrix}\right)$, for example, indicates that p_1's seat is occupied by p_1, p_2's seat is occupied by p_3, and p_3's seat is occupied by p_2. Next she asks the class to consider the problem of a *followed by* b; i.e., to begin with arrangement a and then to follow this with the arrangement b. As a hint she writes $a = \left(\begin{smallmatrix} 1 & 2 & 3 \\ 1 & 3 & 2 \end{smallmatrix}\right)$, $b = \left(\begin{smallmatrix} 1 & 2 & 3 \\ 3 & 2 & 1 \end{smallmatrix}\right) = \left(\begin{smallmatrix} 1 & 3 & 2 \\ 3 & 1 & 2 \end{smallmatrix}\right)$. One pupil immediately remarks that a *followed by* b *is equal to* $\left(\begin{smallmatrix} 1 & 2 & 3 \\ 3 & 1 & 2 \end{smallmatrix}\right)$. The teacher asks him to explain the reason for his answer. He answers "a tells us that 1 is replaced by 1, and b tells us that 1 is replaced by 3, and hence a *followed by* b tells us that 1 is replaced by 3." Then he says "a tells us that 2 is replaced by 3, and b tells us that 3 is replaced by 1, and hence a *followed by* b tells us that 2 is replaced by 1." Then he makes a similar remark that a *followed by* b tells us that 3 is replaced by 2.

Then the teacher introduces the symbol $\odot$ to indicate *followed by* and writes $a = \left(\begin{smallmatrix} 1 & 2 & 3 \\ 1 & 3 & 2 \end{smallmatrix}\right)$, $b = \left(\begin{smallmatrix} 1 & 3 & 2 \\ 3 & 1 & 2 \end{smallmatrix}\right)$, $a \odot b = \left(\begin{smallmatrix} 1 & 2 & 3 \\ 3 & 1 & 2 \end{smallmatrix}\right) = e$. In a similar manner, the teacher and pupils discover that any permutation of the set $\{i, a, b, c, d, e\}$ followed by a permutation of this set is one of these permutations.

From the above classroom episode we observe that $\odot$ is a *binary* operator defined between any *two* of the permutations i, a, b, c, d, e. For simplicity, we shall refer to $a \odot b$, for example, as the *product of a and b* and read $a \odot b$ as *a times b*. The following table exhibits all multiplication facts of this set of permutations.

We read the table from *left* to *right*; for example $a \odot b = e$ but $b \odot a = d$. Hence $a \odot b \neq b \odot a$, and the binary operator $\odot$ is *not* commu-

$\odot$	i	a	b	c	d	e
i	i	a	b	c	d	e
a	a	i	e	d	c	b
b	b	d	i	e	a	c
c	c	e	d	i	b	a
d	d	b	c	a	e	i
e	e	c	a	b	i	d

FIGURE 8.1

tative. Let $P_3 = \{i, a, b, c, d, e\}$. Although $(P_3, \odot)$ is not a commutative group, $(P_3, \odot)$ is a group; i.e., $(P_3, \odot)$ possesses the closure, associative, identity, and inverse properties. The closure property is evident from Figure 8.1. As the proof of the associative property is tedious, it will not be given here. In the exercise you will have an opportunity to *verify* the associative property for a few triplets of permutations. From the table we see that the identity is i (and is unique). Also from the table we see that $i' = i$, $a' = a$, $b' = b$, $c' = c$, $d' = e$, and $e' = d$; i.e., each element of P_3 has a unique inverse.

In summary, we see that $(P_3, \odot)$ *is a group but not a commutative group*, its elements are permutations rather than numbers, and the operator $\odot$, is not one of the familiar operators. The group $(P_3, \odot)$ is called the *symmetric group on three symbols*.

If the number of symbols is *four* rather than *three*, there are 24 permutations. Four of these permutations are $\begin{pmatrix}1\,2\,3\,4\\1\,2\,3\,4\end{pmatrix}$, $\begin{pmatrix}1\,2\,3\,4\\2\,3\,4\,1\end{pmatrix}$, $\begin{pmatrix}1\,2\,3\,4\\3\,4\,1\,2\end{pmatrix}$, and $\begin{pmatrix}1\,2\,3\,4\\4\,1\,2\,3\end{pmatrix}$. The binary operator $\odot$ between permutations on 4 symbols is defined as it was between permutations on 3 symbols. For example $\begin{pmatrix}1\,2\,3\,4\\2\,3\,4\,1\end{pmatrix}\odot\begin{pmatrix}1\,2\,3\,4\\3\,4\,1\,2\end{pmatrix}$ $= \begin{pmatrix}1\,2\,3\,4\\2\,3\,4\,1\end{pmatrix} \odot \begin{pmatrix}2\,3\,4\,1\\4\,1\,2\,3\end{pmatrix} = \begin{pmatrix}1\,2\,3\,4\\4\,1\,2\,3\end{pmatrix}$. Letting P_4 be equal to the set of all 24 permutations on 4 symbols, we can prove that $(P_4, \odot)$ is a group. Similarly, letting P_k be equal to the set of all permutations on k symbols, we can prove that $(P_k, \odot)$ is a group. It is easy to prove that $n(P_k) =$

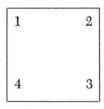

FIGURE 8.2

$(k)(k-1) \ldots (2)(1) = (1)(2) \ldots (k-1)(k)$. For example, the number of permutations on 5 symbols $= n(P_5) = 5(4)(3)(2)(1) = 120$.

Next we consider another group which we call the *group* of *rotations of a square*. You can actually construct the model by cutting out a square sheet of cardboard and labeling the vertices, clockwise, 1, 2, 3, 4, as shown in Figure 8.2.

The elements of this group are *counterclockwise rotations* of the square about its center. The four possible positions of the square are: $\boxed{\begin{smallmatrix}1&2\\4&3\end{smallmatrix}}$, $\boxed{\begin{smallmatrix}2&3\\1&4\end{smallmatrix}}$, $\boxed{\begin{smallmatrix}3&4\\2&1\end{smallmatrix}}$, and $\boxed{\begin{smallmatrix}4&1\\3&2\end{smallmatrix}}$. The rotation which changes the position $\boxed{\begin{smallmatrix}1&2\\4&3\end{smallmatrix}}$ to the position $\boxed{\begin{smallmatrix}1&2\\4&3\end{smallmatrix}}$ is designated by $\left(\begin{smallmatrix}1&2&3&4\\1&2&3&4\end{smallmatrix}\right)$. This is a counterclockwise rotation of $0°$ (or $360°$). The rotation which changes the position $\boxed{\begin{smallmatrix}1&2\\4&3\end{smallmatrix}}$ to the position $\boxed{\begin{smallmatrix}2&3\\1&4\end{smallmatrix}}$ is designated by $\left(\begin{smallmatrix}1&2&3&4\\2&3&4&1\end{smallmatrix}\right)$. This is a counterclockwise rotation of $90°$. The rotation which changes the position $\boxed{\begin{smallmatrix}1&2\\4&3\end{smallmatrix}}$ to the position $\boxed{\begin{smallmatrix}3&4\\2&1\end{smallmatrix}}$ is designated by $\left(\begin{smallmatrix}1&2&3&4\\3&4&1&2\end{smallmatrix}\right)$. This is a counterclockwise rotation of $180°$. The rotation which changes the position $\boxed{\begin{smallmatrix}1&2\\4&3\end{smallmatrix}}$ to the position $\boxed{\begin{smallmatrix}4&1\\3&2\end{smallmatrix}}$ is designated by $\left(\begin{smallmatrix}1&2&3&4\\4&1&2&3\end{smallmatrix}\right)$. This is a counterclockwise rotation of $270°$.

For simplicity, we let $i = \left(\begin{smallmatrix}1&2&3&4\\1&2&3&4\end{smallmatrix}\right)$, $a = \left(\begin{smallmatrix}1&2&3&4\\2&3&4&1\end{smallmatrix}\right)$, $b = \left(\begin{smallmatrix}1&2&3&4\\3&4&1&2\end{smallmatrix}\right)$, and $c = \left(\begin{smallmatrix}1&2&3&4\\4&1&2&3\end{smallmatrix}\right)$.

The multiplication table is given in Figure 8.3. Notice that $a \odot b$ means a counterclockwise rotation of $\boxed{\begin{smallmatrix}1&2\\4&3\end{smallmatrix}}$ through $90°$ *followed by* a counterclockwise rotation through $180°$. Thus $a \odot b = c$, a counterclockwise rotation through $270°$.

$\odot$	i	a	b	c
i	i	a	b	c
a	a	b	c	i
b	b	c	i	a
c	c	i	a	b

FIGURE 8.3

Denoting the set $\{i, a, b, c\}$ by S, we see from Figure 8.3 that $(S, \odot)$ possesses the closure property. Although the proof that $(S, \odot)$ possesses the associative property is tedious, it is not difficult. The identity is i. As $i' = i$, $a' = c$, $b' = b$, and $c' = a$, we see that $(S, \odot)$ possesses the inverse property. The commutative property is evident from Figure 8.3. Consequently, $(S, \odot)$ *is a commutative group*.

Exercise 8.2

I. Verify the associative property in each of the following.

(1) $a = \begin{pmatrix} 1 & 2 & 3 \\ 1 & 3 & 2 \end{pmatrix}$, $b = \begin{pmatrix} 1 & 2 & 3 \\ 3 & 2 & 1 \end{pmatrix}$, $c = \begin{pmatrix} 1 & 2 & 3 \\ 2 & 1 & 3 \end{pmatrix}$

(2) $a = \begin{pmatrix} 1 & 2 & 3 \\ 1 & 3 & 2 \end{pmatrix}$, $b = \begin{pmatrix} 1 & 2 & 3 \\ 3 & 2 & 1 \end{pmatrix}$, $e = \begin{pmatrix} 1 & 2 & 3 \\ 3 & 1 & 2 \end{pmatrix}$

(3) $a = \begin{pmatrix} 1 & 2 & 3 \\ 1 & 3 & 2 \end{pmatrix}$, $b = \begin{pmatrix} 1 & 2 & 3 \\ 3 & 2 & 1 \end{pmatrix}$, $d = \begin{pmatrix} 1 & 2 & 3 \\ 2 & 3 & 1 \end{pmatrix}$

(4) $b = \begin{pmatrix} 1 & 2 & 3 \\ 3 & 2 & 1 \end{pmatrix}$, $c = \begin{pmatrix} 1 & 2 & 3 \\ 2 & 1 & 3 \end{pmatrix}$, $e = \begin{pmatrix} 1 & 2 & 3 \\ 3 & 1 & 2 \end{pmatrix}$

II. Compute each of the following products.

(1) $\begin{pmatrix} 1 & 2 & 3 & 4 \\ 3 & 2 & 1 & 4 \end{pmatrix} \odot \begin{pmatrix} 1 & 2 & 3 & 4 \\ 1 & 3 & 2 & 4 \end{pmatrix}$

(2) $\begin{pmatrix} 1 & 2 & 3 & 4 \\ 1 & 3 & 2 & 4 \end{pmatrix} \odot \begin{pmatrix} 1 & 2 & 3 & 4 \\ 3 & 2 & 1 & 4 \end{pmatrix}$

(3) $\begin{pmatrix} 1 & 2 & 3 & 4 & 5 \\ 2 & 3 & 4 & 5 & 1 \end{pmatrix} \odot \begin{pmatrix} 1 & 2 & 3 & 4 & 5 \\ 1 & 4 & 3 & 2 & 5 \end{pmatrix}$

(4) $\begin{pmatrix} 1 & 2 & 3 & 4 & 5 \\ 1 & 4 & 3 & 2 & 5 \end{pmatrix} \odot \begin{pmatrix} 1 & 2 & 3 & 4 & 5 \\ 2 & 3 & 4 & 5 & 1 \end{pmatrix}$

(5) $\begin{pmatrix} 1 & 2 & 3 & 4 & 5 & 6 \\ 4 & 5 & 6 & 1 & 2 & 3 \end{pmatrix} \odot \begin{pmatrix} 1 & 2 & 3 & 4 & 5 & 6 \\ 6 & 5 & 4 & 3 & 2 & 1 \end{pmatrix}$

(6) $\begin{pmatrix} 1 & 2 & 3 & 4 & 5 & 6 \\ 6 & 5 & 4 & 3 & 2 & 1 \end{pmatrix} \odot \begin{pmatrix} 1 & 2 & 3 & 4 & 5 & 6 \\ 4 & 5 & 6 & 1 & 2 & 3 \end{pmatrix}$

III. Prove that each of the following systems is a commutative group with operator $\odot$.

(1) $\left\{ \begin{pmatrix} 1 & 2 & 3 \\ 1 & 2 & 3 \end{pmatrix}, \begin{pmatrix} 1 & 2 & 3 \\ 3 & 1 & 2 \end{pmatrix}, \begin{pmatrix} 1 & 2 & 3 \\ 2 & 3 & 1 \end{pmatrix} \right\}$

(2) $\left\{ \begin{pmatrix} 1 & 2 & 3 & 4 \\ 1 & 2 & 3 & 4 \end{pmatrix}, \begin{pmatrix} 1 & 2 & 3 & 4 \\ 2 & 1 & 4 & 3 \end{pmatrix} \right\}$

IV. Triangle *ABC* is an equilateral triangle with altitudes *AD*, *BE*, and *CF* which intersect at point *P*.

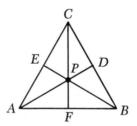

Let $S = \{i, a, b, c, d, e\}$ defined as follows:
i = rotation through $0°$ about P (identity),
a = rotation through $180°$ about AD,
b = rotation through $180°$ about BE,
c = rotation through $180°$ about CF,
d = counterclockwise rotation through $120°$ about P,
e = counterclockwise rotation through $240°$ about P.
Let the operator $\odot$ designate *followed by*.

Thus $a \odot b$ means *rotation a followed by rotation b.*

(1) Write the multiplication table.

(2) Prove that $(S, \odot)$ is a group.

(3) Compare $(S, \odot)$ with the group $(P_3, \odot)$.

8.3 Theorems on Groups

We have already learned that *every* group $(G, \odot)$ possesses the closure, associative, identity, and inverse properties, and some groups possess the commutative property. In this section we shall investigate some theorems which are immediate consequences of the definition of a group and some which are not. The first property which we investigate is the cancellation property. The following theorem states that any group $(G, \odot)$ possesses the cancellation property.

THEOREM 7. If a, b, and c are any elements of a group $(G, \odot)$ and $c \odot a = c \odot b$, then $a = b$.

Proof. Let $c \odot a = c \odot b$.

Then $c' \odot (c \odot a) = c' \odot (c \odot b)$ (by closure property).

$(c' \odot c) \odot a = (c' \odot c) \odot b$ (by associative property).

$i \odot a = i \odot b$ (by inverse property).

Hence $a = b$ (by identity property).//

The following theorem states that the equation $a \odot x = b$ has a unique solution.

THEOREM 8. If a and b are any elements of a group $(G, \odot)$, then the equation $a \odot x = b$ has the unique solution $a' \odot b$.

Proof. Now $a \odot x = b \rightarrow a' \odot (a \odot x) = a' \odot b$ (by closure property)

$\rightarrow (a' \odot a) \odot x = a' \odot b$ (by associative property

$\rightarrow i \odot x = a' \odot b$ (by inverse property)

$\rightarrow x = a' \odot b$ (by identity property)

Moreover, $x = a' \odot b \rightarrow i \odot x = a' \odot b$ (by identity property)

$$\rightarrow (a' \odot a) \odot x = a' \odot b \quad \text{(by inverse prop-erty)}$$

$$\rightarrow a' \odot (a \odot x) = a' \odot b \quad \text{(by associative property)}$$

$$\rightarrow a \odot x = b \quad \text{(by cancellation property)}.$$

Thus $a \odot x = b$ if and only if $x = a' \odot b$.

Hence $a' \odot b$ is the unique solution of the equation $a \odot x = b$.//

The following theorem, which we shall not prove, is a statement of the *generalized associative property* in any group $(G, \odot)$.

THEOREM 9.   If $a_1, a_2, \ldots, a_k$ are any elements of a group $(G, \odot)$, then all punctuations of $a_1 \odot a_2 \odot \ldots \odot a_k$ yield the same element of $(G, \odot)$.

The following theorem is a statement of the *generalized commutative and associative property* in any *commutative* group $(G, \odot)$.

THEOREM 10.   If $a_1, a_2, \ldots, a_k$ are any elements of a commutative group $(G, \odot)$, then all arrangements and punctuations of $a_1 \odot a_2 \odot \ldots \odot a_k$ yield the same element of $(G, \odot)$.

The proofs of Theorems 9 and 10 depend on the *postulate of finite induction*, which we have not included in this text.

Recall that $(P_3, \odot)$ is a group with the six elements $i = \left(\begin{smallmatrix} 1 & 2 & 3 \\ 1 & 2 & 3 \end{smallmatrix}\right)$, $a = \left(\begin{smallmatrix} 1 & 2 & 3 \\ 1 & 3 & 2 \end{smallmatrix}\right)$, $b = \left(\begin{smallmatrix} 1 & 2 & 3 \\ 3 & 2 & 1 \end{smallmatrix}\right)$, $c = \left(\begin{smallmatrix} 1 & 2 & 3 \\ 2 & 1 & 3 \end{smallmatrix}\right)$, $d = \left(\begin{smallmatrix} 1 & 2 & 3 \\ 2 & 3 & 1 \end{smallmatrix}\right)$, $e = \left(\begin{smallmatrix} 1 & 2 & 3 \\ 3 & 1 & 2 \end{smallmatrix}\right)$. Recall also that the three elements $i = \left(\begin{smallmatrix} 1 & 2 & 3 \\ 1 & 2 & 3 \end{smallmatrix}\right)$, $d = \left(\begin{smallmatrix} 1 & 2 & 3 \\ 2 & 3 & 1 \end{smallmatrix}\right)$, and $e = \left(\begin{smallmatrix} 1 & 2 & 3 \\ 3 & 1 & 2 \end{smallmatrix}\right)$ form a group with operator $\odot$. Observe that $\{i, d, e\} \subset \{i, a, b, c, d, e\}$. Whenever a group contains a subset which is itself a group, we give this subset a special name.

DEFINITION 3. $(S, \odot)$ is said to be a *subgroup* of the group $(G, \odot)$ if and only if $S \subset G$ and $(S, \odot)$ is a group.

For example, denoting the set $\{i, d, e\}$ by A, we see that $(A, \odot)$ is a subgroup of $(P_3, \odot)$. Notice that $n(A) = 3$ and $n(P_3) = 6$ and hence $n(A) \mid n(P_3)$. As another example, consider the set $S = \{i, a, b, c\} = \{\left(\begin{smallmatrix} 1 & 2 & 3 & 4 \\ 1 & 2 & 3 & 4 \end{smallmatrix}\right), \left(\begin{smallmatrix} 1 & 2 & 3 & 4 \\ 2 & 3 & 4 & 1 \end{smallmatrix}\right), \left(\begin{smallmatrix} 1 & 2 & 3 & 4 \\ 3 & 4 & 1 & 2 \end{smallmatrix}\right), \left(\begin{smallmatrix} 1 & 2 & 3 & 4 \\ 4 & 1 & 2 & 3 \end{smallmatrix}\right)\}$ of Section 8.2. Recall that $(S, \odot)$ is a group. Moreover, recall that $(P_4, \odot)$ is a group. Since $S \subset P_4$, we see that $(S, \odot)$ is a *subgroup* of $(P_4, \odot)$. Notice that $n(S) = 4$ and $n(P_4)$

$= 24$ and hence $n(S) \mid n(P_4)$. The following theorem, known as *Lagrange's Theorem*, states that the number of elements of any subgroup of a finite group divides the number of elements of the group. We do not include the proof.

THEOREM 11. If $(G, \odot)$ is a finite group and $(S, \odot)$ is a subgroup of $(G, \odot)$, then $n(S) \mid n(G)$.

Another important theorem in abstract algebra is a theorem known as *Cayley's Theorem*. Before we state Cayley's theorem, we shall consider two apparently different groups and show that they are abstractly identical. First, we consider the set $B = \{1_{17}, 4_{17}, 16_{17}, 13_{17}\}$ of equivalence classes and write the multiplication table shown in Figure 8.4.

×	1	4	16	13
1	1	4	16	13
4	4	16	13	1
16	16	13	1	4
13	13	1	4	16

FIGURE 8.4

It is easy to prove that $(B, \times)$ is a group with identity 1. Next we reconsider the group $(S, \odot)$ consisting of the elements $i = \left(\begin{smallmatrix}1&2&3&4\\1&2&3&4\end{smallmatrix}\right)$, $a = \left(\begin{smallmatrix}1&2&3&4\\2&3&4&1\end{smallmatrix}\right)$, $b = \left(\begin{smallmatrix}1&2&3&4\\3&4&1&2\end{smallmatrix}\right)$, and $c = \left(\begin{smallmatrix}1&2&3&4\\4&1&2&3\end{smallmatrix}\right)$. Since $n(B) = n(S)$, we see that $B \approx S$ (i.e., B is equivalent to S). Is the group $(B, \times)$ *abstractly identical* with the group $(S, \odot)$? That is, is the group $(B, \times)$ *identical with the group* $(S, \odot)$ *except for notation*? To answer this question, we compare the table in Figure 8.3 with the table in Figure 8.4. For convenience, we reproduce both tables in Figure 8.5.

$\odot$	i	a	b	c
i	i	a	b	c
a	a	b	c	i
b	b	c	i	a
c	c	i	a	b

×	1	4	16	13
1	1	4	16	13
4	4	16	13	1
16	16	13	1	4
13	13	1	4	16

(a) $\qquad\qquad\qquad\qquad$ (b)

FIGURE 8.5

Observe that Figure 8.5(a) is identical with Figure 8.5(b) *except for notation.* That is, in Figure 8.5(a) if we replace $\odot$ by $\times$, i by 1_{17}, a by 4_{17}, b by 16_{17}, and c by 13_{17}, we obtain Figure 8.5(b). In other words, the one-to-one correspondence

$$i \leftrightarrow 1_{17}$$
$$a \leftrightarrow 4_{17}$$
$$b \leftrightarrow 16_{17}$$
$$c \leftrightarrow 13_{17}$$

is operation-preserving; i.e., $a \odot b \leftrightarrow 4_{17} \times 13_{17}$, $a \odot c \leftrightarrow 4_{17} \times 13_{17}$, $b \odot c$ $\leftrightarrow 16_{17} \times 13_{17}$, etc. In general, a one-to-correspondence between two groups $(A, \odot)$ and $(B, \times)$ is *operation-preserving* if and only if $(a_i \odot a_j$ $\leftrightarrow b_i \times b_j)$ whenever $a_i \leftrightarrow b_i$ and $a_j \leftrightarrow b_j$. We are now prepared to give precise meaning to the term *abstractly identical.*

DEFINITION 4.   Two groups are said to be *abstractly identical* (or *isomorphic*) if and only if there exists an operation-preserving one-to-one correspondence between the groups.

Thus $(B, \times)$ is abstractly identical with the subgroup $(S, \odot)$ of $(P_4, \odot)$. Moreover, $n(S) = 4$, and the elements of S are permutations on 4 symbols.

In summary, we observe that $(B, \times)$ is a group of four elements, and $(B, \times)$ is abstractly identical with a group of *four* permutations on *four* symbols. Moreover, the group of *four* permutations on *four* symbols is a subgroup of $(P_4, \odot)$. *Cayley's theorem*, which we state without proof, tells us that this result is true in general.

THEOREM 12.   Every finite group consisting of k elements is abstractly identical with a subgroup of $(P_k, \odot)$.

Since the theory of permutation groups has been investigated carefully, Cayley's theorem is extremely important to pure mathematicians. The reason for this is that any finite group of k elements may be replaced by a subgroup of $(P_k, \odot)$; the theory of permutation groups is then immediately applicable to the given finite group. Mathematicians appreciate the elegance of a theorem such as Cayley's theorem, which unifies the theory of finite groups. In addition, it is very useful in the applications of group theory to physical problems.

Exercise 8.3

I. Prove each of the following.

   (1) If a, b, and c are any elements of a group $(G, \odot)$ and $a \odot c$ $= b \odot c$, then $a = b$.

(2) If a and b are any elements of a group $(G, \odot)$, then the equation $x \odot a = b$ has the unique solution $b \odot a'$.

(3) If a is any element of a group $(G, \odot)$, then $(a')' = a$.

(4) If a and b are any elements of a commutative group $(G, \odot)$, then $a \odot (b \odot a') = b$.

(5) If a and b are any elements of a *(not necessarily commutative)* group $(G, \odot)$, then $(a \odot b')' = b \odot a'$.

II. (1) Let $E = \{2n: n \in I\} = \{\ldots, {}^-4, {}^-2, 0, 2, 4, \ldots\}$. Prove that $(E, +)$ is a commutative group.

  (2) Let $O = \{2n + 1: n \in I\} = \{\ldots, {}^-3, {}^-1, 1, 3, \ldots\}$. Is $(O, +)$ a group? Is $(O, \times)$ a group?

III. (1) Give an example of a commutative subgroup of a noncommutative group.

  (2) List the subgroups of $(I_6, +)$.

  (3) List the subgroups of $(I_7, +)$.

  (4) Let $G = \{1_5, 2_5, 3_5, 4_5\}$. Prove that $(G, \times)$ is a commutative group.

IV. Prove that the group $(I_5, +)$ is abstractly identical with the following subgroup $(S, \odot)$ of $(P_5, \odot)$:

$$S = \left\{\begin{pmatrix}1\,2\,3\,4\,5\\1\,2\,3\,4\,5\end{pmatrix}, \begin{pmatrix}1\,2\,3\,4\,5\\2\,3\,4\,5\,1\end{pmatrix}, \begin{pmatrix}1\,2\,3\,4\,5\\3\,4\,5\,1\,2\end{pmatrix}, \begin{pmatrix}1\,2\,3\,4\,5\\4\,5\,1\,2\,3\end{pmatrix}, \begin{pmatrix}1\,2\,3\,4\,5\\5\,1\,2\,3\,4\end{pmatrix}\right\}.$$

8.4 Fields

Recall from Chapter 1 that a system $(F, +, \times)$ is a *field* if and only if it possesses the following properties:

F1. If a and b are any elements of F, then $a + b$ is a unique element of F (closure property for addition).

F2. If a, b, and c are any elements of F, then $(a + b) + c = a + (b + c)$ (associative property for addition).

F3. There exists a unique element 0 of F such that $a + 0 = a$ for any element of F (identity property for addition).

F4. If a is any element of F, then there exists a unique element ${}^-a$ of F such that $a + {}^-a = 0$ (inverse property for addition).

F5. If a and b are any elements of F, then $a + b = b + a$ (commutative property for addition).

F6. If a and b are any elements of F, then $a \times b$ is a unique element of F (closure property for multiplication).

F7. If a, b, and c are any elements of F, then $(a \times b) \times c = a \times (b \times c)$ (associative property for multiplication).

F8. There exists a unique element 1 of F such that $a \times 1 = a$ for any element a of F (identity property for multiplication).

F9. If a is any nonzero element of F, then there exists a unique element $1/a$ of F such that $a \times 1/a = 1$ (inverse property for multiplication).

F10. If a and b are any elements of F, then $a \times b = b \times a$ (commutative property for multiplication).

F11. If a, b, and c are any elements of F, then $a(b + c) = ab + ac$ (distributive property).

We have already learned that the rational number system, the real number system, the complex number system, and the system of equivalence classes modulo any prime are fields. Notice that we required that the identity elements 0 and 1 be unique, that each element have a unique additive inverse, and that each element *except 0* have a unique multiplicative inverse. The following definition of field is less restrictive than the above definition.

DEFINITION 5. A system $(F, +, \times)$ is called a *field* if and only if it possesses all of the following properties:

F1. If a and b are any elements of F, then $a + b$ is a unique element of F (closure property for addition).

F2. If a, b, and c are any elements of F, then $(a + b) + c = a + (b + c)$ (associative property for addition).

F3. There exists an element 0 of F such that $a + 0 = a$ for any element of F (identity property for addition).

F4. If a is any element of F, then there exists an element ^-a of F such that $a + {^-a} = 0$ (inverse property for addition).

F5. If a and b are any elements of F, then $a + b = b + a$ (commutative property for addition).

F6. If a and b are any elements of F, then $a \times b$ is a unique element of F (closure property for multiplication).

F7. If a, b, and c are any elements of F, then $(a \times b) \times c = a \times (b \times c)$ (associative property for multiplication).

F8. There exists an element 1 of F such that $a \times 1 = a$ for any element a of F (identity property for multiplication).

F9. If a is any nonzero element of F, then there exists an element $1/a$ of F such that $a \times 1/a = 1$ (inverse property for multiplication).

F10. If a and b are any elements of F, then $a \times b = b \times a$ (commutative property for multiplication).

F11. If a, b, and c are any elements of F, then $a(b + c) = ab + ac$ (distributive property).

Observe the difference between Definition 5 and the previous definition of field: in Definition 5 there is no requirement of *uniqueness* of identities and inverses. In fact, according to Definition 5, it appears possible that a field may have more than one additive (or multiplicative) identity and that an element may have more than one additive (or multiplicative) inverse. If this is actually the case, then Definition 5 does not agree with the original definition of field. Before we prove that the original definition of field is equivalent to Definition 5, we make the following observations:

(1) Properties $F1$ through $F5$ are precisely the properties of Definition 1 with F replacing G and $+$ replacing $\odot$;

(2) Properties $F6$ through $F10$ are precisely the properties of Definition 1 with F replacing G and $\times$ replacing $\odot$, except that 0 is not required to have an inverse;

(3) Property $F11$ is a property involving both operations $+$ and $\times$. Consequently, we can rewrite Definition 5 as follows.

A system $(F, +, \times)$ is a *field* if and only if it possesses all of the following properties:

(a) $(F, +)$ is a commutative group;
(b) $(F \smallsetminus \{0\}, \times)$ is a commutative group;
(c) if a, b, and c are any elements of F, then $a(b + c) = ab + ac$.

Since $(F, +)$ is a commutative group, we know from Theorem 1 that the additive identity 0 is unique and from Theorem 2 that each element of F has a unique additive inverse. Similarly, since $(F \smallsetminus \{0\}, \times)$ is a commutative group, we know from Theorem 1 and Theorem 2 that the multiplicative identity is unique and that each element of $F \smallsetminus \{0\}$ has a unique multiplicative inverse. Thus *the original definition of field is* *a consequence of Definition 5.* Obviously *Definition 5 is a consequence of the original definition of field.* Hence the two definitions are *equivalent.* This is an excellent illustration of the economy of abstraction. Having proved uniqueness in a group, we were able to prove uniqueness in a field. If the uniqueness of each identity and of inverses in a field had been available to us when we developed the rational numbers and the real numbers* our task would have been simplified. Similarly, our development in Chapters 6 and 7 would have been simplified.

We have already studied four systems which are fields. Now we shall reconsider some systems, studied previously, which are not fields. The counting number system $(C_0, +, \times)$ is not a field because $(C_0, +)$ is not a group. The reason $(C_0, +)$ is not a group is that 0 is the only element of C_0 which has an additive inverse in C_0. The system of integers $(I, +, \times)$ is not a field because $(I \smallsetminus \{0\}, \times)$ is not a group. The reason $(I \smallsetminus \{0\}, \times)$ is not a group is that 1 is the only element of $I \smallsetminus \{0\}$ which has a multiplicative inverse in $I \smallsetminus \{0\}$. If m is a composite number, the system $(I_m, +, \times)$ is not a field because some nonzero element of I_m does not have a multiplicative inverse in I_m. For example, 2_6 does not have a multiplicative inverse in I_6.

In pure mathematics, a mathematician formulates a basic set of undefined terms, definitions, and postulates and builds an abstract mathematical system from these. In applied mathematics, a mathematician applies these general results to specific problems whose mathematical models can be formulated in the abstract system. For example, a mathematician known as an *algebraist* proves theorems about groups, fields, and other abstract systems. The primary interest of the pure mathematician is *creating* mathematics for its own beauty. He is especially interested in any theorem which *unifies* different branches of mathematics. Although our primary interest in this text has been the *algebraic structure of the common number systems,* in closing we mention that there are many other branches of pure mathematics; for example, *analysis, topology,* and *geometry.*

Exercise 8.4

I. Let $S = \{a + b\sqrt{3}: a \in R \land b \in R\}$.
   Prove that $(S, +, \times)$ is a field.

II. Let $K = \{a + b\sqrt{3}: a \in I \land b \in I\}$.
    Prove that $(K, +, \times)$ is *not* a field.

* Ohmer, Aucoin, and Cortez, *Elementary Contemporary Mathematics* (1964). New York: Blaisdell Publishing Company.

APPENDIX

A *sentence* is any declarative statement which is either true or false, but not both true and false.

A statement which contains a variable is called an *open sentence* if and only if it is not a sentence but becomes a sentence upon replacement of the variable by a name for a specific number, person, or object.

An open sentence is not really a sentence. However, an open sentence can be converted to a sentence by the replacement of the variable by the name for a specific number, person, or object. For example, the open sentence "$x + 2 = 7$" is converted to the true sentence "$5 + 2 = 7$" by replacement of the variable x by the numeral 5. The replacement method is not the only method of converting an open sentence to a sentence; we may *quantify* the variable. For example, although "$x + 2 = 7$" is not a sentence, "for some x, $x + 2 = 7$" is a sentence.

The terms *all* (or *any*, or *each*, or *every*), *some* (or *there exists*), and *no* (or *none*) are called *quantifiers*.

A quantifier is *expressed* if and only if it appears explicitly in a sentence. For example, "for all x, $x + 3 = 3 + x$" contains the expressed quantifier *all*.

A quantifier is *implied* if and only if it does not appear explicitly in a sentence but must be supplied by the reader. For example, the quantifier *all* is implied in the (open) sentence "$x^2 - 9 = (x - 3)(x + 3)$."

The connectives are *not* ($\sim$), *or* ($\vee$), *and* ($\wedge$), *if . . . then* ($\rightarrow$), and *if and only if* ($\leftrightarrows$).

223

Sentences may be denoted by the lower case letters p, q, r, etc. The following sentences illustrate the use of the connectives.

Negation	$\sim p$	not p
Disjunction	$p \vee q$	p or q
Conjunction	$p \wedge q$	p and q
Conditional	$p \rightarrow q$	if p, then q or p only if q
Biconditional	$p \leftrightarrows p$	p if and only if q

Although the word *set* is undefined in mathematics, we *refer* to any collection of elements as a *set*.

We *name* a set by a capital letter A, B, C, etc., and we indicate that *a is an element of A* by $a \in A$ and *a is not an element of A* by $a \notin A$.

We may *list* the elements of a set in braces. For example, the set of one digit positive integers is $\{1, 2, 3, 4, 5, 6, 7, 8, 9\}$.

The *empty set*, or *null set*, is the set which contains no elements. It is denoted by the Greek letter ϕ or by the empty braces, $\{\ \}$.

The *complement* of A, denoted by $\tilde{A}$, or $U \smallsetminus A$, is the set of all elements in the universe, U, which are not in A. That is, $\tilde{A} = \{x : x \in U \wedge x \notin A\}$. For example, if $U = \{1, 2, 3, 4, 5\}$ and $A = \{1, 3, 5\}$, then $\tilde{A} = \{2, 4\}$.

The *union* of A and B, denoted by $A \cup B$, is the set of all elements which belong to A *or* to B (or both). That is, $A \cup B = \{x : x \in A \vee x \in B\}$. This is read *A union B is the set of all x such that x is an element of A or x is an element of B.*

The *intersection* of A and B, denoted by $A \cap B$, is the set of all elements which belong to A *and* to B. That is, $A \cap B = \{x : x \in A \wedge x \in B\}$. This is read *A intersection B is the set of all x such that x is an element of A and x is an element of B.*

A is a *subset* of B, written $A \subset B$, if and only if every element of A is an element of B.

A is *equal* to B, written $A = B$, if and only if $A \subset B$ and $B \subset A$.

A relation **R** on a set S is an *equivalence relation* if and only if the following three properties are satisfied:

(a) Reflexive Property (if $a \in S$, then a **R** a);
(b) Symmetric Property (if $a \in S$, $b \in S$, and a **R** b, then b **R** a);
(c) Transitive Property (if $a \in S$, $b \in S$, $c \in S$, and a **R** b, and b **R** c, then a **R** c).

An equivalence relation on a set S separates S into mutually exclusive (disjoint) subsets whose union is S and such that a **R** b if and only if a and b are in the same subset of S.

The *Cartesian product* $(A \times B)$ of the set A and the set B is the set of all ordered pairs (a, b) such that $a \in A$ and $b \in B$. That is, $A \times B = \{(a, b): a \in A \text{ and } b \in B\}$. Similarly, $B \times A = \{(b, a): b \in B \text{ and } a \in A\}$. In general, $A \times B \neq B \times A$ and $(a, b) \neq (b, a)$.

The *number of elements* of a set A is denoted by $n(A)$.

The finite set A *is equivalent* to the finite set B if and only if the number of elements of A is the same as the number of elements of B. That is, $A \approx B$ if and only if $n(A) = n(B)$.

ARCHIMEDEAN PROPERTY

If a is any positive integer and b is any counting number such that $a < b$, then there exists a positive integer k such that $b < ak$.

WELL-ORDERING PROPERTY

If A is any nonempty subset of C_0, then there is one and only one element a_0 of A which is less than any other element of A. The element a_0 is called the *least element*.

For any integer a and any positive integer m,
$$a^m = \underbrace{a \times a \ldots \times a.}_{m\text{-factors}}$$

The number a is called the *base*,
the number m is called the *exponent*, and
the number a^m is called an *exponential*.

If a is any nonzero real number and k is any integer, then
$$a^0 = 1$$
$$a^{-k} = \frac{1}{a^k}$$

If k and m are any integers and a is any nonzero real number, then
$a^k a^m = a^{k+m}$.

If k and m are any integers and a is any nonzero real number, then
$a^k \div a^m = a^{k-m}$.

The *difference* $a - b$ in the subtraction of the counting number b from the counting number a is the counting number $n(A \smallsetminus B)$, in which $n(A) = a$, $n(B) = b$, $B \subset A$, and $A \smallsetminus B = \{x: x \in A \wedge x \notin B\}$. [That is, $a - b = n(A) - n(B) = n(A \smallsetminus B)$.]

If a and b are any integers, then the difference $a - b$ is the integer c if and only if $a = b + c$. (That is $a - b = c$ if and only if $a = b + c$.)

The integer b divides the integer a (written $b \mid a$) if and only if there exists an integer k such that $a = bk$.

If a, b, and c are any integers such that $c \mid b$ and $b \mid a$, then $c \mid a$.

If a, b, and c are any integers such that $c \mid a$ and $c \mid b$, then $c \mid (a + b)$.

If a, b, and c are any integers such that $c \mid a$ and $c \mid b$, then $c \mid (a - b)$.

The positive integer p is said to be a *prime number* (or simply a *prime*) if and only if $p \neq 1$ and the only positive divisors of p are 1 and p.

The positive integer c is said to be a *composite number* (or simply a *composite*) if and only if $c \neq 1$ and c is not a prime.

The positive integer 1 is called a *unit*.

If p is any prime and a and b are any positive integers such that $p \mid ab$, then $p \mid a$ or $p \mid b$.

If p is any prime and $a_1, a_2, \ldots, a_k$ are any positive integers such that $p \mid a_1 a_2 \ldots a_k$, then $p \mid a_1$ or $p \mid a_2$ or ... or $p \mid a_k$.

The integer b is a *divisor* (or *factor*) of the integer a if and only if $b \mid a$.

UNIQUE PRIME FACTORIZATION THEOREM

Every composite may be expressed uniquely as a product of primes, except for order.

The *greatest common divisor* (*gcd*) of the positive integers a and b is the largest integer which divides both a and b. The *gcd* of a and b is denoted by (a, b).

The positive integers a and b are said to be *relatively prime* if and only if $(a, b) = 1$.

The positive integer a is a *multiple* of the positive integer b if and only if $b \mid a$. That is, a is a *multiple* of b if and only if b is a divisor of a.

The *least common multiple* (*lcm*) of the positive integers a and b is the smallest positive integer which is a multiple of both a and b. The *lcm* of a and b is denoted by $[a, b]$.

The *least common denominator* (*lcd*) of two rational numbers a/b and c/d is the least common multiple of b and d.

If the positive integer a divides the counting number b and if $b < a$, then $b = 0$.

DIVISION ALGORITHM

If a and b are any positive integers and $b < a$, then there exist a unique positive integer q and a unique counting number r such that $a = bq + r$ and $0 \leq r < b$.

EUCLIDEAN ALGORITHM

If a and b are any positive integers and $d = (a, b)$, then there exist integers j and k such that $d = ja + kb$. Moreover, if c is any common divisor of a and b, then $c \mid d$. The integers j and k are not unique.

The *absolute value* of the real number a (written $|a|$) is the real number

(a) ^-a if a is negative,

(b) 0 if and only if $a = 0$,

(c) a if a is positive.

A *counting number* is a member of the set C_0.
$$C_0 = \{ 0, 1, 2, 3, \ldots \}$$

A *negative integer* is a member of the set I^-.
$$I^- = \{^-1, ^-2, ^-3, \ldots \}$$

A *positive integer* is a member of the set I^+.
$$I^+ = \{1, 2, 3, \ldots \}$$

An *integer* is a member of the set I.
$$I = \{\ldots, ^-3, ^-2, ^-1, 0, 1, 2, 3, \ldots \}$$

A *fraction* is an ordered pair $\frac{a}{b}$ of integers such that $b \neq 0$.

A *rational number* is an equivalence class of fractions. The set of rational numbers is denoted by R_a.
$$R_a = \{a/b : a \in I, b \in I^+, \text{ and } (a, b) = 1 \}.$$

A *real number* is an infinite decimal which does not contain infinitely many consecutive repeating 9's. The set of real numbers is denoted by R.
$$R = \text{the set of all real numbers.}$$

ANSWERS TO PROBLEMS

CHAPTER 1

Exercise 1.1 (page 5)

I. (5) $F1$, $F2$, $F5$
   (7) $F6$, $F7$, $F8$, $F9$, $F10$

Exercise 1.2 (page 9)

I. (1) 3   (3) 3/2   (5) 7/2   (7) 7/6   (9) 5
III. (1) ⁻10   (3) ⁻6   (5) 8   (7) 160   (9) 24

Exercise 1.4 (page 16)

I. (1) 0   (3) 17   (5) 2
III. (1) The smallest element of B is 7
    (3) The largest element of A is ⁻5
    (5) No, because $A \cup B \neq R$

CHAPTER 2

Exercise 2.1 (page 23)

I. (1) 3   (3) $\sqrt{2}$ (5) 17   (7) 3   (9) $(⁻2/3 + 4)$
III. (1) Multinomial   (3) Multinomial   (5) Monomial
    (7) Multinomial   (9) Multinomial
V. (1) Equation   (3) Equation   (5) Not an equation
    (7) Not an equation   (9) Equation   (11) Equation
    (13) Not an equation   (15) Equation   (17) Equation
    (19) Equation

229

Exercise 2.2 (page 26)

III. (1) $-30x$ (3) $-20 + 130x - 60x^2$ (5) $22x + 20$ (7) $10x + 5$
    (9) $24x + 6$ (11) 0 (13) $90x^2 + 54x + 6$ (15) $-x - 9$
    (17) $-11x + 6$ (19) -3 (21) $30x^2 - 27x - 27$
    (23) $30x^2 - 45x - 3$ (25) $11x$ (27) $3x + xy - 10y^2$
    (29) $6x^2 + 2y^2 + 8xy + 6xz + 2yz + 4x + 4y + 4z$
    (31) $x^2 + 4xy + 4y^2 + 6xz + 12yz + 9z^2$ (33) $a^3 + 3a^2x + 3ax^2 + x^3$
    (35) $x^2 - 4a^2$ (37) $x^3 + 8$ (39) $x^3 - 3xy^2 + 2y^3$

Exercise 2.3 (page 31)

I. (1) $\{-6\}$ (3) $\{1\}$ (5) $\{5/2\}$ (7) $\{-1/2\}$ (9) $\{88/225\}$

Exercise 2.4 (page 36)

I. (1) 34, 35, 36 (3) 45, 47, 49 (5) None
   (7) 35 nickels, 42 pennies (9) 14 pennies, 19 nickels, 9 quarters
  (11) Elaine is 10 and her father is 30
  (13) Joseph is 15 and his father is 35 (15) 7:00 PM (17) 9:00 AM
  (19) Width, 60 ft. and length, 90 ft. (21) 142, 143, 144
  (23) $-1, 0, 1$ (25) Yvonne, 8 mph and Sylvia, 12 mph

Exercise 2.5 (page 41)

I. (1) Yes (3) Yes (5) Yes (7) No (9) Yes
  (11) Yes (13) Yes (15) Yes (17) Yes (19) Yes

Exercise 2.6 (page 44)

I. (1) $\{x:x \le 1\}$ (3) $\{x: -1/2 \le x\}$ (5) U (7) ϕ
   (9) $\{x: -1 \le x \le 1\}$ (11) ϕ (13) $\{x: -5 < x < 5\}$
  (15) U (17) $\{x: (x \le 5) \wedge (3 < x)\}$ (19) $\{x: (x \le 5) \vee (3 < x)\}$
  (21) $\{8, 10\}$ (23) $\{x: (x < 5) \wedge (2 \le x)\}$
  (25) $\{x: (x < 5) \vee (15 < x)\}$ (27) $\{x: 7 \le x \vee x \le -7\}$
  (29) $\{x: 3/5 \le x \vee x \le -1\}$

Exercise 2.7 (page 46)

I. (1) 20 marbles (3) 6 miles (5) $\$21,600 \le x \le \$28,800$
  (7) \$225 (9) 18,000 pounds per sq. inch.

CHAPTER 3

Exercise 3.1 (page 53)

I. (1) $\{(2, 0)\}$ (3) $\{(-1, 1), (-1, 2), (0, 1), (0, 2), (1, 1), (1, 2)\}$
  (5) $\{(0, 0), (1, 0), (2, 0), \ldots, (0, 1), (1, 1), (2, 1), \ldots\}$
  (7) $\{(0, a): a \in R\}$ (9) $\{$(Tom, Mary), (Tom, Jane),
(Dick, Mary), (Dick, Jane), (Harry, Mary), (Harry, Jane)$\}$
III. (1) ϕ (3) $\{1\}$ (5) B (7) A (9) ϕ

Exercise 3.2 (page 59)

I. (1) Function (3) Function (5) Not a function (7) Function
  (9) Function (11) Not a function (13) Function
  (15) Not a function (17) Function (19) Not a function

Exercise 3.3 (page 64)

I. (1) Reals   (3) Reals   (5) Reals   (7) Reals   (9) Reals
III. (1) ⁻4   (3) 9   (5) 14   (7) ⁻65   (9) 17
V. (1) 0   (3) 1.   (5) ⁻2   (7) ⁻1   (9) 1
VII. {3, 6, 9, 12}

Exercise 3.5 (page 76)

I. (1) Linear   (3) Linear   (5) Not a linear function
   (7) Not a linear function   (9) Not a linear function
III. (1) $y = (-2/3)x + 7/3$, slope is ⁻2/3   (3) $y = x + 3$, slope is 1/1
   (5) $y = 10x - 2$, slope is 10/1
   (7) $y = (-1/5)x$, slope is ⁻1/5   (9) $y = 2x + 5/2$, slope is 2/1
VII. (1) $\{(0, 2)\}$ (3) $\{(0, 5)\}$ (5) $\{(0, 0)\}$

Exercise 3.6 (page 81)

I. (1) Not a quadratic function   (3) Not a quadratic function
   (5) Quadratic function   (7) Not a quadratic function
   (9) Quadratic function

CHAPTER 4

Exercise 4.1 (page 99)

I. (1) ⁻2, 5   (3) 2, 1   (5) 10, ⁻3   (7) $\{(x, y): x = 2y + 3\}$
   (9) $\{(x, y): 2x - 3y = 4\}$
III. (1) 3/2, 1/2   (3) 33/2, 121/10   (5) 2, 5
   (7) 5/2, ⁻5/2   (9) 16/11, ⁻17/11

Exercise 4.2 (page 103)

I. (1) ⁻3, 2   (3) ϕ (5) $\{(x, y): x + 4y = 3\}$ (7) ϕ
   (9) $\{(x, y): 2x - 3y = 4\}$ (11) ⁻20/11, ⁻41/11
   (13) 0, 0   (15) ϕ
III. (1) 18/5, 2/5   (3) 1, ⁻2   (5) $\{(x, y): 7x - 5y = 0\}$
   (7) ϕ (9) 3, 3

Exercise 4.3 (page 107)

I. (1) 42 pennies, 35 nickels   (3) Diana is 12 and her father is 36
   (5) Vicky is 14 and her mother is 34   (7) 8 oz. of $12 per oz.
   and 12 oz. of $7 per oz.   (9) 36 qt. of 4% and 42 qts. of 30%
   (11) 39 years old   (13) 45   (15) 12 or 24 or 36 or 48
   (17) 200 mph, 250 mph   (19) air speed—90 mph, wind speed—45 mph

Exercise 4.4 (page 114)

II. (1) 8, ⁻8¼   (3) 26, ⁻17⅗   (5) 19, 1   (7) 6, 0

Exercise 4.5 (page 117)

I. 10 lathes from W_1 to Lafayette, 0 lathes from W_1 to Baton Rouge, 10
   lathes from W_2 to Lafayette, 25 lathes from W_2 to Baton Rouge
III. M_1 should operate 30 hours and M_2 should not operate
V. 80 acres of crop A and 20 acres of crop B

CHAPTER 5

Exercise 5.1 (page 122)

II. (1) $(5, 0)$ and $(2, 0)$ (3) $(0, 0)$ and $(-10, 0)$
(5) $(-4, 0)$ and $(3, 0)$ (7) $(-6, 0)$ and $(-2, 0)$
(9) $(0, 0)$ and $(5, 0)$

Exercise 5.2 (page 127)

I. (1) $6x^2 - 6x + 21$ (3) $-15ax^4 + -25x^3 + 35x^2 + 20x$
(5) $-2x^2y + -6xy^2 + 2x^3y + 8x^2y^2 + -14xy$ (7) $9x^2 - 1$
(9) $9x^2 - 6x + 1$ (11) $9x^2 - 4$ (13) $25x^2 + 40x + 16$
(15) $1 - 49x^2$ (17) $16x^2 + 8x + 1$ (19) $x^2 + 7x + 6$
(21) $5x^2 - 13x + 6$ (23) $6x^2 + 7x - 49$ (25) $8x^2 + 35x - 25$
(27) $3x^2 + 5x - 12$ (29) $9x^2 - 6x + 18xy - 12y$

II. (1) $7(x^3 - 3x^2 + 2x + 4)$ (3) $11x(x^2 + 3x - 5)$
(5) $(x + 5)(x - 5)$ (7) $(3x + 4y)(3x - 4y)$
(9) $32(x + 2y)(x - 2y)$ (11) $(x + 2)(x + 2)$
(13) $(5x + 1)(5x + 1)$ (15) $(x - 6)(x - 6)$
(17) $(x + 3)(x + 1)$ (19) $(2x - 1)(x + 2)$
(21) $(2x - 3)(2x - 3)$ (23) $(2x - 1)(2x - 9)$
(25) $(4x + 1)(x + 9)$ (27) $(x + 1)(4x + 9)$
(29) $2x(3x - 2)(x + 2)$

Exercise 5.3 (page 132)

I. (1) $\{5, -5\}$ (3) $\{4/3, -4/3\}$ (5) $\{2, -2\}$ (7) $\{-2\}$ (9) $\{-1/5\}$
(11) $\{6\}$ (13) $\{-1, -3\}$ (15) $\{3/2\}$ (17) $\{1/2, 9/2\}$
(19) $\{4/9, 1\}$

III. (1) 5 or -5 (3) $4/3$ or $-4/3$ (5) 2 or -2 (7) -2 (9) $-1/5$

(11) 6 (13) -1 or -3 (15) $3/2$ (17) $1/2$ or $9/2$ (19) $4/9$ or 1

V. (1) $\dfrac{2x - 3}{(x - 1)(3x - 2)}$ (3) $\dfrac{x + y}{2x - y}$ (5) $\dfrac{(x - 3y)(x - 3y)}{(x + y)(x + y)}$
(7) $\dfrac{(x + 2y)(x + 2y)}{(2x - y)(2x - y)}$ (9) $\dfrac{(x + 4)(x - 3)(2x - 5)(2x + 3)}{(2x + 5)(2x - 3)(x - 4)(x + 3)}$

Exercise 5.4 (page 137)

I. (1) $\{\sqrt{5}, -\sqrt{5}\}$ (3) $\{2 + \sqrt{6}, 2 - \sqrt{6}\}$ (5) $\{-1 + \sqrt{6}, -1 - \sqrt{6}\}$
(7) $\{1/2 + \sqrt{3}/2, 1/2 - \sqrt{3}/2\}$ (9) ϕ

Exercise 5.5 (page 140)

I. (1) $\{3, 1\}$ (3) $\{-1, 2\}$ (5) $\left\{\dfrac{1 + \sqrt{17}}{4}, \dfrac{1 - \sqrt{17}}{4}\right\}$

(7) $\{1/3, -2\}$ (9) ϕ (11) $\left\{\dfrac{3 + 3\sqrt{21}}{10}, \dfrac{3 - 3\sqrt{21}}{10}\right\}$

(13) $\{-3/2, 2/3\}$ (15) ϕ (17) ϕ (19) $\left\{\dfrac{5 + \sqrt{2}}{3}, \dfrac{5 - \sqrt{2}}{3}\right\}$

Exercise 5.6 (page 144)

I. (1) 9 yrs. old   (3) Donald has 6 pencils and Bud has 31 pencils
(5) William's speed is 8 mph and Homer's speed is 3 mph
(7) 20 problems   (9) 29 miles the first day and 35 miles altogether
(11) Velma worked 10 and Laureen worked 4

(13) He might have been, but -9 could also be the number
(15) 0 and 6   (17) Vertex is (5/16, 101⁹⁄₁₆)   (19) 10   (21) 210

CHAPTER 6

Exercise 6.1 (page 150)

I. (1) $a = -7, d = 5$ (3) $c = -6, d = -3$ (5) $6 \neq 7$
(7) $a = 10, b = 5$ (9) $a = -10/3, b = -11/6$
III. (1) $83 + 66i$ (3) $(35/2)i$ (5) 58   (7) -10   (9) $5 + 12i$

Exercise 6.2 (page 155)

I. (1) -5   (3) $(-6/7)i$ (5) $-1 + -3i$ (7) $5 + -3i$
(9) $6/5 + (2/3)i$ (11) $0 + 0i$
III. (1) $3/25 + (4/25)i$ (3) $-7/625 + (-24/625)i$

Exercise 6.3 (page 159)

I. (1) $-1 + 5i$ (3) $-6 + 10i$ (5) $-5 + i$ (7) $6i$ (9) $3 + 6i$

Exercise 6.4 (page 162)

I. (1) $3/4 + (\sqrt{7}/4)i$ or $3/4 - (\sqrt{7}/4)i$ (3) $1/2 + (\sqrt{23}/2)i$
or $1/2 - (\sqrt{23}/2)i$ (5) $\left(\frac{-7 + \sqrt{13}}{2}\right)$ or $\left(\frac{-7 - \sqrt{13}}{2}\right)$
(7) $-5/6 + (\sqrt{13}/6)i$ or $-5/6 - (\sqrt{13}/6)i$ (9) 1 or -5
(11) $\left(\frac{-3 + \sqrt{5}}{2}\right)$ or $\left(\frac{-3 - \sqrt{5}}{2}\right)$ (13) $\sqrt{2}\, i$ or $-\sqrt{2}\, i$
(15) 0 or $\frac{7}{3}$ (17) $3i$ or $-3i$ (19) $3 + \sqrt{11}$ or $3 - \sqrt{11}$

CHAPTER 7

Exercise 7.1 (page 170)

III.

Clock number	1	3	5	7	9	11
Additive inverse	11	9	7	5	3	1

V. (1) 6   (3) 6   (5) 6   (7) True for all t (9) 2

Exercise 7.3 (page 180)

I. (1) False   (3) True   (5) True   (7) True   (9) False

Exercise 7.4 (page 184)

I. (1) 5_7 (3) 0_7 (5) 2_5 (7) 9_{12} (9) 0_4
III. (1) 3_5 (3) 3_5 (5) 0_6 (7) 0_6 (9) 11_{12}

Exercise 7.5 (page 189)

III. (1) Not a commutative group   (3) Commutative group
(5) Not a commutative group   (7) Commutative group

Exercise 7.6 (page 193)

I. (1) $x \equiv 2 \pmod 3$ (3) $x \equiv 2 \pmod 5$ (5) $x \equiv 3 \pmod{17}$
(7) $x \equiv 2 \pmod{17}$ (9) $x \equiv 8 \pmod{11}$

Exercise 7.7 (page 196)

I. (1) 9 $\nmid$ 27,638   (3) 9 | 85,419   (5) 9 $\nmid$ 26,893
  (7) 9 $\nmid$ 173,287   (9) 9 | 654,723

Exercise 7.8 (page 204)

I. (1) $\{(x, y): x = 3k \wedge y = {}^-7 - k \wedge k \in I\}$
  (3) $\{(x, y): x = 4 + 6k \wedge y = 5k \wedge k \in I\}$
  (5) $\{(x, y): x = 2 + 8k \wedge y = 1 + 9k \wedge k \in I\}$

III. (1)

4¢	15¢
128	0
113	4
98	8
83	12
68	16
53	20
38	24
23	28
8	32

(3) 92

CHAPTER 8

Exercise 8.1 (page 209)

III. (1) Commutative group   (3) Not a group   (5) Commutative group

Exercise 8.2 (page 214)

III. (1) $\begin{pmatrix} 1 & 2 & 3 & 4 \\ 2 & 3 & 1 & 4 \end{pmatrix}$ (3) $\begin{pmatrix} 1 & 2 & 3 & 4 & 5 \\ 4 & 3 & 2 & 5 & 1 \end{pmatrix}$ (5) $\begin{pmatrix} 1 & 2 & 3 & 4 & 5 & 6 \\ 3 & 2 & 1 & 6 & 5 & 4 \end{pmatrix}$

INDEX

ABCDEFGHIJ   0698765

ABOUT THE AUTHORS

MERLIN M. OHMER received his B.S. and M.S. degrees from Tulane University and his Ph.D. degree in mathematics from the University of Pittsburgh. In 1948 he joined the staff of the mathematics department at the University of Southwestern Louisiana, where he became full professor in 1956. Since 1959 he has been an associate director and lecturer in National Science Foundation summer and in-service institutes at the University. His lectures on the changing mathematical curricula in the elementary and secondary schools have reached wide audiences throughout the U. S. and Canada. Professor Ohmer is a member of the Mathematical Association of America, the National Council of Teachers of Mathematics, the Louisiana Academy of Sciences, the Louisiana Teachers Association, the American Association of University Professors, and is active in civic, church, and school affairs. He is a commander in the U. S. Naval Reserve and commanding officer of a Naval Reserve Officers' School. Dr. Ohmer is a visiting lecturer for the Mathematical Association of America, a visiting scientist for the Louisiana Academy of Sciences, and a member of the advisory board to the Louisiana State Department of Education. He conducts a state-wide television program in mathematics for elementary school teachers and parents.

CLAYTON V. AUCOIN received his B.S. degree from Louisiana College and his M.S. and Ph.D. degrees in mathematics from Auburn University. Subsequently, he spent a year at Stanford University on an N.S.F. faculty fellowship studying operations research and stochastic processes. From 1959 to 1963 he was a member of the mathematics department at the University of Southwestern Louisiana, where he was promoted to Associate Professor in 1962. In 1963 he joined the staff of the mathematics department at Clemson University and became department chairman in 1964. While he was at the University of Southwestern Louisiana, Professor Aucoin lectured in N.S.F. summer and in-service institutes. Dr. Aucoin is a member of the Mathematical Association of America, the Society for Industrial and Applied Mathematics, and the Association for Computing Machinery.

MARION J. CORTEZ received his B.S. and M.Ed. degrees from the University of Southwestern Louisiana. In 1959 he became mathematics teacher at Lafayette High School. Presently, as mathematics teacher at Northside High School and supervising teacher for the University, he is responsible for supervising student teachers of mathematics. His lectures on mathematics in the elementary schools have reached wide audiences throughout Louisiana. Mr. Cortez is a member of the Mathematical Association of America, the National Council of Teachers of Mathematics, the National Education Association, and the Louisiana Teachers Association.